Introduction to Biophysical Chemistry

INTRODUCTION TO BIOPHYSICAL CHEMISTRY

R. BRUCE MARTIN

Associate Professor of Chemistry
University of Virginia
Charlottesville, Virginia

McGraw-Hill Book Company

New York   San Francisco
Toronto   London

Introduction to
Biophysical Chemistry

40629

Preface

Our knowledge of living organisms has now attained a state of development in which the fundamental unit of biological study is the molecule, rather than the cell. This shift means that biology is becoming a molecular, or chemical, science. Biologically significant molecules are often complex; some of the most important are macromolecules. Many of the properties of biological molecules which enable them to perform their functions and which account for their specificities are due to their physical as well as their chemical properties. Biophysical chemistry, the topic of this book, is concerned primarily with the physical chemical properties of biological molecules.

Beginning with the application of fundamental principles to small molecules of biological significance, this volume proceeds through a discussion of the methods for characterizing biopolymers to a study of their properties and interrelationships. Throughout, the aim is an appreciation for, but not a detailed analysis of, the topics covered. Questions at the ends of the chapters are intended to emphasize chapter content without being arithmetically or algebraically tedious. The contents of a book dealing with a field as broad as biophysical chemistry clearly must be somewhat subjective and eclectic. Obviously, for reasons of length, the book cannot be authoritative in any one field, but it is hoped that it will serve as an introduction to several areas of contemporary study. Anyone desiring more specific information should consult the references listed at the end of each chapter. These references are not distinguished by their number, but they do provide cogent sources of further information on higher levels of understanding and detail.

In this book we consider the thermodynamic basis of biological reactions, offer a systematic presentation of acid-base equilibria, and cover within a single volume the properties, functions, and interrelationships of the biologically important macromolecules, proteins and nucleic acids. As the approach is primarily chemical, chemistry occurs as a noun in the title, with biophysical in a modifying position. The book should be of value to chemists interested in biological problems and to biological chemists who seek to learn more of the physical-chemistry approach to their field. Though suitable for use as a textbook in an advanced undergraduate or graduate course, the book is also designed for collateral reading.

Such a survey as this book attempts must depend on the publications of many authors. I wish to express my deep indebtedness to workers throughout this field, and I hope that the presentation of their contributions is a faithful, if in most cases unacknowledged, rendition of their views. Though some of the ideas in the book are a product of my own reflection, I imagine that similar thoughts have occurred to others and do not make great claims for originality. I am indebted to Drs. L. G. Hepler, D. W. Kupke, P. N. Schatz, and R. J. P. Williams for helpful comments on portions of the volume. For her dedication and inexhaustible patience in reading and rereading, checking and rechecking, typing and retyping the pages of the manuscript, I owe the greatest thanks to my wife, Fran.

R. Bruce Martin

Contents

1 | Introduction

Molecules in biological systems display enormous complexity and a bewildering variety of properties. In presenting such an intricate subject, we begin with a discussion of some physical properties of representative small molecules. Only later are large molecules and specialized techniques considered. For instance, we first discuss the acid-base properties of amino acids; we then amplify the study to include the acid-base equilibria of a chain of amino acids strung end to end: a *polypeptide* or *protein*.

In discussing macromolecules, it is essential to consider the special methods used in their characterization. Even so familiar a concept as molecular weight requires such specific treatment that most of Chap. 6 is devoted to it. Many of the theories and techniques now applied to biological macromolecules were developed from a study of proteins and later extended to nucleic acids. For this reason the first portion of the book deals mainly with examples from protein chemistry. Where appropriate, however, applications to nucleic acid chemistry are included. A more thorough discussion of nucleic acids appears later in the text.

This opening chapter introduces three topics: amino acids, their optical rotatory properties, and biopolymers. Much of the discussion of the first few chapters is centered on the amino acids. The brief treatment of biopolymers gives some orientation relative to an overall view of macromolecules of biological significance.

1-1 AMINO ACIDS

The 20 amino acids commonly occurring as amino acid residues in proteins are shown in Table 1-1. They are all α-amino acids. At the right of the table title is represented the general configuration of an

1

TABLE 1-1 L-*Amino Acid* R *Groups*

$$
\begin{array}{c}
R \\
| \\
C \\
\end{array}
$$

NH₃⁺   H   COO⁻

Predisposed toward	Nonpolar side chains	Polar
		Basic

α-helical structure	—CH₃
	 Alanine
	
	 —CH₂— ⬡
	 Phenylalanine
	
	 —CH₂—CH—CH₃
	         CH₃
	 Leucine
		—CH₂—CH₂—CH₂
		             CH₂
		             NH₃⁺
		 Lysine
		
		 —CH₂—CH₂—CH₂
		             NH
		          ⁺C—NH₂
		           NH₂
		 Arginine
		
		 —CH₂—C══CH
		     HN N(H⁺)
		       C
		       H
		 Histidine

Non-α structures	CH₃
	 —CH
	       CH₂CH₃
	 Isoleucine
	
	       CH₃
	 —CH
	       CH₃
	 Valine
	
	 —H
	 Glycine
	
	 O CH₂—CH₂
	 ‖
	 —C—CH CH₂
	 O ⁺NH₂
	 Proline	

R groups table showing L-amino acid side chains.

side chains

Neutral	Acidic
—CH₂—CONH₂ Asparagine	—CH₂—COO⁻ Aspartic acid
—CH₂—CH₂—CONH₂ Glutamine	—CH₂—CH₂COO⁻ Glutamic acid
—CH₂—⬡—OH Tyrosine	
—CH₂— (indole ring with N, H) Tryptophan	
—CH₂—CH₂—S—CH₃ Methionine	
—CH₂SH Cysteine	
—CH₂OH Serine	
—CHOH CH₃ Threonine	

α-L-amino acid. Depending on the arrangement of the four different groups about the tetrahedral carbon atom, two possible nonsuperimposable mirror-image forms give rise to two distinct isomers. Amino acids found in proteins are almost always L-amino acids, so called because their configuration corresponds to that of L-glyceraldehyde. The sign of rotation of a plane of polarized light upon passage through a solution of an L-amino acid may be either positive or negative and is strongly pH- and wavelength-dependent. If the ammonium group of an L-amino acid were held in the left hand, and the carboxylate group in the right, so that the H atom and R group both pointed upwards, the R group would be nearer the holder, and the H atom farther away. To put it another way, if, in an extended hand, a triangularly disposed thumb, forefinger, and index finger represent the H atom, ammonium group, and carboxylate group, respectively, then the R group is in the position of the left arm in an L-amino acid, and the right arm in a D-amino acid. Differences between L and D isomers are significant when interaction with optically active surfaces takes place. In general L-amino acids taste more bitter than their D counterparts.

Several of the amino acid side chains in Table 1-1 deserve further comment. In glycine the R group is only an H atom. Since this amino acid already contains an H atom bound to a tetrahedral carbon atom, there are no optical isomers for glycine. Threonine and isoleucine, on the other hand, possess two asymmetrically substituted carbon atoms, so that four optical isomers are possible in these two cases. The complete amino acid, not just the R group, is drawn for proline, because in this special case the R function cannot be shown conveniently without including the ring which contains the asymmetrically substituted carbon atom. The positively charged end of the arginine R group is a resonance structure with the center of the positive charge residing on the carbon atom. Thus both lysine and arginine contain a positive charge about the same distance from the asymmetric carbon. Histidine contains an imidazole residue which, when protonated, yields a structure with resonance possibilities in the ring. Note that the acid moiety of the R groups of aspartic and glutamic acids may be amidated in proteins to yield two quite different amino acid residues. Tryptophan possesses an indole residue.

When two or more amino acids are combined by the elimination of water to yield an amide bond, the resulting compound is called a *peptide* if the amino acid sequence is short, a *polypeptide* if the sequence is long, and a *protein* if the sequence is long and specifically determined in nature. In peptides and proteins an amide bond is frequently referred to as a peptide bond. That part of an amino acid which occurs in a polypeptide or protein is called an amino acid *residue*. For example, in the naturally occurring tripeptide glutathione,

$$\begin{array}{c}
\text{NH}_3{}^+ \hspace{5.5cm} \text{CH}_2\text{SH}\\
\diagdown \hspace{6cm} |\\
\text{CH—CH}_2\text{—CH}_2\text{—C—NH—CH—C—NH—CH}_2\text{—COOH}\\
\diagup \hspace{2.8cm} \| \hspace{2.1cm} \|\\
{}^-\text{OOC} \hspace{3.1cm} \text{O} \hspace{2.1cm} \text{O}
\end{array}$$

or γ-glutamylcysteinylglycine, the central amino acid residue is called a *cysteinyl residue*. Note that in this peptide the γ- instead of the α-carboxyl group is linked to the nitrogen atom of the cysteinyl residue. Since unusual linkages of this kind seldom occur in proteins, we shall not consider them. By convention, peptide chains, which are usually written with the ammonium or N terminus on the left and the carboxylate or C terminus on the right, are named from left to right, as in the above example.

In Table 1-1 the amino acid R groups are arranged according to two criteria: their side-chain polarities in the vertical columns and their predisposition toward forming an α helix or a non-α structure when in a polypeptide or protein. The polar amino acid R groups are straight-chained, while nonpolar R groups tend to be branched. The divisions made are not always sharp, however. Helices are discussed further in Sec. 14-1; the amino acid groups are listed here in this way for convenient reference. We merely note now that all naturally occurring amino acids with charged side chains seem to be predisposed toward formation of an α helix. Not all amino acids predisposed toward helix formation when components of polymers form helices of the same strength or even of the same screw sense.

1-2 OPTICAL ROTATION

Sugars are the prime examples of compounds which rotate a plane of polarized light. This property of sugars is due to their common possession of at least one asymmetric carbon atom with four different groups bound in a tetrahedral fashion such that nonsuperimposable mirror-image forms give rise to two distinct optical isomers. Measurements are usually conducted in a polarimeter, an instrument containing two nicol prisms, the first to polarize incident monochromatic light (often sodium D line) before passage through a sample, and the second used as an analyzer prism. Insertion of an optically active sample into the light path requires that the angle between polarizer and analyzer prisms be changed in order to restore passage of light comparable to that observed prior to introduction of a sample. At a given temperature and wavelength of monochromatic radiation, the specific rotation $[\alpha]$ is defined as

$$[\alpha]_\lambda^T = \frac{100\alpha}{lc}$$

where α is the measured angle of rotation for a solution containing c grams of optically active substance in 100 ml of solution, and l is the path length in decimeters. If measurements are performed at 25° with a sodium lamp which produces doublet D lines at 5,890 and 5,896 A, the specific rotation is denoted as $[\alpha]_D^{25}$. *Molar rotation* is defined as

$$[M] = \frac{M[\alpha]}{100} \tag{1-1}$$

where M is the molecular weight of the optically active solute. The solvent dependence of $[M]$ may be eliminated by dividing Eq. (1-1) by $(n^2 + 2)/3$, where n is the refractive index at each wavelength of a solvent which does not interact with the solute and $[M']$ is the vacuum value of the molar rotation:

$$[M'] = \frac{3[M]}{n^2 + 2} = \frac{3[\alpha]M}{(n^2 + 2)100}$$

For substances composed of repeating subunits such as proteins, it is frequently convenient to define a *mean residue rotation* as follows, where MRW is the mean residue weight:

$$[m'] = \frac{3[m]}{n^2 + 2} = \frac{3[\alpha]\,\mathrm{MRW}}{(n^2 + 2)100}$$

Since mean residue weights for proteins are frequently about 110, $[m]$ is only about 10% greater than $[\alpha]$. For aqueous solutions,

$$[m'] = [m]/1.26 = 0.9[\alpha]$$

Thus solvent-corrected mean residue rotations have almost the same numerical values as specific rotations.

A beam of plane-polarized light may be thought of as composed of right and left circularly polarized components. When both components are transmitted with equal velocities through a medium, no rotation occurs, and $\alpha = 0$. If refractive indices for transmission of the two components differ by 1 part in 10^6, then the circularly bire-fringent emergent beam exhibits a phase difference and a rotation of the plane of polarization which yields $[\alpha]_D \simeq 100$. If optical rotation measurements are performed over a range of wavelengths, greater rotations are obtained as an optically active absorption band is approached, as shown by the solid curve of Fig. 1-1. Rotatory-dispersion curves of this shape and sign are termed *plain negative;* the optical isomer would exhibit a plain positive curve of the same magnitude and opposite sign. Plain dispersion curves may cross the horizontal line of zero rotation.

When the two components, with unequal velocities, of a circularly birefringent beam are also unequally absorbed, the emergent beam is elliptically polarized and exhibits circular dichroism. The combination of circular birefringence and circular dichroism gives rise to the anomalous dashed curve of Fig. 1-1. Such a rotatory-dispersion curve containing a peak at longer wavelengths than a trough is said to exhibit a positive Cotton effect; the optical isomer would yield an identical curve reflected by the horizontal line of zero rotation and would therefore display a negative Cotton effect. The point at which the Cotton-effect curve crosses the line of zero rotation is often close to the center of an optically active absorption band. All plain dispersion curves would eventually become anomalous if the measurements could be extended into the region of an optically active absorption

FIG. 1-1   Plain dispersion curve (solid line) and curve with positive Cotton effect (dashed line). The Cotton-effect curve crosses the line of zero rotation at 458 mμ. The absorption band of acriflavine dye is at 457 mμ. Poly-L-glutamic acid in the helical form displays no Cotton effect in the visible spectral region, while an induced Cotton effect appears on binding of optically inactive acriflavine (Sec. 16-4). [From E. R. Blout and L. Stryer, *Proc. Natl. Acad. Sci. U.S.*, **45**, 1591 (1959).]

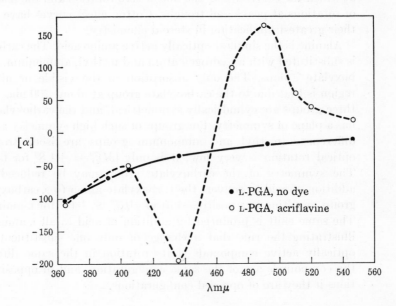

band. Not all absorption bands are optically active. A substance is better characterized by measurement of its optical rotatory dispersion, the optical rotation over a range of monochromatic wavelengths, than by determination of optical rotation at a single wavelength.

A plain dispersion curve is quantitatively characterized by the simple Drude equation

$$[\alpha] = \frac{K}{\lambda^2 - \lambda_c^2} \tag{1-2}$$

In the region in which the curve is plain, a dispersion constant λ_c may be determined from the slope of a $\lambda^2[\alpha]$ versus $[\alpha]$ plot. From the theory of optical rotation, it may be shown that there are at least two optically active transitions in any molecule possessing rotatory power. Therefore, λ_c must be a weighted average consisting of contributions from two or more wavelengths. If the optically active absorption bands are widely separated on the wavelength scale, an experimental λ_c may correspond closely to the center of an optically active absorption band which exhibits strong rotatory activity. As an absorption band is approached, the dispersion becomes complex, and a two-term or longer Drude equation with at least four adjustable parameters fits the data:

$$[\alpha] = \frac{K_1}{\lambda^2 - \lambda_1^2} + \frac{K_2}{\lambda^2 - \lambda_2^2} \tag{1-3}$$

Cotton-effect curves are frequently characterized by the wavelength at which the curve crosses the line of zero rotation and the magnitudes of rotations at peaks and troughs. Cotton-effect curves have received their greatest application in steroid chemistry.

Alanine is the simplest optically active amino acid. The carbon atom is substituted with a hydrogen atom and methyl, ammonium, and carboxylate groups. The only absorption in the visible or ultraviolet region is that due to the carboxylate group at about 200 mμ. The first three groups are cylindrically symmetrical, and the carboxylate anion has a plane of symmetry. For groups of such high symmetry and small differences (methyl and ammonium groups are isoelectronic) the optical rotation is very low; it is only $[M]_D^{20} = +1.8°$ for L-alanine. The symmetry of the carboxylate group may be reduced by the addition of acid to convert the carboxylate anion to a carboxylic acid group, resulting in a positive shift of $[M]_D^{20} \simeq +15°$ for L-amino acids. The same shift is produced by addition of acid to all L-amino acids, illustrating the rule that a change of only one substituent in two optically active compounds shifts rotation in the same direction if the compounds are of the same configuration, and in opposite directions if they are of opposed configurations.

Optical rotations of amino acids are usually compared in acid solutions because comparisons are more easily made when all groups are uniformly protonated. Optical rotatory-dispersion curves of amino acids are plain down to about 250 mμ, and the simple Drude plot yields a dispersion constant λ_c consistent with the carboxylic acid group as the optically active chromophore. Due to the low wavelength region (200 mμ) of this chromophore, Cotton effects are not observed unless the amino acid is coupled with other groups absorbing at higher wavelengths. Dithiocarbamates of amino acids exhibit Cotton effects, and when the absolute configuration of one amino acid is established by x-ray diffraction, the nature of the Cotton effect may be used to establish the configurations of other amino acids. Transition-metal ion chelates of L-amino acids often exhibit easily observed negative Cotton effects in the visible region of the spectrum.

The more distant a chromophoric group is from an asymmetric center in a molecule, the less is its influence on the optical rotations. Other than alanine all optically active amino acids are β-substituted alanines, and any chromophore of the R group is at least one carbon atom removed from the center of asymmetry. Amino acids with aromatic R groups absorb too stongly for direct observation of the Cotton effect, but analysis of a two-term Drude equation indicates that the aromatic chromophore contributes to the optical rotation. Though threonine and isoleucine possess two asymmetric centers, their optical rotatory-dispersion curves are similar to that of alanine, because the second center of asymmetry is not a chromophore.

Restricted rotation about single bonds in the cyclic amino acid proline results in a greater asymmetry than in alanine, markedly increasing the rotatory properties. The trough of a negative Cotton effect appears at about 265 mμ.

The sulfhydryl-containing amino acid cysteine has $[M]_D = -13°$, only slightly larger than alanine. Oxidation of two cysteine molecules to yield the disulfide cystine dramatically increases $[M]_D$ to $-507°$, a value which becomes even greater in neutral solutions. The negative Cotton-effect curve shows a trough at 268 mμ close to the disulfide absorption band at 255 mμ. The high rotation of cystine and other optically active disulfides may be ascribed to restricted rotation in the disulfide linkage (Sec. 16-1).

Glutathione does not exhibit the marked increase in levorotation on oxidation that is shown by cysteine. In aqueous solutions the specific rotation of glutathione is $[\alpha]_D = -17°$, while that of oxidized glutathione is $[\alpha]_D = -108°$. To the extent that glutathione may be taken as a model for sulfhydryl groups in proteins, an increase in levorotation of $108°/2 - 17° = 37°$ occurs for each cysteine residue that becomes linked in a disulfide bond. If even 10% of a protein is composed of cysteine residues, the alteration in specific rotation of only $-3.7°$ on forming all possible disulfide bonds would scarcely be discernible among the greater effects accompanying the usual changes in folding of proteins discussed in Sec. 16-4.

1-3 BIOPOLYMERS

All three classes of naturally occurring macromolecules, i.e., polysaccharides, proteins, and nucleic acids, are large, relatively simple molecules in that they consist of repeating structural units in a linear array, usually with a minimum of cross-linking. The three principal polysaccharides are starch, glycogen, and cellulose. Starch and glycogen are energy stores in plants and animals, respectively; cellulose is the structural element of plants. Polysaccharides are long polydisperse chains of repeating units, D-glucose in the three substances mentioned. Their complex stereochemistry differs, however, since their chains are not linked together in the same way. Chain branching occurs in glycogen and in the amylopectin constituent of starch. Lower viscosities are obtained with branched-chain polymers than with straight-chain amylose of the same molecular weight. Only the amylose fraction of starch can absorb nearly 20% of its weight in iodine to give a blue complex which consists of equally spaced iodine atoms lined down the center of a helical molecule. Polysaccharides bind water by hydrogen bonding through their numerous OH groups and often occur in combination with lipids, proteins, and nucleic acids.

Proteins comprise an extremely diverse group of compounds of large molecular weight and characteristic composition consisting in a uniform backbone of repeating peptide links. Significantly, only α-L-amino acids occur in proteins, because the presence of only one β- or D-amino acid would prevent the constant repeat along the backbone essential to the structures discussed in Chap. 14. Amino acids other than the α variety are found in biological systems, but not as constituents of proteins. The sequence of the 20 or so L-amino acids is under genetic control and is uniform for a given molecule unless the molecule is abnormal. Certain abnormal human hemoglobins are discussed in Sec. 12-3. Folding of proteins must be regular and fairly uniform, because crystals can be made from them. Extensive folding, usually essential for enzyme activity, can also occur in solution, because proteins take on compact shapes.

Responsible for the specific amino acid sequences of proteins are the two naturally occurring, linear, long-chain nucleic acids whose structure and properties are considered in Chaps. 17 to 19. Neither deoxyribosenucleic acid (DNA) nor ribosenucleic acid (RNA) consists of homogeneous material within a cell. DNA, found mainly in the chromosomes of the nucleus, is the genetic material; the sequence of its bases contains the genetic code. Two molecules of DNA have been compared to two different books that superficially look alike, except that one may be about elephants and the other about ants. Consideration of the wide variety of traits incorporated into DNA chains shows why many kinds of DNA may exist in one cell. Several different types of RNA also occur within a cell. The main concentration is in the cytoplasm, where the protein-synthesizing machinery resides. How the varieties of RNA are intimately involved in protein synthesis is discussed in Sec. 20-4.

SELECTED BIBLIOGRAPHY

1 J. P. Greenstein and M. Wintz, "Chemistry of the Amino Acids," 3 vols., John Wiley & Sons, Inc., New York, 1961.

2 A. Meister, "Biochemistry of the Amino Acids," Academic Press Inc., New York, 1957.

3 C. Djerassi, "Optical Rotatory Dispersion," McGraw-Hill Book Company, Inc., New York, 1960.

4 B. Jirgensons, "Natural Organic Macromolecules," Pergamon Press, New York, 1962.

QUESTIONS

1-1 Write resonance structures for phenylalanine, tyrosine, tryptophan, arginine, and histidine (protonated and unprotonated).

1-2 Write out the structure of α-glutamylcysteinylglycine, a tripeptide that has not yet been found naturally.

1-3 What are the molar rotations for glutathione and oxidized glutathione?

1-4 Calculate the solvent-dependent and solvent-independent mean residue rotations for glutathione and oxidized glutathione.

2 | Principles of Equilibria

All living systems depend on chemical reactions. Biochemists have worked out the details of many of these complex reactions and their relationships to each other. But knowledge of the principles of physical chemistry is essential for quantitative assessment of the way in which the driving force or energy available serves to place a particular reaction into a series of coupled reactions occurring in a living system. In this chapter we consider the application of thermodynamics to measurement of the tendency of reactions to attain an equilibrium. As thermodynamics disregards the time factor, our only concern here is how far a reaction can go. How fast it goes (rate) is the subject of Chap. 21.

2-1 FREE ENERGY

The tendency for a reaction to take place is measured by the free-energy change ΔG (commonly denoted as ΔF by American physical chemists). The absolute free energy of a compound is not known. It is the difference in free energy between reactants and products that is measured and recorded. The free-energy change is a function only of the initial and final states of the system and is independent of the path or the time taken to reach the final condition. For a system in equilibrium at constant temperature and pressure, the free-energy change $\Delta G = 0$.

The relationship of free energy to the effective concentration or activity a of a substance is expressed by the equation

$$G - G^o = nRT \ln \frac{a}{a_o}$$

where G^o, a_o = free energy and activity, respectively, in some standard state

n = number of moles
R = universal gas constant, 1.987 cal/deg mole
T = absolute temperature

and ln denotes natural logarithm. Note the dimensionless character of the logarithmic term. In the standard state $a_o = 1$, and we have

$$G - G^o = nRT \ln a = RT \ln a^n \qquad (2\text{-}1)$$

This equation may be taken as a definition of activity. For unit activity, $G = G^o$.

Activity is a measure of the active concentration of a component. Molal activity is related to the concentration by the equation $a = m\gamma$, where a is the activity, m the number of moles of the component per 1,000 g of solvent (molality), and γ the molal activity coefficient. Molar activity is the product of the concentration, expressed as the number of moles per liter of solution (molarity), and a corresponding molar activity coefficient. It is preferable to assign the same units to activity and to concentration, making activity coefficients dimensionless. Relationships between these and other systems for representing activities, concentrations, and activity coefficients are described in standard physical-chemistry and thermodynamics texts. For dilute solutions, differences between the several systems are unimportant.

Consider the general reaction of a moles of substance A with b moles of substance B, etc., to yield p moles of substance P and q moles of substance Q, etc.:

$$aA + bB + \cdots \rightleftharpoons pP + qQ + \cdots \qquad (2\text{-}2)$$

For each component of Reaction (2-2), the free-energy function of Eq. (2-1) may be written

$$\begin{aligned}
G_A &= G_A{}^o + RT \ln (A)^a \\
G_B &= G_B{}^o + RT \ln (B)^b \\
&\cdots\cdots\cdots\cdots\cdots \\
G_P &= G_P{}^o + RT \ln (P)^p \\
G_Q &= G_Q{}^o + RT \ln (Q)^q \\
&\cdots\cdots\cdots\cdots\cdots
\end{aligned} \qquad (2\text{-}3)$$

where the parentheses in the logarithmic terms denote activities of the components. The overall free-energy change of Reaction (2-2) is given by

$$\Delta G = G_P + G_Q + \cdots - G_A - G_B - \cdots$$

Substitution of Eqs. (2-3) yields

$$\Delta G = \Delta G^o + RT \ln \frac{(P)^p(Q)^q \cdots}{(A)^a(B)^b \cdots} \qquad (2\text{-}4)$$

If all components have unit activity, $\Delta G = \Delta G^o$. The particular standard free-energy change denoted by ΔG^o frequently refers to a standard state of 1 atm pressure and unit activity. At equilibrium $\Delta G = 0$, and Eq. (2-4) gives

$$\Delta G^o = -RT \ln \frac{(P)^p(Q)^q \cdots}{(A)^a(B)^b \cdots}$$

At constant temperature the quotient in the logarithmic term is constant, and we may define an equilibrium constant

$$K^o = \frac{(P)^p(Q)^q \cdots}{(A)^a(B)^b \cdots}$$

We then write

$$\Delta G^o = -RT \ln K^o \tag{2-5}$$

and Eq. (2-4) becomes

$$\Delta G = -RT \ln K^o + RT \ln \frac{(P)^p(Q)^q \cdots}{(A)^a(B)^b \cdots} \tag{2-6}$$

Thus, if the standard free-energy change or the equilibrium constant at some temperature is known, the first term on the right of Eq. (2-4) or (2-6) is also known. If the ratios in the logarithmic term are determined, the free-energy change ΔG for the reaction may be calculated. Conversely, the logarithmic term may be computed if ΔG is known.

Let us assume substance A reacts to yield product substance P $(A \rightleftarrows P)$. If α is the fraction of the total moles of A and P that are products at some stage in the course of the reaction, then $1 - \alpha$ is the fraction of the reactants remaining. Equation (2-4) becomes

$$\Delta G = \Delta G^o + RT \ln \frac{\alpha}{1 - \alpha}$$

In Fig. 2-1 the values of ΔG are plotted as a function of α for different assumed values of ΔG^o at 25°C. Initially, values of ΔG are negative, and the reactants slide down the curves until the equilibrium value of $\Delta G = 0$ is attained at the horizontal line. Dashed portions of the curves are not attained without help from another energy source.

In the second lowest curve of Fig. 2-1, $\Delta G^o = 0$, and equilibrium is reached at a value of $\alpha = 0.5$. For more negative values of ΔG^o, equilibrium occurs at larger values of α. In the lowest curve, where ΔG^o is taken as $+1$ kcal/mole, the reaction proceeds until a value of $\alpha = 0.15$ is attained. Even with a positive standard free-energy change, some of the initial reactants are converted to products.

For values of ΔG^o more negative than -10 kcal/mole, equilibrium would not be reached for all practical purposes until α was nearly unity, i.e., until only products were present. Conversely, in the situation in which $\Delta G^o > +10$ kcal/mole, only reactants would ordinarily be detectable.

In the vicinity of $\alpha \simeq 0.5$ in Fig. 2-1, there is a relatively small change in ΔG for a variation in α. An acid-base system in this position is said to be *buffered*, while an oxidation-reduction system in the $\alpha \simeq 0.5$ range is referred to as *poised*.

FIG. 2-1 Free-energy change ΔG kcal/mole versus the fraction of the initial reactant A converted to product P for varying values of ΔG^o at 25°C.

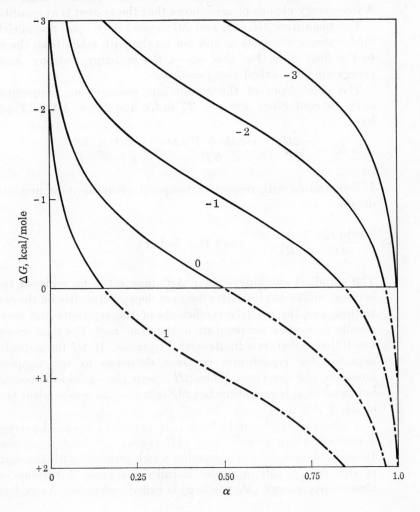

Free-energy changes consist of two parts: $\Delta G = \Delta H - T \Delta S$. Both parts are important in determining the equilibrium position of a reaction. The change in enthalpy ΔH is a measure of the degradation of chemical energy into heat. By convention, exothermic processes are denoted by a negative enthalpy change. The entropy change ΔS indicates the extent to which the system has rearranged into a more disordered array. An increase in disorder is denoted by a positive entropy change. A spontaneous reaction will have a negative free-energy change; that is, ΔG is negative. The more negative the value of ΔG, the greater the innate driving force under the assumed conditions. Enthalpy and entropy effects often oppose each other; the sign of the free energy is then determined by the larger quantity. A positive value of ΔG indicates that the reaction is not spontaneous as written. A free-energy change of zero shows that the system is at equilibrium.

The quantities ΔH, ΔS, and ΔG depend only upon the initial and final states of the system, and not on the path taken from the initial to the final state. For this reason the enthalpy, entropy, and free energy are often called *state functions*.

The dependence of the equilibrium constant on temperature is easily derived. Since $\Delta G^o = -RT \ln K^o$, and $\Delta G^o = \Delta H^o - T \Delta S^o$, we have

$$\ln K^o = \frac{-\Delta G^o}{RT} = \frac{-\Delta H^o + T \Delta S^o}{RT} = \frac{-\Delta H^o}{RT} + \frac{\Delta S^o}{R}$$

Differentiating with respect to temperature at constant pressure, we obtain

$$\frac{d(\ln K^o)}{dT} = \frac{\Delta H^o}{RT^2} \qquad \text{van't Hoff isobar}$$

The standard enthalpy change ΔH^o may often be replaced by ΔH because, unlike ΔG, the latter does not depend explicitly on the concentration, and the activity coefficients of the reactants and products usually depend on temperature in the same way. The final result, the van't Hoff isobar, is a fundamental equation. If ΔH for a reaction is negative, the equilibrium constant decreases as the temperature increases, and vice versa. When ΔH is zero, the equilibrium constant is independent of temperature, but ΔG^o is temperature-dependent because of the $T \Delta S^o$ term.

A reaction which emits heat (ΔH negative) is called *exothermic;* a reaction which absorbs heat (ΔH positive) is termed *endothermic*. In an analogous fashion a reaction which proceeds with the emission of free energy (ΔG negative) is called *exergonic*. A reaction which absorbs free energy (ΔG positive) is called *endergonic*. An endergonic reaction cannot take place, however, unless it is coupled with an exergonic reaction through a common intermediate.

Coupling of an exergonic with an endergonic reaction is illustrated by the synthesis of sucrose (the free-energy values quoted are those estimated for biological conditions):

$$\text{glucose} + \text{fructose} \rightleftarrows \text{sucrose} + \text{H}_2\text{O} \qquad \Delta G = +5 \text{ kcal}$$

This endergonic reaction does not proceed spontaneously but is driven in the forward direction by coupling with the very exergonic reaction

$$\text{ATP} + \text{H}_2\text{O} \rightarrow \text{ADP} + \text{P} \qquad \Delta G = -12 \text{ kcal}$$

The abbreviation ATP represents adenosine triphosphate; ADP, adenosine diphosphate; and P, phosphate. Coupling is achieved via the intermediate glucose-1-P as follows:

$$\text{ATP} + \text{glucose} \rightarrow \text{glucose-1-P} + \text{ADP} \qquad \Delta G = -7 \text{ kcal}$$
$$\text{glucose-1-P} + \text{fructose} \rightarrow \text{sucrose} + \text{P} \qquad \Delta G = 0 \text{ kcal}$$

Since free-energy changes are additive, the net result is

$$\text{ATP} + \text{glucose} + \text{fructose} \rightarrow \text{sucrose} + \text{ADP} + \text{P} \qquad \Delta G = -7 \text{ kcal}$$

This example is typical of the coupling occurring in many biological reactions in which the exergonic nature of one reaction drives an endergonic reaction to completion. Though favored thermodynamically, the reaction takes place at a significant rate only in the presence of enzymes.

2-2 FREE ENERGIES OF FORMATION

Since the free energy is a state function, the free-energy change ΔG is dependent only upon the initial and final states of the system. This important property enables us to calculate the free-energy change of a reaction by subtracting the free energies of formation of the reactants from those of the products. If the requisite free-energy data are known, equilibrium constants may be calculated by Eq. (2-5). For these reasons it is convenient to define and tabulate standard free energies of formation ΔG_f° of compounds. Then the standard free-energy change of a reaction may be obtained by suitable combination of the standard free energies of formation of reactants and products. The standard free energies of formation of several compounds are listed in the second column of Table 2-1. These values are referred to the normal conditions of the substances at a standard state of 1 atm pressure and 25°C. ΔG_f° for any element in the standard state is assigned a value of zero.

Many biological reactions occur in aqueous media. It is pertinent, therefore, to consider the free energies of formation at unit activity in aqueous solution $\Delta \widetilde{G}_f{}^o$. Representative values of $\Delta \widetilde{G}_f{}^o$ are listed in the third column of Table 2-1. The free energy of formation of hydrogen ion at unit activity in aqueous solution is taken as zero. In most cases the differences between the values of columns 2 and 3 of Table 2-1 are small. They are important, however, because the figures are added

TABLE 2-1 *Standard Free Energies of Formation in kilocalories per mole at 25°C and 1 atm*

Compound	$-\Delta G_f{}^o$	$-\Delta \widetilde{G}_f{}^o$
Acetic acid	93.8	95.5
Acetate⁻		89.0
NH_3	4.0	6.4
$NH_4{}^+$		19.0
CO_2	94.3	92.3
$HCO_3{}^-$		140.3
Cysteine	82.1	81.2
Cystine	163.6	159.0
Ethanol	41.8	43.4
α-D-glucose	217.6	219.2
Glycine	88.6	89.3
H^+		0.00
OH^-		37.6
Lactate⁻		123.8
Pyruvate⁻		113.4
Urea	47.1	48.7
Water	56.7	

and subtracted in such a way that the final result is often a difference of large numbers.

We may use Eq. (2-1) to illustrate how $\Delta \widetilde{G}_f{}^o$ may be calculated from $\Delta G_f{}^o$ for α-D-glucose. The reaction is the conversion of solid glucose to an aqueous solution of glucose at unit activity.

Glucose (a_{solid}) → glucose (unit activity in water)

Equation (2-1) becomes

$$\Delta \widetilde{G}_f{}^o = \Delta G_f{}^o + RT \ln \frac{1}{a_{\text{solid}}} = -217.6 - RT \ln a_{\text{solid}} \qquad (2-7)$$

A saturated solution of a compound is in equilibrium with the solid phase; therefore, the activity of glucose in a saturated solution is identical with the activity of the solid. The difference between the two free energies of formation is equal to the difference between the free energy of 1 mole of glucose in a solution at unit activity and its free energy in a saturated solution. The activity of glucose in a saturated solution is 16.6. Substitution into Eq. (2-7) gives

$$\Delta \tilde{G}_{f}^{o} = -217.6 - 2.3 \times 1.987 \times 10^{-3} \times 298 \log 16.6$$
$$= -217.6 - 1.36 \times 1.22 = -219.3 \text{ kcal/mole}$$

This result agrees with the value in the third column of Table 2-1.

The energy made available by the complete oxidation of glucose is a physical-chemistry aspect of a significant biochemical reaction:

$$C_6H_{12}O_6 + 6O_2 \rightarrow 6CO_2 + 6H_2O$$

The standard free-energy change for this reaction in aqueous solution at 25° may be determined from the values for the standard free energies of formation of the components shown in the third column of Table 2-1.

$$\Delta \tilde{G}^{o} = 6 \Delta \tilde{G}_{f}^{o} (CO_2) + 6 \Delta \tilde{G}_{f}^{o} (H_2O) - \Delta \tilde{G}_{f}^{o} (\text{glucose}) - 6 \Delta \tilde{G}_{f}^{o} (O_2)$$
$$= 6(-92.3) + 6(-56.7) - (-219.2) - 6(0)$$
$$= -675 \text{ kcal/mole glucose}$$

This large amount of energy is not released all at once in biological systems. More efficient utilization of the available energy is made possible by its release in smaller amounts, usually less than 10 kcal, in a complex series of reactions involving phosphorylation, acylation, hydrolysis, and dehydrogenation.

The negative sign of the free-energy change for the oxidation of glucose is a general result for organic compounds. In an atmosphere of oxygen all organic compounds are thermodynamically unstable and potentially oxidizable to carbon dioxide. Frequently, however, such reactions occur only indirectly or very slowly, because no convenient direct reaction pathway is available at ordinary temperatures.

2-3 CONTRIBUTION OF ACID - BASE IONIZATION TO THE OVERALL FREE - ENERGY CHANGE

If any of the components of a reaction ionize, the calculated value of ΔG^{o} will not adequately describe the driving force of the reaction. The contribution of ionization to the overall free-energy change at a specified pH may be determined if the ionization constant is known. A pH value of 7.0 is often selected as typical of biological systems.

For the ionization of a weak acid of any charge type, $HA \rightleftarrows H^+ + A$, where H^+ is an abbreviation for the hydrated proton, and HA is the conjugate acid of the base A. The equilibrium constant K_a is equal to $(H^+)(A)/(HA)$, where the parentheses represent activities or, as an approximation, concentrations. The fraction of the total acid in all forms that is ionized is $\alpha = (A)/[(HA) + (A)]$; therefore, $K_a = (H^+)\alpha/(1 - \alpha)$, $\alpha = K_a/[(H^+) + K_a]$, and

$$1 - \alpha = \frac{(H^+)}{[(H^+) + K_a]}$$

If the conjugate acid of an acid-base pair enters into or is produced by a reaction, we are concerned with the effect of its change of concentration on the free-energy change of the reaction.

HA (unit activity in aqueous solution) $\rightleftarrows$ HA (less activity)

Applying Eq. (2-4), we obtain

$$\Delta G = \Delta \tilde{G}^o + RT \ln \frac{(HA)}{(1)}$$

The relative concentration of the acid form is $1 - \alpha$. The contribution to the overall free-energy change due to the ionization of the acid is

$$\Delta G_a = \Delta G - \Delta \tilde{G}^o = RT \ln (1 - \alpha) = 2.3RT \log \frac{(H^+)}{(H^+) + K_a}$$

$$= 1.36 \log \frac{10^{-7.0}}{10^{-7.0} + K_a} \quad \text{kcal/mole} \tag{2-8}$$

The last equality is for the special case of 25°C and pH 7.0. Equation (2-8) simplifies to

$$\Delta G_a = 1.36(pK_a - 7.0) \text{ kcal/mole} \qquad pK_a < 5.5 \tag{2-9}$$

and

$$\Delta G_a = 1.36 \log \frac{10^{-7.0}}{10^{-7.0}} = 0 \qquad pK_a > 8.5 \tag{2-10}$$

In the last case, ionization of the acid contributes nothing to the free energy of the compound because the acid is not ionized appreciably at pH 7.0. When $5.5 < pK_a < 8.5$, the complete Eq. (2-8) must be used.

For the successive ionizations of phosphoric acid H_3PO_4 at 25°, $pK_1 = 2.1$, $pK_2 = 7.2$, and $pK_3 = 12.4$. Contributions of the free energy of ionization to the free energy of phosphoric acid at pH 7.0

are $-\Delta G_{a_1} = 6.7$, $-\Delta G_{a_2} = 0.3$, and $-\Delta G_{a_3} = 0.0$ kcal/mole, yielding a total of $-\Delta G_a = 7.0$ kcal/mole for this tribasic acid.

If the conjugate base form is the reactant or product, we have

$$\Delta G_b = 1.36 \log \frac{K_a}{10^{-7.0} + K_a} \tag{2-11}$$

Thus ammonium ion with $pK_a = 9.3$ yields $-\Delta G_b = 3.1$ kcal/mole if NH_3 is the reactant or product, but $-\Delta G_a = 0$ for NH_4^+ as a reaction component.

2-4 PEPTIDE - BOND HYDROLYSIS

The free energy of hydrolysis, at 25° and pH 7, of the amide bond of dipeptides such as glycylglycine and alanylglycine is about $\Delta G = -4$ kcal/mole. The alanylglycine hydrolysis reaction is

$$NH_3^+CHCH_3CONHCH_2COO^- + H_2O \rightleftarrows NH_3^+CHCH_3COO^- \\ + NH_3^+CH_2COO^-$$

The reverse reaction, combination of alanine and glycine residues to form alanylglycine and water, requires the interaction of the negatively charged carboxylate group of alanine and the positively charged ammonium group of glycine. However, the positively charged ammonium group of alanine repels the same group on glycine. A similar repulsion occurs between the carboxylate groups of the two amino acids. Acylation of the alanyl ammonium group and esterification or amidation of the glycyl carboxylate group would reduce the charge repulsion. The synthesis reaction is thereby more favored in the modified amino acids, and the free energy of hydrolysis is correspondingly less negative. Therefore, dipeptides with no terminal charges or peptide bonds in longer chains where the electrostatic effects are reduced should also have less negative free energies of hydrolysis. In support of this view, the free energy of hydrolysis of the uncharged N-benzoyltyrosyl–glycinamide is only $\Delta G = -0.4$ kcal/mole at 25° and pH 7.

In amide-bond hydrolysis near neutral pH, the carboxylic acid and amino groups ionize to yield carboxylate and ammonium ions. We can determine the contribution of these ionizations to the overall free-energy change at pH 7 by the methods of the previous section. The pK_a value of the carboxylic acid group of N-benzoyltyrosine is 3.8. From Eq. (2-9), $\Delta G_a = -4.4$ kcal/mole. The pK_a value of the ammonium group of glycinamide is 7.9. Equation (2-11) yields $\Delta G_b = -1.3$ kcal/mole. At pH 7 the ionizations thus contribute a total of -5.7 kcal/mole to the free energy of hydrolysis of N-benzoyltyrosylglycinamide. If the ionizations did not occur, the free-energy change for the hydrolysis reaction would be

$$\Delta G = -0.4 - (-5.7) = 5.3 \text{ kcal/mole}$$

This relatively high positive value indicates that the reverse or synthesis reaction is favored in the absence of the ionizations. The result is of general validity. The driving force of amide-bond hydrolysis at biological pH is the ionization of the groups produced, particularly the carboxylic acid group. We might expect peptide bonds to be synthesized in living systems under conditions of esterification and perhaps acylation such that one or both of the reacting groups are uncharged.

2-5 FREE ENERGY OF HYDROLYSIS OF ATP

Energy made available by the oxidation of glucose is stored in several "high-energy" compounds before it is utilized in living processes. These high-energy compounds include acetyl coenzyme A (a thiol-ester), amino acid esters, phosphoacetic acid, 1,3-diphosphoglyceric acid, phospho-enol-pyruvic acid, creatine and arginine phosphates, adenosine diphosphate (ADP), and adenosine triphosphate (ATP). ATP is the primary agent for converting the energy produced in biological reactions into work. In muscle, for example, energy is stored as creatine phosphate and transferred to ATP for use in the contractile process. The structure of ATP, shown in Fig. 2-2, consists of the purine base, adenine, linked to ribose, which in turn is bonded through the 5' carbon to a triphosphate residue.

The structure of the triphosphate residue cannot be depicted on paper. Figure 2-3 indicates some of the resonance forms of the inorganic terminus of ATP. The compound does not exist in first one resonance form and then another; its properties are best explained by a structure

FIG. 2-2 Structure of adenosine triphosphate (ATP).

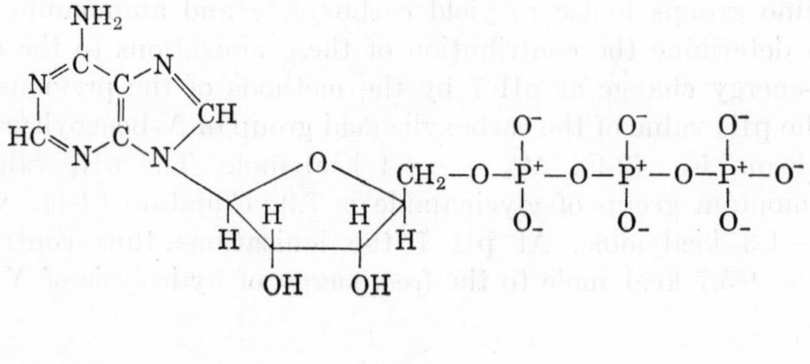

which is a combination of the forms drawn and others, but which is never at any time any one of them. The reader must abstract mentally from the resonance structures a composite structure to which each resonance form makes a contribution. The absence of some important resonance forms in Fig. 2-3 is substantiated by molecular orbital calculations which indicate that the three internal oxygen atoms in the triphosphate residue of ATP each possess a fractional positive charge of about $+0.2$ while the three phosphorus atoms each contain a charge of about $+0.4$ and the seven external oxygen atoms each possess a -0.8 charge.

Determination of the value of the free energy of hydrolysis of ATP in aqueous solutions is a problem of continuing interest. Many of the uncertainties and confusions of the past have now been clarified. We may write the hydrolysis equation at pH 7.5 as

$$ATP^{4-} + H_2O \rightleftarrows ADP^{3-} + HPO_4^{=} + H^+ \tag{2-12}$$

Both reactants and products undergo the loss and gain of protons, but the equation represents the predominant forms at pH 7.5. Due to the highly exergonic nature of the reaction, the equilibrium is far to the right, and the free-energy change cannot be measured by the direct determination of the equilibrium constant,

$$K_T = \frac{[ADP^{3-}][HPO_4^{=}]}{[ATP^{4-}]}$$

where the brackets represent molar concentrations. The activities of the components of the reaction would be quite different from the concentrations, because some of the species are highly charged ions.

FIG. 2-3 Some resonance forms of the triphosphate terminus of ATP.

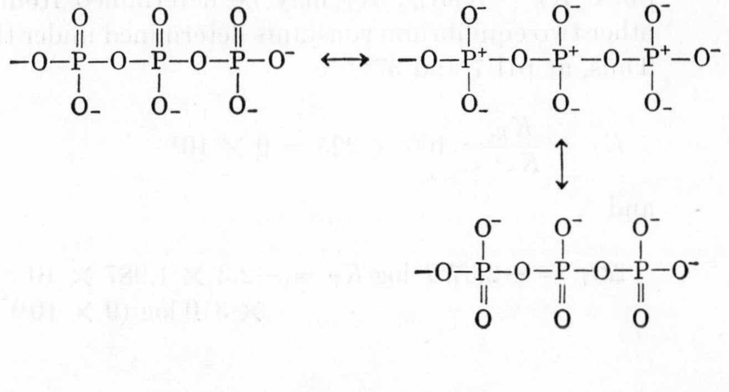

Since the activity coefficients are not known, the thermodynamic or infinite dilution value of K_T cannot be computed.

The concentration equilibrium constant K_T has been determined by coupling the exergonic hydrolysis reaction with an endergonic reaction of known equilibrium constant and evaluating the overall equilibrium constant for the coupled reactions. The reaction of glutamate with ammonium ion to yield glutamine and water proceeds rapidly to an equilibrium position in the presence of the enzyme glutaminase:

$$\underset{\substack{| \\ NH_3^+ \\ Glu^-}}{COO^-}CHCH_2CH_2COO^- + NH_4^+ \rightleftarrows \underset{\substack{| \\ NH_3^+ \\ Glu}}{COO^-}CHCH_2CH_2CONH_2 + H_2O$$

$$(2\text{-}13)$$

A catalyst does not alter the equilibrium position of the reaction but facilitates its determination by promoting the rate of attainment of equilibrium. The delicate technique of heatburst microcalorimetry was used to determine the following thermodynamic equilibrium constant, where the parentheses represent activities of the components:

$$K_{G^o} = \frac{(Glu)}{(Glu^-)(NH_4^+)} = \frac{1}{225} \qquad \text{at pH 7 and 37°C}$$

The sum of Eqs. (2-12) and (2-13) yields

$$ATP^{4-} + Glu^- + NH_4^+ \rightleftarrows ADP^{3-} + HPO_4^= + Glu + H^+$$

The equilibrium constant for the coupled reaction is

$$K_E = \frac{[ADP^{3-}][HPO_4^=](Glu)}{[ATP^{4-}](NH_4^+)(Glu^-)} = 400 \qquad \begin{array}{l} \text{at pH 7 and 37°C in} \\ \text{presence of excess Mg}^{++} \text{ at} \\ 0.2\ M \text{ ionic strength} \end{array}$$

Since $K_E = K_T K_{G^o}$, K_T may be determined from the values of the other two equilibrium constants determined under the same conditions. Thus, at pH 7 and 37°,

$$K_T = \frac{K_E}{K_{G^o}} = 400 \times 225 = 9 \times 10^4$$

and

$$\Delta G_T = -2.3RT \log K_T = -2.3 \times 1.987 \times 10^{-3}$$
$$\times 310 \log (9 \times 10^4) = -7.0 \text{ kcal/mole}$$

This value is obtained in the presence of Mg^{++} ion. Because of differential binding of Mg^{++} ion to the reactants and products of Eq. (2-12), ΔG is about 1.6 kcal/mole more negative in the absence of Mg^{++} ion. The value of ΔG obtained from these careful measurements is less than the -12 kcal/mole previously assumed. The last is, however, a good estimate of the value prevailing under physiological conditions of concentration. Even if $[ADP^{3-}] = [ATP^{4-}]$ in the expression for K_T, any value of $[HPO_4^=] < 1$ M will make ΔG more negative than ΔG^o according to Eq. (2-4).

The importance of ATP has promoted inquiries into its mode of synthesis in biological systems. In aerobic cells more than 90% of the ATP is synthesized in intact mitochondria by oxidative phosphorylation. The exact mechanism is a subject of intense current study. The sites of phosphorylation occur in a very complex series of coupled reactions termed the *respiratory chain*. Energy made available by the oxidation of 1 mole of glucose is passed in small increments through a series of reactions which finally yield 38 moles of ATP. We have already determined that complete oxidation of glucose to CO_2 and H_2O has a free-energy change of -675 kcal/mole. Physiological production of 38 moles of ATP requires the input of about $12 \times 38 = 456$ kcal. Thus about 67% of the energy made available by the oxidation of glucose is transformed into a form utilizable for conversion to work. This transformation occurs with a high degree of efficiency for so complex a reaction sequence.

Phosphate esters of organic compounds have been classified into two groups, depending upon whether the free energy of hydrolysis under biological conditions of temperature and pH has a high negative value as in ATP or a value more positive than about -7 kcal/mole as in glucose-6-phosphoric acid and 3-phosphoglyceric acid. Compounds of the former group are often said to contain high-energy bonds, and those of the latter low-energy bonds. The high-energy bonds of ADP and ATP are often denoted $A—P{\sim}P$ and $A—P{\sim}P{\sim}P$, respectively, where the wavy line represents the high-energy bond.

Several features of the high-energy-bond concept require further comment. In the first place, the nomenclature is just opposite that used in chemical thermodynamics, where the term high-energy bond would denote great stability. In the case of the phosphate esters, high-energy bond means a bond that is easily hydrolyzed, hence of low energy in the thermodynamic sense. Compounds with high-energy bonds have less negative standard free energies of formation than their low-energy counterparts.

The terminology high-energy bond is misleading because it implies that the energy is stored in a single bond. We have already indicated the resonance character of the phosphate terminus of the ATP molecule. This general smearing out of the distribution of electron density precludes localization of energy in any one bond.

The implied presence of two high-energy bonds in A—P∼P∼P is not correct. Formulation of the splitting of ATP to yield ADP and phosphate as A—P∼P∼P → A—P∼P + P is self-consistent. However, when splitting of ATP yields adenosine monophosphate (AMP) and pyrophosphate, A—P∼P∼P → A—P + PP, consistency requires that pyrophosphate contain a high-energy bond. In fact, the free energy of hydrolysis of pyrophosphate is only about −2 kcal/mole. These considerations demonstrate the inadvisability of considering localization of energy in a bond or bonds.

Reasons for the high negative free energies of hydrolysis of some phosphate esters have been determined. At pH 7.5 the contribution of the free energy of ionization accounts for about 60% of the free energy of hydrolysis of ATP to ADP. Once this portion has been allowed for, the enthalpy ΔH contributes the remainder, whereas the entropy is negative and has the effect of making the overall ΔG less negative. The pattern is not the same for all high-energy phosphate esters. Although all have negative ΔH terms, the contribution of ionization and entropy terms may be positive or negative, depending upon the particular compound considered. In fact the ionization and entropy terms usually oppose each other at pH 7.5. No simple general explanation exists for the high free energies of hydrolysis of some phosphate esters.

The foregoing discussion has indicated the importance of considering the phosphate residue as a whole and the inadvisability of localizing the free energy of hydrolysis in a bond or two. It seems more appropriate to state that these compounds have a high *group-transfer potential.* Group-transfer potential is a measure of the tendency of a compound to donate a particular group to another compound. For hydrolysis this latter compound is water. The high group-transfer potentials of certain phosphate groups in biological reactions is akin to the high group-transfer potentials of some acyl groups in organic acylations. Inclusion of the word potential emphasizes the kinetic aspect of the situation. In spite of high group-transfer potentials, the reactions may proceed at convenient rates only in the presence of enzymes.

2-6 OXIDATION - REDUCTION

A substance that is oxidized undergoes a loss of electrons and functions as a reducing agent. In living organisms the most important electron donors are hydrogen atoms of organic molecules. This oxidation process is often called *dehydrogenation.* When one substance loses electrons, the presence of an electron acceptor is implied. The substance that gains electrons is said to be reduced, and it functions as an oxidizing agent. Oxygen is the most important electron acceptor in aerobic organisms. Since oxidation cannot occur without concomitant reduction, the process is referred to as oxidation-reduction.

$$ox_1 + red_2 \rightleftarrows red_1 + ox_2 \tag{2-14}$$

where ox_1 and red_1 are the oxidized and reduced forms of substance 1, and similarly for substance 2. In living systems oxygen does not receive hydrogen atoms directly. A complex series of reactions such as the above proceeds by means of electron carriers which have intermediate potentials.

The tendency for oxidation-reduction reactions to occur may be determined by potentiometric measurements of electromotive force (emf). It is not convenient to determine the emf for every conceivable oxidation-reduction system. For this reason half-reactions are considered:

$$ox + ne \rightleftarrows red \tag{2-15}$$

where ox is the oxidized form, red the reduced form, and n the number of electrons transferred per molecule of oxidant or reductant. As it is not possible to determine the absolute electrode potential of any half-reaction, the standard hydrogen-electrode half-reaction

$$H^+ (a = 1) + e^- \rightleftarrows \tfrac{1}{2}H_2 \text{ (1 atm)}$$

is assigned a potential of 0.000 volts at any temperature. In all other standard half-reactions, emf values are compared directly or indirectly with the assigned value for the standard hydrogen electrode.

The writing of a free electron in Eq. (2-15) and other equations does not mean that a free electron is thought to exist in solution; Eq. (2-15) is only a half-reaction. For electron transfer to take place, another half-reaction system is needed to give an overall result similar to that of Eq. (2-14). The mechanism of reactions for which n is 2 in Eq. (2-15) has been the subject of much discussion. Is there a simultaneous transfer of two electrons, or do two successive one-electron transfers occur? To the extent that the process occurs by atom transfer, the debate is unnecessary. In aqueous solutions OH or H atom transfer is equivalent to a one-electron process, and hydride ion or O atom transfer to a two-electron process. Water is a good solvent for transfer reactions because it provides both kinds of transfer species. Many oxidation-reduction reactions probably involve some kind of atom transfer. Since this is a chapter about equilibria, we are concerned only with the initial and final states of the system. The thermodynamic result is independent of the mechanism or path taken.

Several conventions regarding the choice of sign for standard half-reactions are in use. A convention must be chosen and used consistently, or incorrect conclusions may result. The convention chosen here has been widely adopted, except by American physical chemists. It has the advantage of assigning a negative potential to the half-reaction occurring at the electrode at which oxidation takes place (anode) in the emf cell. Consistent with this choice of convention, we shall write half-reactions as reductions, assign a negative sign to the standard half-reactions of oxidizing agents stronger than hydrogen ion at unit activity, and refer to tabulations of such half-reactions as tables of standard reduction potentials. Tables of standard reduction potentials are prepared with reference to a standard state of unit activity in aqueous solution at 25°C and 1 atm pressure. The American physical chemist writes half-reactions as oxidations, tabulates standard oxidation potentials, and reverses the sign of the numerical values.

The free-energy change is related to the potential,

$$\Delta G = -nF\mathcal{E} \tag{2-16}$$

where $\mathcal{E}$ is the potential in volts, and F is the Faraday, equal to 96,500 coulombs/equiv. Thus the more positive the value of $\mathcal{E}$, the more negative the value of ΔG and the greater the driving force of the reaction. Since 1 volt-coul = 1 joule and there are 4.184 joules/cal

$$1 \text{ Faraday} = \frac{96,500 \text{ coul/equiv}}{4.184 \text{ volt-coul/cal}} \times 10^{-3} \text{ kcal/cal}$$

$$= 23.06 \text{ kcal/volt-equiv}$$

Substitution of Eqs. (2-15) and (2-16) into Eq. (2-4) yields

$$\mathcal{E} = \mathcal{E}^o + \frac{2.30RT}{nF} \log \frac{(\text{ox})}{(\text{red})} \tag{2-17}$$

where $\mathcal{E}^o$ is the standard reduction potential. This equation is of the same form as those plotted in Fig. 2-1; only the units differ. At 25°C the prelogarithmic term of Eq. (2-17) becomes

$$\frac{2.30RT}{nF} = \frac{2.30 \times 1.987 \text{ cal/deg-mole} \times 298° \times 10^{-3} \text{ kcal/cal}}{n \text{ equiv/mole} \times 23.06 \text{ kcal/volt-equiv}}$$

$$= \frac{0.0592}{n} \text{ volt}$$

To illustrate how these principles are applied, we shall consider the reduction of pyruvic to lactic acid:

$$CH_3C{-}COOH + 2H^+ + 2e^- \rightleftarrows CH_3CH{-}COOH$$

with O double-bonded below the first carbon and OH below the second.

The reduction potential for this system at 35° and pH 7 is $\varepsilon = -0.179$ volt. We wish to determine the standard reduction potential ε^o at the same temperature. At 35° the ionization constants are $K_P = 3.2 \times 10^{-3}$ for pyruvic acid and $K_L = 1.55 \times 10^{-4}$ for lactic acid. These values indicate that at pH 7 both acids exist predominantly in their ionized or basic forms. Since the standard reduction potential ε^o is the value at unit activity of hydrogen ion in aqueous solution, allowance must be made for the alteration in the nature of the oxidant and reductant with the change in pH.

Application of Eq. (2-17) to this system yields

$$\varepsilon = \varepsilon^o + \frac{0.0611}{2} \log \frac{(HP)(H^+)^2}{(HL)} \tag{2-18}$$

For pyruvic acid, $K_P = (P^-)(H^+)/(HP)$. The total molar concentration of pyruvic acid in its acidic and basic forms is $C_P = (HP) + (P^-)$. Solving the two simultaneous equations yields

$$(HP) = (H^+)C_P/[(H^+) + K_P].$$

Similarly, $(HL) = (H^+)C_L/[(H^+) + K_L]$. Thus Eq. (2-18) becomes

$$\varepsilon = \varepsilon^o + 0.0306 \log \frac{C_P}{C_L} + 0.0306 \log \frac{(H^+) + K_L}{(H^+) + K_P} - 0.0611 \, pH \tag{2-19}$$

At unit activity of (H^+) or pH 0, $(H^+) \gg K_L$ or K_P, and

$$\varepsilon = \varepsilon^o + 0.0306 \log \frac{(HP)}{(HL)}$$

At pH 7.0, we have

$$\varepsilon = -0.179 = \varepsilon^o + 0.0306 \log \frac{(P^-)}{(L^-)} + 0.0306 \log \frac{K_L}{K_P} - 0.0611 \times 7.0$$

$$\varepsilon = \varepsilon^o + 0.0306 \log \frac{(P^-)}{(L^-)} - 0.0402 - 0.4277 \tag{2-20}$$

Therefore, $\varepsilon^o = -0.179 + 0.0402 + 0.4277 = +0.289$ volt. The equation for the potential at any pH at 35° is given by Eq. (2-19) with

$\mathcal{E}^o = +0.289$ volt. Reduction is more favored in acid solutions because pyruvic acid is a stronger acid than lactic acid ($K_P > K_L$).

Many $\mathcal{E}$ values are determined under conditions considerably removed from unit activity of hydrogen ion, as in the case just described. To determine $\mathcal{E}^o$, accurate values of the ionization constants at the same temperature are required. Precise evaluation of $\mathcal{E}^o$ is necessary if any temperature-variation studies are to be made, because the standard hydrogen electrode is assigned a zero value at any temperature only at unit activity of hydrogen ion. The standard cannot be changed to pH 7 or any other pH without introduction of the unknown temperature dependence of the hydrogen electrode. Therefore, unless the $\mathcal{E}^o$ value and its temperature dependence are known, measurements of $\mathcal{E}$ performed at other than unit activity of hydrogen ion must be separately determined at each temperature of interest.

The ratio of pyruvate to lactate may be calculated easily. At equilibrium $\mathcal{E} = 0$, so that we have, at pH 7 and 35°, from Eq. (2-20),

$$\mathcal{E} = 0 = +0.289 + 0.0306 \log \frac{(P^-)}{(L^-)} - 0.468$$

Therefore,

$$\log \frac{(P^-)}{(L^-)} = \frac{0.179}{0.0306} = 5.85$$

or $(P^-)/(L^-) = 7 \times 10^5$. This result means that at equilibrium lactate is almost completely oxidized to pyruvate at pH 7 and 35°.

It is not always possible to calculate the $\mathcal{E}^o$ value for a half-reaction from data taken in a pH range removed from pH 0. Such would have been the case in the example if the ionization constants of pyruvic and lactic acids were not known at 35°. In the pH 7 region, $d\mathcal{E}/d(\text{pH}) = -0.0611$ from Eq. (2-19). The observed value, at pH 7, of $\mathcal{E} = -0.179$ volt may be extrapolated to pH 0 without regard for the change to the acidic form of oxidant and reductant. The value so obtained,

$$\tilde{\mathcal{E}} = -0.179 + 0.4277 = +0.249 \text{ volt} = \mathcal{E}^o + 0.0306 \log \frac{K_L}{K_P}$$

is the standard reduction potential for the reaction

$$CH_3COCOO^- + 2H^+ + 2e^- \rightleftarrows CH_3CH(OH)COO^- \tag{2-21}$$

with all ions at unit activity. $\tilde{\mathcal{E}}$ is a hypothetical potential because the acid anions cannot exist at unit activity in the presence of hydrogen ion at unit activity.

The standard free-energy change of the reaction in Eq. (2-21) may be evaluated directly from Table 2-1 because all components of the reaction are at unit activity.

$$\Delta \tilde{G} = -123.8 - (-113.4) = -10.4 \text{ kcal/mole}$$

$$\tilde{\varepsilon} = \frac{-\Delta \tilde{G}}{nF} = \frac{10.4 \text{ kcal/mole}}{2 \text{ equiv/mole} \times 23.06 \text{ kcal/volt-equiv}}$$

$$= 0.225 \text{ volt at } 25°C$$

This value cannot be compared directly with the potentiometric results for $\tilde{\varepsilon}$ because the latter was determined at 35°.

SELECTED BIBLIOGRAPHY

1 W. J. Moore, "Physical Chemistry," 3d ed., Prentice-Hall, Inc., Englewood Cliffs, N.J., 1962.

2 G. N. Lewis and M. Randall, revised by K. S. Pitzer and L. Brewer, "Thermodynamics," 2d ed., McGraw-Hill Book Company, Inc., New York, 1961.

3 I. M. Klotz, "Chemical Thermodynamics," Prentice-Hall, Inc., Englewood Cliffs, N.J., 1950.

4 H. Netter, "Theoretische Biochemie," Springer-Verlag OHG, Berlin, 1959.

5 E. Baldwin, "Dynamic Aspects of Biochemistry," 3d ed., Cambridge University Press, New York, 1957.

6 H. A. Krebs and H. L. Kornberg, A Survey of the Energy Transformations in Living Matter, *Ergeb. Physiol.*, **49**, 212–298 (1957). In English, with an appendix by K. Burton, as "Free Energy Data of Biological Interest."

7 T. Benzinger, C. Kitzinger, R. Hems, and K. Burton, Free Energy Changes of the Glutaminase Reaction and the Hydrolysis of the Terminal Pyrophosphate Bond of Adenosine Triphosphate, *Biochem. J.*, **71**, 400–407 (1959).

8 P. George and R. J. Rutman, The High Energy Phosphate Bond Concept, *Progr. in Biophys. Biophys. Chem.*, **10**, 1–53 (1960).

9 W. M. Clark, "Oxidation-Reduction Potentials of Organic Systems," The Williams & Wilkins Company, Baltimore, 1960.

QUESTIONS

2-1 Find the values of ΔG^o corresponding to the following values of equilibrium constants at 25°: $K = 10^{-3}, 10^{-2}, 10^{-1}, 10^0, 10, 10^2, 10^3, 10^6$.

2-2 Construct curves of Fig. 2-1 for $\Delta G^o = +5$ and -5 kcal/mole.

2-3 Construct a plot analogous to that of Fig. 2-1 for equimolar amounts of reactants in the reaction $A + B \rightleftharpoons P + Q$.

2-4 Calculate the equilibrium constant for the complete oxidation of glucose in aqueous solution. How does a solution of glucose in contact with oxygen manage to exist?

2-5 A saturated solution of glycine is 3.3 molal with $-\log \gamma = 0.137$ at 25°. Given that $\Delta G_f{}^o = -88.6$ kcal/mole, find $\Delta \tilde{G}_f{}^o$.

2-6 The vapor pressure of pure liquid ethanol at 25° is 56.5 mm. A 1 M solution of ethanol in water has a vapor pressure of ethanol of 3.65 mm. Given that $\Delta G_f{}^o = -41.8$ kcal/mole, what is $\Delta \tilde{G}_f{}^o$?

2-7 Calculate the free-energy change in the commercially important reaction catalyzed by enzymes from yeast,

$$C_6H_{12}O_6 \rightarrow 2CO_2 + 2C_2H_5OH$$

2-8 Calculate the first ionization constant of carbonic acid from the information given in Table 2-1.

2-9 Calculate the free energy of formation in aqueous solution of N-acetylcysteine.

2-10 What percent peptide is present at equilibrium at pH 7 for initial solutions of N-benzoyltyrosyl–glycinamide 10^{-1} and 10^{-4} M in peptide?

2-11 Calculate the contribution of the ionization of the products to the free energy of hydrolysis of alanylglycine. The pK_a values are 2.4 for the carboxyl group of alanine and 9.7 for the ammonium group of glycine. About what would the free-energy change be in the absence of ionizations of the newly formed product groups? How does this compare with the value for N-benzoyltyrosyl–glycinamide?

2-12 For the formation reaction of many carboxylic acid esters, acid + alcohol $\leftrightarrows$ ester + H_2O, the molar equilibrium constant is about 3 under a wide variety of conditions of solvent and temperature. Show that the free energy of hydrolysis of many carboxylic acid esters is -1.7 kcal/mole at 25° in dilute aqueous solution. (Note that the molar concentration of water is used in the equilibrium constant, while water is considered to be at unit activity in calculating ΔG.)

2-13 Pursue further the result of the previous question by calculating the free energies of hydrolysis of ethyl acetate and glycine ethyl ester at pH 7, and, in effect, calculate the contribution of ionization to the overall free-energy change at this pH. For acetic acid and glycine, the pK_a values are 4.7 and 2.4, respectively.

2-14 In what regards is the term high-energy bond misleading?

2-15 Write resonance structures for PO_4^{3-} and ADP.

2-16 From statements in the text deduce whether Mg^{++} is bound more strongly to ADP^{3-} or ATP^{4-}.

2-17 It has been said that the value of the free energy of hydrolysis of ATP under physiological conditions of 12 kcal/mole is the currency of living organisms. How many volts of potential is this?

2-18 What is the potential of a hydrogen electrode at pH 7?

2-19 The oxygen electrode is not reversible, but the standard reduction potential has been calculated by indirect methods to be $\mathcal{E}^o = +0.401$ volt at 25°. The electrode equation is

$$\tfrac{1}{2}O_2 \text{ (1 atm)} + H_2O \text{ } (l) + 2e^- \leftrightarrows 2OH^-$$

Calculate the potential of the oxygen electrode in air at pH 7.0 and 25°.

2-20 The oxidized and reduced forms of the enzyme cofactor nicotinamide adenine dinucleotide are related by

$$NAD^+ + H^+ + 2e^- \leftrightarrows NADH$$

where, at 30°, $\tilde{\mathcal{E}} = -0.107$ volt. Derive the relationship between potential and pH in the physiological pH range.

2-21 What is the standard free-energy change in aqueous solution for the reduction of cystine to cysteine? How is the result dependent upon pH? What is the value of the equilibrium constant?

3 | Solubility

So many factors affect the solubilities of substances that this chapter cannot attempt to exhaust the subject. Only the main outlines of variations in solubility for aqueous solutions will be described. The ideas and equations introduced in this description will be used in succeeding chapters, especially Chap. 4. In the past, separation of proteins by solubility techniques (either salting out with added salts or precipitation by addition of nonaqueous liquids such as ethanol) was of great importance. Such procedures, though still useful, have now been largely replaced by chromatographic techniques. Our discussion, therefore, treats only a fraction of the concepts and applications of solubility.

3-1 HYDROGEN BONDING

"Like dissolves like" is the simplest rule of solubility and should be appreciated early in a student's training. Application of this rule leads one to expect mutual solubilities of hydrocarbons and, by negative inference, insolubility of hydrocarbons in water.

Addition of a hydroxy group to a hydrocarbon to yield an alcohol markedly increases the solubility in water. Propane gas is nearly insoluble in water; liquid propyl alcohol is miscible with water in all proportions. The higher boiling points and greater solubilities in water of alcohols, as compared with the corresponding hydrocarbons, are attributed mainly to hydrogen bonding in alcohols. Hydrogen bonds may be formed in compounds containing hydrogen bound to electronegative F, O, N, or S atoms, yielding a relatively unshielded, partially positive H atom which may interact electrostatically with another electronegative atom. Examples of such compounds are water, alcohols, and carboxylic acids. The last form dimers in the vapor phase at low temperatures, in the solid state, and in non-hydrogen-bonding solvents:

$$R—C \overset{\displaystyle O \text{------} H—O}{\underset{\displaystyle O—H \text{------} O}{\Big\langle}} C—R$$

where the dotted line represents a hydrogen bond. Only in special cases, such as bifluoride ion FHF^-, is the hydrogen equidistant from the two electronegative atoms. Hydrogen bonds are only about 10% as strong as ordinary covalent bonds.

In solvents such as water, which is highly hydrogen-bonded, dimer formation of carboxylic acids does not occur at low concentrations because extensive hydrogen bonding occurs between solute and excess solvent. Since biological systems contain an aqueous milieu, competition between solute-solute and solute-solvent hydrogen bonding is a common concern in such systems. Hydrogen bonds are of enormous importance in living organisms, and further discussion and examples of hydrogen-bonded structures are presented in this chapter and in Chaps. 14 to 19.

3-2 DIPOLE MOMENT AND DIELECTRIC CONSTANT

Of the numerous factors affecting solubility, the dielectric constant of the solvent appears to be one of the more important. Since dielectric-constant measurements are useful in determining dipole moments, we shall discuss both these topics in a single section.

When a bond is formed between two atoms of differing electronegativity, a dipole is formed. The dipole moment μ_D is defined as the product of the charge q and the distance between charges r; $\mu_D = qr$. Since the electronic charge is 4.8×10^{-10} esu, and interaction distances are of the order of 1 A or 10^{-8} cm, the dipole moment μ_D is of the order of 10^{-18} esu-cm, called 1 *Debye unit*. In polyatomic molecules, in which several bonds may exhibit dipoles, the net dipole moment for the molecule as a whole may be obtained by vector addition of the component bond moments if orientation of all dipoles is known. Molecules exhibiting appreciable permanent dipole moments are called *polar*, while molecules with little or no permanent dipole moments are termed *nonpolar*.

Dipole moments of nonpolar molecules may be determined from measurements of the dielectric constants of dilute solutions of the molecules in nonpolar solvents. The determination of dipole moments of amino acids and proteins is more difficult, because they form highly conducting solutes in water and are usually insoluble in nonpolar solvents. In such determinations polar solvents such as water must be used, but the simple theoretical considerations applicable to nonpolar molecules no longer apply. In practice high-frequency alternating fields are used to minimize complications arising from conductance effects.

If two charged plates produce a uniform electric field of strength E_0, the introduction of nonpolar molecules between the plates reduces

TABLE 3-1 *Dielectric Constants of Liquids*†

Liquid	Dielectric constant
Hexane	1.9
Dioxane	2.2
Benzene	2.3
Chloroform	5
Acetone	21
Ethanol	24
Methanol	33
Nitrobenzene	35
Acetonitrile	37
N-dimethylformamide	37
N-dimethylacetamide	38
Acetamide	74 (extrapolated)
Water	78.5
Hydrogen fluoride	84 (0°)
Hydrogen peroxide	94
Sulfuric acid	101
Hydrogen cyanide	107
Formamide	110
N-methylpropionamide	172
N-methylacetamide	179 (30°)
N-methylformamide	182

† The temperature is 25° unless otherwise specified.

the field strength to E, because dipoles induced in the molecules by the electric field act in opposition to the applied field. The dielectric constant of the medium, $\epsilon = E_0/E$, is always greater than unity. Dielectric constants of nonpolar substances are often determined by measuring the capacitance of a capacitor in an alternating electric field both with and without the dielectric medium. If the capacitance in a vacuum is C_0, the introduction of a medium increases it to C. The dielectric constant is found from the ratio of the capacitances:

$$\epsilon = C/C_0.$$

In Table 3-1 are collected the dielectric constants of several liquids. In general, molecules usually thought to be the most polar and associated exhibit the greatest dielectric constants. All the liquids displaying high dielectric constants are capable of extensive hydrogen bonding among molecules, often producing long chains. Except for formic and acetic acids, in which the opposite trend is observed, the dielectric constant always decreases with an increase in temperature at constant pressure. In contradistinction to the usual effect, increased temperature disrupts cyclic hydrogen-bonded dimers of formic and acetic acids and permits a more polymeric type of association, which raises the dielectric constant.

The extraordinarily high dielectric constants of pure liquid *N*-monomethyl amides are accounted for by polymeric association through hydrogen bonding of planar trans structures. Contributions from the resonance forms yield a hybrid structure

with 40% double-bond character in the C—N bond. Since rotation about double bonds is restricted, planarity is enforced on the molecule. Steric considerations favor the trans structure. Nitrogen-bonded hydrogens are linked by hydrogen bonds to the carbonyl oxygens of neighboring molecules throughout the medium:

N-unsubstituted and *N*-disubstituted amides have lower moments because cyclic hydrogen-bonded structures are permitted in the former, while no hydrogen-bond donor is present in the latter. In reference to the two resonance structures depicted above, it is important to appreciate that neither structure ever exists, and that there is no oscillation between the two structures. The double-headed arrow implies that the correct representation is a hybrid structure, not easily drawn on paper, which the reader must abstract mentally from the pictured resonance forms. Molecular orbital calculations yield a net charge of -0.40 on the oxygen atom and charges of about $+0.14$ and $+0.26$ on nitrogen and peptide carbon atoms, respectively.

Experimentally determined dielectric constants of solutions of dipolar ions in water at 25° are accurately represented by the linear equation $\epsilon = 78.54 + \delta C$, where C is the molar concentration. Smaller and negative values of δ are obtained for solutions of salts in water. This equation is valid up to the limits of solubility of dipolar ions, which are often well over 1 M. The molar dielectric increment δ, constant for a given amino acid, is about 23 for α-amino acids, 35 for β-amino acids, 51 for γ-amino acids, 63 for δ-amino acids, 75 for ϵ-amino acids, and 87 for ζ-amino acids and increases as the charge separation becomes greater. For pentaglycine, $\delta = 215$; for the protein, β-lactoglobulin, $\delta = 60 \times 10^3$, a value which would be much greater if all the plus charges were at one end of the molecule and all the minus charges at the opposite end. The δ values for β-lactoglobulin and other proteins indicate a generally even charge distribution over the surface of the protein. Molar dielectric increments are approximately proportional to the square of the dipole moments. As calculation of dipole moments from polarization data for polar substances is complicated, the reader is referred to Chap. 6 of Ref. 1 for some of the details. The results obtained are in agreement with those deduced from structural arguments. Since the distance between positive and negative charges on the glycine molecule $NH_3^+CH_2COO^-$ is about 3 A, the dipole moment from structural considerations is

$$4.8 \times 10^{-10} \text{ esu} \times 3 \times 10^{-8} \text{ cm} = 15 \times 10^{-18} \text{ esu-cm}$$
$$= 15 \text{ Debye units}$$

3-3 ION-ION INTERACTIONS

Since ions bear at least one whole unit of electrostatic charge, the intense electrostatic field produced alters the properties of neighboring solvent molecules and affects other ions according to Coulomb's law, $F = q_1q_2/\epsilon r^2$, where F is the force between two charges q separated by a distance r in a medium of dielectric constant ϵ. Even in aqueous solutions in which the dielectric constant is high, the interactions between ions are appreciable and take place over long distances. Ideal behavior is therefore not observed in electrolyte solutions. We shall consider the determination of the departure from ideality in terms of activity coefficients from solubility measurements and the Debye-Hückel theory for estimating activity coefficients in dilute solutions.

Activity Coefficients from Solubility. Dissolution of a slightly soluble salt such as thallous chloride to give aqueous ions is represented by

$$TlCl \ (s) \rightleftarrows Tl^+ \ (aq) + Cl^- \ (aq)$$

The solubility under various conditions may be calculated from the solubility-product constant, $K^o = (Tl^+)(Cl^-)$, where the parentheses indicate activities, so that K^o is the thermodynamic or zero ionic strength solubility-product constant. At $25°$, $K^o = 2.04 \times 10^{-4}$. Activities a are related to concentrations C by $a = C\gamma$, where γ is an activity coefficient. Activity coefficients allow for nonideality; the thermodynamic activity or effective concentration is usually not numerically equal to the measured concentration. Since solutions of TlCl are of necessity dilute, we shall, for the moment, consider the activity coefficients to be near unity and write

$$K = [Tl^+][Cl^-] = 2 \times 10^{-4} \tag{3-1}$$

where the brackets represent molar concentrations. In solutions containing only TlCl, $K = S^2$, and the molar solubility S

$$[Tl^+] = S = [Cl^-] = 1.4 \times 10^{-2} M$$

If a common ion is added to the solution by the introduction of C moles/liter of KCl, we have $[Tl^+] = S \neq [Cl^-] = C + S$. In combination with Eq. (3-1) we obtain $K = S(C + S) = 2 \times 10^{-4}$. The molar solubility S may be determined by solving a quadratic equation, but more commonly $C \gg S$, so that $S = K/C$. Experimentally, values of S are found to be slightly larger than the calculated values because of the neutral-salt effect.

The effect of adding a neutral salt such as KNO_3 to a solution of TlCl can be assessed only if the exact solubility-product constant is considered. We have

$$K^o = (Tl^+)(Cl^-) = [Tl^+][Cl^-]\gamma_{Tl}{}^+\gamma_{Cl}{}^- = K\gamma_\pm{}^2 = S^2\gamma_\pm{}^2 \tag{3-2}$$

where parentheses represent activities, brackets concentrations, and $\gamma_\pm$ is the mean ion activity coefficient of the slightly soluble salt, $\gamma_\pm{}^2 = \gamma_{Tl}{}^+\gamma_{Cl}{}^-$. Mean ion activity coefficients are unity for infinitely dilute solutions and decrease as the concentrations of neutral salts such as KNO_3 increase. Since K^o is a constant, the solubility S must increase to compensate for the decrease in $\gamma_\pm$. Writing Eq. (3-2) in logarithmic form gives

$$\log S = \tfrac{1}{2} \log K^o - \log \gamma_\pm \tag{3-3}$$

A plot of $\log S$ versus the square root of ionic strength yields a nearly straight line with ordinate intercept $\tfrac{1}{2} \log K^o$. Once K^o is determined by extrapolation to zero salt concentration, its value may be used to calculate $\gamma_\pm$ at any desired S through Eq. (3-3). Results of such measurements for TlCl at 25° are presented in Table 3-2. Even in the solution with no added KNO_3, the mean ion activity coefficient of TlCl is less than unity, owing to the ions introduced by the slight solubility of the salt. Activity coefficients are also determined from measurements of electromotive force and freezing-point depression.

The ionic strength of a solution is defined as $\mu = \frac{1}{2}\Sigma C_i z_i^2$, where C is the concentration of ion with charge z. The sum is taken over all ions in the solution. For 0.1 M KNO$_3$, the ionic strength is

$$\mu = \frac{1}{2}(0.1 \times 1^2 + 0.1 \times 1^2) = 0.1$$

In general, ionic strength is numerically the same as concentration for uni-univalent electrolytes. For 0.1 M K$_2$SO$_4$,

$$\mu = \frac{1}{2}(0.2 \times 1^2 + 0.1 \times 2^2) = 0.3$$

A mixture of 0.1 M KNO$_3$ and 0.1 M K$_2$SO$_4$ has $\mu = 0.4$. The virtue of ionic strength compared with other methods for expressing ionic concentrations is that in plots such as those of Eq. (3-3) a single curve is obtained for ions of different charge types. If the solubility were

TABLE 3-2 *Solubility of* TlCl *in* KNO$_3$ *Solutions at 25°*

C_{KNO_3}	S_{TlCl}	$\mu = C + S$	$\gamma_{\pm}$
0.00 M	0.0162 M	0.0162	0.882
0.02 M	0.0173 M	0.0373	0.826
0.05 M	0.0184 M	0.0684	0.776
0.10 M	0.0198 M	0.1198	0.721
0.31 M	0.0238 M	0.3338	0.600
1.05 M	0.0322 M	1.0822	0.444

plotted against concentrations of added salts instead of ionic strengths, KNO$_3$, K$_2$SO$_4$, and ZnSO$_4$ would all yield separate curves, whereas use of ionic strength would accommodate all points on a single curve. Finally, we may note that at zero ionic strength $\gamma_{\pm} = 1$, so that the solubility at zero ionic strength S_0 equals $(K^o)^{1/2}$, from which Eq. (3-3) may be written

$$\log \frac{S_0}{S} = \log \gamma_{\pm} \tag{3-4}$$

Debye-Hückel Theory of Activity Coefficients. Up to this point, we have treated activity coefficients on a strictly thermodynamic basis. No model has been assumed; we have simply expressed the deviation of TlCl solubility from ideality in terms of the mean ion activity coefficient. Mean ion activity coefficients and mean ion activities are all that may be determined from thermodynamic measurements; it is not possible to determine the activity coefficient or activity of a single ion without introducing some extra-thermodynamic considerations. In 1923, P. Debye and E. Hückel proposed that the deviations from ideal behavior of strong electrolytes are related to electrostatic interactions of positive and negative ions in solution. They considered each ion to be surrounded by an atmosphere of oppositely charged ions. By assuming Coulomb's law, Boltzmann's distribution law, and the activity of the solute proportional to its mole fraction (Henry's law), Debye and Hückel showed, after simplifying assumptions in the mathematical derivation, that for small single ions

$$- \ln \gamma = z^2 \frac{e^2}{2\epsilon kT} \frac{\kappa}{1 + a\kappa} \tag{3-5}$$

where e = electronic charge

k = Boltzmann's constant, R/N

a = mean distance of closest approach of ions measured from centers

$\kappa = (8\pi e^2 \mu/\epsilon kT)^{\frac{1}{2}}$

For a given solvent and temperature, κ is a function only of the ionic strength; at 25° in aqueous solutions, $\kappa = 0.33\mu^{\frac{1}{2}}$ Å^{-1}. The reciprocal $1/\kappa$ is the distance from the surface of the central ion to the maximum in charge distribution of the ion atmosphere. The activity coefficient calculated by Eq. (3-5) is based on mole fractions although we have been

T A B L E 3 - 3   *Debye-Hückel Constants for Aqueous Solutions*

Temperature, °C	A	B
0	0.492	0.325×10^8
18	0.505	0.328×10^8
25	0.512	0.329×10^8
38	0.524	0.332×10^8
100	0.609	0.349×10^8

assuming molal or molar activity coefficients. We shall ignore this discrepancy, but we point out that the differences among the various activity coefficients are negligible only in very dilute solutions. Since most calculations in which we are interested strain the high-concentration range of validity of the Debye-Hückel theory, refinements in the use of activity coefficients would not appear worthwhile.

Rewriting Eq. (3-5) gives

$$- \log \gamma = \frac{Az^2\mu^{\frac{1}{2}}}{1 + Ba\mu^{\frac{1}{2}}} \tag{3-6}$$

where A is a constant proportional to $(\epsilon T)^{-\frac{3}{2}}$, and $B = \kappa/\mu^{\frac{1}{2}}$. Values of A and B for aqueous solutions at several temperatures are presented in Table 3-3. At low ionic strengths, when the B-containing term in the denominator of Eq. (3-6) is small compared to unity, we have

$$- \log \gamma = Az^2\mu^{\frac{1}{2}} \tag{3-7}$$

This is the Debye-Hückel limiting law, which is always valid for sufficiently dilute solutions.

With the exception of the a term, Eq. (3-6) indicates that activity coefficients are independent of the nature of the ions and a function only of the ionic strength. This independence is particularly apparent at low ionic strengths, since no a term appears in the limiting law. For a single electrolyte it may be shown that Eq. (3-6) becomes

$$\log \gamma_\pm = \frac{A z_+ z_- \mu^{1/2}}{1 + B a \mu^{1/2}} \tag{3-8}$$

where the z_+ is the charge on the cation, and z_- the anionic charge. As only $\gamma_\pm$, and not γ_+ or γ_-, can be determined experimentally, Eq. (3-8) is often used. If $\log \gamma_\pm$ is plotted against $\mu^{1/2}$, the slope is a function of the charge type and is given by $A z_+ z_-$ in the limit of dilute solutions. An uncharged molecule has $\log \gamma = 0$ and hence $\gamma = 1$.

The a term in Eq. (3-6) cannot be determined independently; it may therefore be treated as an adjustable parameter. When the a value is so treated, values of several angstrom units are obtained for it as expected if a is considered as the distance of closest approach of the ions. For small inorganic ions, for which a is of the order of 3 A, Eq. (3-6), at reasonable temperatures, becomes

$$- \log \gamma = \frac{0.5 z^2 \mu^{1/2}}{1 + \mu^{1/2}} \tag{3-9}$$

whereas for larger organic ions the following is more appropriate:

$$- \log \gamma = \frac{0.5 z^2 \mu^{1/2}}{1 + 2 \mu^{1/2}} \tag{3-10}$$

The Debye-Hückel equation may only be applied to solutions of low ionic strength. It is applicable up to about $\mu = 0.1$ M for singly charged ions, and to lesser ionic strengths for multiply charged particles. At higher concentrations, effects not considered in the derivation render the equation incomplete. In an attempt to extend the range of validity, a term linear in ionic strength has been added to Eq. (3-6) to give

$$- \log \gamma = \frac{A z^2 \mu^{1/2}}{1 + B a \mu^{1/2}} - K_S \mu \tag{3-11}$$

In effect, a second adjustable parameter is introduced by addition of the constant K_S.

Since the variation of a with ionic size is not easily obtained, it is common practice in physical chemistry to assign the value unity to Ba for inorganic ions and take up any ionic size variation in K_S. Then K_S values are calculated empirically and may vary with concentration

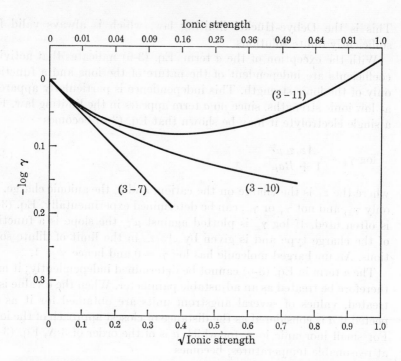

FIG. 3-1 Negative logarithm of the activity coefficient for a singly charged ion versus the square root of ionic strength. Numbers near curves refer to equation numbers in text. The constant A is taken as 0.5, Ba as 2, and K_S as 0.2 in this example.

if an accurate equation is desired for high concentrations of electrolyte. Although it is not necessary to do so, K_S values are often given a chemical interpretation. Occasionally K_S in Eq. (3-11) is negative, a fact which may be ascribed to association. Usually, however, the positive K_S value obtained may be interpreted as due to hydration of ions and a concomitant decrease in the activity of water. For this reason K_S is often called a *salting-out constant*. Values of salting-out constants generally increase as ionic size increases. In Fig. 3-1, differences between the several forms of the Debye-Hückel equations are illustrated. Note that Eq. (3-11) with the salting-out term can account for activity coefficients greater than unity at high ionic strengths.

3-4 ION-DIPOLE INTERACTIONS

In the preceding section it was shown how the deviation from ideality of the solubility of a slightly soluble salt may be thermodynamically expressed in terms of a mean ion activity coefficient. Also, the extra-thermodynamic Debye-Hückel theory was shown to account quantitatively for the observed values of the mean ion activity coefficient in very dilute solutions. For ion-dipole interactions, we may also describe the deviations from ideality in terms of activity coefficients. Theoretically, however, the complexities of the interactions are great enough so that no formulation yet proposed approaches the general applicability that the Debye-Hückel theory has for ion-ion interactions.

Effects of Salts on Uncharged Molecules. Gases and slightly soluble organic molecules are usually rendered less soluble in water by the addition of salts. Since $\log \gamma = \log (S_0/S)$, the activity coefficients of most uncharged molecules are increased by the addition of neutral salts. Empirically, a plot of $\log (S_0/S)$ is found to vary linearly with the molal concentration of added salt, $\log \gamma = Km_3$ (component 1 is solvent, and component 2 is uncharged molecule), as shown in Fig. 3-2. The salting-out constant K is inversely proportional to the difference between the reciprocal dielectric constants of solution and water, $1/\epsilon - 1/\epsilon_0$, so that acetone, which lowers the dielectric constant of water, is salted out, while HCN, which raises the dielectric constant of water, is salted in (K is negative). These results may be accounted for by preferential solvation of the ions by the higher-dielectric constant component. Theoretical considerations also indicate that K is dependent upon the valence type of the salt and is inversely proportional to the mean ionic radius of the salt. Thus the highly solvated lithium ion has less effect than the sodium or potassium ion. We have already noted that glycine increases the dielectric constant of aqueous solutions and hence is salted in like HCN on addition of salts.

Effects of Salts on Proteins. Concentrated solutions of $(NH_4)_2SO_4$, Na_2SO_4, or phosphate buffers have long been used to salt proteins out of solution. Those water-soluble proteins salted out by half-saturated $(NH_4)_2SO_4$ are called *globulins;* those remaining in the supernatant are called *albumins* and are salted out by saturated $(NH_4)_2SO_4$ solutions. Though high ionic strengths are required to salt out proteins, precipitation occurring over a small range of ionic strength once the requisite region is attained provides for sharp separations in mixtures of proteins.

Figure 3-3 illustrates the effects of several salts on the solubility of horse carboxyhemoglobin. Note that the salts mentioned in the previous paragraph are more effective as salting-out agents than the alkali chlorides. Before the linear salting-out region at high ionic strength is reached, proteins exhibit an initial salting-in region at low ionic strengths. For this reason the extrapolation of the straight-line salting-out portion of the curve will not intersect the ordinate at $\log (S/S_0) = 0$, but at some greater value. The salting-out constant

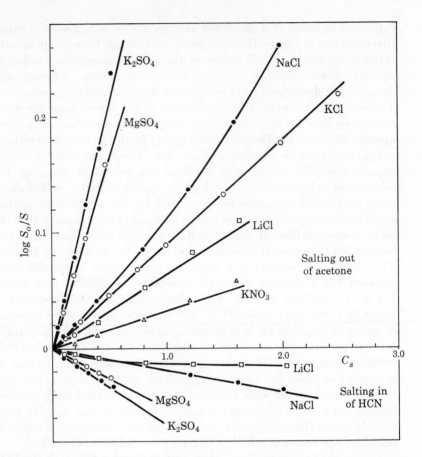

FIG. 3-2 log (S_o/S) for acetone (upper curve) and HCN (lower curve) versus molality of added salt in aqueous solutions. (After Ref. 1, p. 271.)

K' is then defined by the equation log $(S/S_i) = -K'\mu$, where S_i is the intercept value of the extrapolation. Though the solubility is dependent on temperature and pH, K' depends upon neither quantity. The nature of the salt and the protein size and shape are the main factors determining K', and, in general, the larger a protein molecule, the greater the K'. Amino acids with no net charge behave similarly to proteins, but the effects of added salts are quantitatively much less.

Development of a theoretical treatment of ion-dipole interactions analogous to the Debye-Hückel theory for ion-ion reactions is difficult. J. G. Kirkwood has given a theoretical treatment for ion-dipole interactions in the limit of infinite dilution, but in order to obtain final results he found it necessary to assume models, the simplest of which

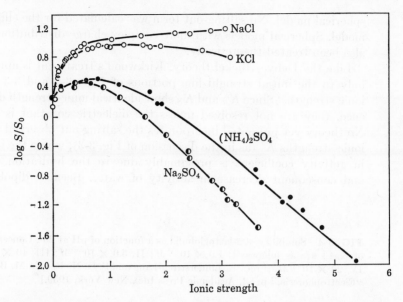

FIG. 3-3 Logarithm of the relative solubility of horse carboxyhemoglobin in salt solutions at varying ionic strengths. The section of the curves at ionic strengths less than 0.1 is linear. (From E. J. Cohn and J. T. Edsall, "Proteins, Amino Acids and Peptides," p. 608, Reinhold Publishing Corporation, New York, 1943.)

is a sphere with a point dipole at its center. In all the models he investigated, for the dipolar molecule, $- \log \gamma$ was equal to $K\mu$, exhibiting a first-power dependence on ionic strength in contrast to the square-root dependence for ion-ion interactions. The value of K is dependent upon the model assumed. For the spherical model it is divisible into two parts, $K = K_R - K_S$, a salting-in term K_R and a salting-out term K_S. The salting-in term arises from electrostatic interactions between the dipole and surrounding ions and is proportional to $(\mu_D/\epsilon T)^2$. No dependence upon the dipole moment appears in the salting-out term, which is proportional to $1/\epsilon T$ and is dependent upon the shape of the dipolar molecule considered as a cavity of low dielectric constant in a medium of high dielectric constant. This salting-out term arises only because of the explicit consideration of the dipolar molecule as a cavity with a microscopic dielectric constant much less than the bulk dielectric constant of the solvent. Kirkwood has also derived the salting-in term for a prolate ellipsoid of revolution with charges at the foci. In this model the salting-in term is proportional to $\mu_D/(\epsilon T)^2$. The first-power dependence of the dipole moment agrees better with experiment than the square dependence of the spherical model. No salting-out term was calculated for the ellipsoidal model. Spherical models with more complex charge distributions have also been treated theoretically.

Like the Debye-Hückel theory, Kirkwood's treatment is applicable only to the initial straight-line portions of Figs. 3-2 and 3-3 at low ionic strengths. Since K_R and K_S show identical ionic-strength dependence, they are not resolved unless the dielectric constant is varied. No theory yet presented incorporates the salting out observed at high ionic strengths K' (as in the discussion of Fig. 3-3), where the increase in activity coefficient is presumably due to the hydration of ions and consequent decrease in activity of water. Because dipolar ions

FIG. 3-4 Solubility of β-lactoglobulin as a function of pH at 25°. Concentrations of NaCl are as follows: I, 1.0×10^{-3} M; II, 5.0×10^{-3} M; III, 10×10^{-3} M; IV, 20×10^{-3} M. [From K. Linderstrøm-Lang and S. O. Nielsen, in M. Bier (ed.), "Electrophoresis," p. 83, Academic Press Inc., New York, 1959.]

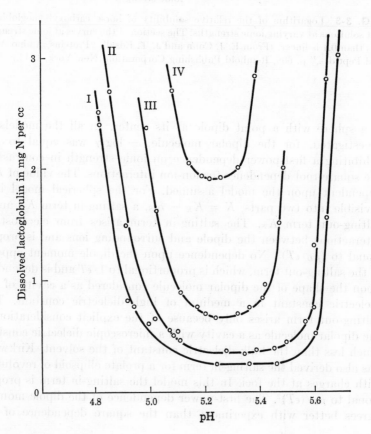

increase the dielectric constant of the solution, they also salt in proteins, but to a lesser extent than salts.

Effects of pH *and Salts on Protein.* In the discussion so far, pH has been assumed constant, but properties of proteins are pH-dependent. Figure 3-4 shows the solubility of β-lactoglobulin as a function of pH at different low concentrations of NaCl. β-Lactoglobulin is a typical globulin, quite insoluble in water at the isoelectric point, but showing a pronounced salting in as the salt concentration is raised at constant pH.

SELECTED BIBLIOGRAPHY

1 J. T. Edsall and J. Wyman, "Biophysical Chemistry," chaps. 5 and 6, Academic Press Inc., New York, 1958.

2 C. P. Smyth, "Dielectric Behavior and Structure," McGraw-Hill Book Company, Inc., New York, 1955.

3 R. A. Robinson and R. H. Stokes, "Electrolyte Solutions," 2d ed., Butterworth Scientific Publications, London, 1959.

4 H. S. Harned and B. B. Owen, "The Physical Chemistry of Electrolytic Solutions," 3d ed., Reinhold Publishing Corporation, New York, 1958.

5 G. C. Pimentel and A. L. McClellan, "The Hydrogen Bond," W. H. Freeman and Company, San Francisco, 1960.

QUESTIONS

3-1 Draw two resonance structures for benzene, and describe their relation to the structure of benzene.

3-2 What is the approximate contribution of each additional methylene group to the molar dielectric increment of amino acids?

3-3 Estimate the molar dielectric increment of triglycine.

3-4 Calculate the solubility of TlCl in the presence of 0.01 M, 0.10 M, and 1 M KCl.

3-5 From the data in the first three columns of Table 3-2, evaluate the thermodynamic solubility-product constant of TlCl, and obtain the mean ion activity coefficients of the fourth column.

3-6 Compare the mean ion activities of TlCl in a saturated solution of TlCl with and without the presence of 0.10 M KNO$_3$.

3-7 What is the ionic strength of a solution 0.15 M in KNO$_3$, 0.10 M in ZnSO$_4$, and 0.20 M in MgCl$_2$?

3-8 Derive the general relationships between ionic strength and concentration for 1-1, 1-2, 2-1, 2-2, 1-3, 3-1, 2-3, and 3-2 electrolytes.

3-9 Calculate the distance of the maximum in charge distribution about a central ion for 10^{-4}, 10^{-3}, 10^{-2}, and 10^{-1} ionic strength aqueous solutions at 25°.

3-10 Calculate the mean ion activity coefficients according to Eq. (3-8) for each solution in Table 3-2. Ion-pair formation at higher ionic strengths accounts for the unexpectedly l w values of the experimental mean ion activity coefficients.

3-11 The dipole moments of glycine, diglycine, and triglycine are 15, 27, and 35, respectively. If the salting-in constant for glycine is 0.33, estimate the salting-in constants of the peptides using Kirkwood's ellipsoidal model.

3-12 Estimate the salting-in constant of β-lactoglobulin at the isoelectric point from the data in Fig. 3-4.

4 | Acid-Base Equilibria

4-1 FUNDAMENTAL DEFINITIONS

Acids and Bases. According to the classical definition of acids and bases, an acid is a substance which furnishes a hydrogen ion, and a base a substance that furnishes a hydroxyl ion. This definition was broadened in 1923 by J. N. Brønsted to take into account the role of the solvent in acid-base equilibria. According to his definition, an acid is a substance which furnishes a proton, and a base a substance which accepts a proton. A proton is 10^{-4} times as large as a hydrogen atom and will polarize the neighboring solvent molecules due to its high charge density. This interaction of the proton with solvent or other solution components implies that free protons do not exist in solution. Protons are only transferred from one solution component to another.

In aqueous solutions, the solvent may function as a base by accepting a proton from an acid:

$$HB + H_2O \rightleftarrows H_3O^+ + B^- \tag{4-1}$$

The bases H_2O and B^- compete for the proton. The acid HB and the base B^- are said to be *conjugate* to one another, as are the acid H_3O^+ and the base H_2O. Processes such as those represented by Eq. (4-1) are called *ionizations*, to emphasize the role of the solvent, with its high dielectric and solvating properties, in effecting the conversion of non-ionic HB to the ions B^- and a hydrated proton. Compounds already ionic in the solid state (such as KCl) are not ionized on dissolution in water, but only dissociated. Ions in solution are hydrated to some unknown extent. Though we have written the hydrated proton as H_3O^+ to emphasize the role of the solvent, it may be considered more heavily hydrated, as $H(H_2O)_4^+$, for instance. Because of uncertainties regarding the hydration of ions, we shall make no attempt to specify hydration numbers and shall often abbreviate the hydrated proton as H^+.

In nonaqueous solvents the hydrogen ion has a much different character because it is solvated by species other than water. For instance, when an alcohol functions as a base,

$$HB + ROH \rightleftarrows ROH_2^+ + B^-$$

In solutions of pure acetic acid, addition of a strong acid such as HCl forces acetic acid to function as a base, because no other proton acceptor is available:

$$HCl + CH_3COOH \rightleftarrows CH_3COOH_2^+ + Cl^-$$

Thus whether a given compound functions as an acid or a base depends upon the relative proton-donating and proton-accepting powers of that compound and the other reagents in the system.

Water may also function as an acid by donating a proton to a base such as ammonia,

$$H_2O + NH_3 \rightleftarrows NH_4^+ + OH^- \tag{4-2}$$

to yield the conjugate acid ammonium ion. Note that NH_3 is a base in the Brønsted sense, but not by the classical definition. Equation (4-2), when generalized, gives

$$H_2O + B \rightleftarrows HB^+ + OH^- \tag{4-3}$$

Both Eqs. (4-1) and (4-3) are of the more general form

$$acid_1 + base_1 \rightleftarrows acid_2 + base_2$$

where the only charge specification is that $acid_2$ must have one more positive charge than $acid_1$, and that $base_2$ must have one less positive charge than $base_1$.

Solvents such as water which exhibit both acid and basic properties are called *amphiprotic* and undergo self-ionization,

$$H_2O + H_2O \rightleftarrows H_3O^+ + OH^-$$

where one molecule of water functions as an acid, and the other as a base. Applying the mass-action principle, we may write

$$K = (H_3O^+)(OH)^-/(H_2O)^2$$

where parentheses indicate activities of the components. In dilute aqueous solutions the activity of water is nearly constant and may be incorporated with the equilibrium constant K. Abbreviating the hydrated proton as H^+, we obtain,

$$K_w = (H^+)(OH^-) \tag{4-4}$$

where K_w is the ion-product constant for water. The value of K_w is 1.0×10^{-14} at 25°; it increases about 8% per degree rise in temperature, becoming 2.4×10^{-14} at 37°. We shall make use of the 25° value in our calculations.

pH *and* pcH.   According to Eq. (4-4) for the ion-product constant of water, the hydrogen-ion concentration in going from strongly acid to strongly basic solutions ranges over more than 15 powers of 10. As in other instances in which many powers of 10 are involved, a logarithmic scale is often more convenient. Therefore, we define

$$pcH = - \log [H^+] \tag{4-5}$$

and

$$pH = - \log (H^+) \tag{4-6}$$

where brackets represent molar concentration, and parentheses activity. According to Eq. (4-5), for 1.0, 0.10, and 0.01 M solutions of the strong acid HCl, the pcH is 0, 1, and 2, respectively. Equation (4-5) corresponds to the original definition of pH given by Sørenson in 1909, a definition arising in part from his studies of enzymatic reactions.

The activity of hydrogen ion is equal to the product of the concentration and the activity coefficient γ_{H^+}:

$$(H^+) = [H^+]\gamma_{H^+}$$

Taking the negative logarithm of both sides, we obtain

$$pH = pcH - \log \gamma_{H^+}$$

As discussed in the preceding chapter, only mean ion activity coefficients may be determined experimentally, so that we may only estimate $- \log \gamma_{H^+}$. Single-ion activity coefficients may be approximated by the Debye-Hückel equation (3-9), discussed in the previous chapter:

$$- \log \gamma = \frac{0.5z^2\mu^{\frac{1}{2}}}{1 + \mu^{\frac{1}{2}}}$$

For 0.10 M HCl, $- \log \gamma = 0.12$, so that pH = 1.12. A solution 10^{-2} M in HCl has $- \log \gamma = 0.05$ and hence a pH of 2.05. If the latter solution is made 9×10^{-2} M in KCl, the pH is 2.12, but for both solutions pcH = 2.00. In pure water, pH and pcH are both equal to 7.00 at 25°.

Since we are most interested in the activity of hydrogen ion or pH, and only mean ion activity coefficients may be experimentally determined, how can we correlate the former with the latter? No wholly satisfactory relationship exists for relating single-ion activities to experimentally determinable quantities. Usually hydrogen ion activity is defined in terms of the hydrogen electrode discussed in Sec. 2-6. Hydrogen electrodes, however, are inconvenient and not in general use. A detailed analysis indicates that in most cases suitably calibrated glass-electrode pH meters measure a characteristic quite close to what we have defined as pH. A 0.10 M HCl solution reads pH = 1.11 on the pH meter. The usual practice is to call pH what the pH meter reads. If one wishes to determine pcH, then $- \log \gamma_{H^+}$ must be estimated from Debye-Hückel theory or in some other way. Occasionally mean ion activity coefficients will have been determined by electromotive force or other measurements and the results tabulated. Seldom, however, will this determination have been made for a particular solution under study.

4-2 TITRATIONS

Strong Acid–Strong Base. Since strong acids and strong bases are completely ionized in aqueous solutions of the pH range of interest in biological reactions, it is simple to calculate the pH change when a strong base such as NaOH is added to a strong acid such as HCl. The curve obtained on titration of 0.10 N HCl with 0.10 N NaOH is shown in Fig. 4-1. Note the large change in pH for a small addition of base at the equivalence point. The pH at the equivalence point is 7.00 because the titration reaction is

$$H^+ + OH^- \rightleftarrows H_2O$$

and, at the equivalence point, $[H^+] = [OH^-]$.

Weak Acid–Strong Base. Figure 4-1 shows the titration curve for titration of 0.10 N acetic acid with 0.10 N NaOH. Acetic acid, or any weak acid HB, ionizes in water to yield a hydrated proton and the conjugate base of the acid:

$$HB + H_2O \rightleftarrows H_3O^+ + B^- \tag{4-7}$$

If we remember the constant activity of water in dilute solutions and abbreviate the hydrated proton as H^+, the equilibrium constant for Eq. (4-7) may be written

$$K_a{}^o = \frac{(H^+)(B^-)}{(HB)} \tag{4-8}$$

where $K_a{}^o$ is the thermodynamic or zero-ionic-strength acid ionization constant for the weak acid HB. In practice, concentrations rather

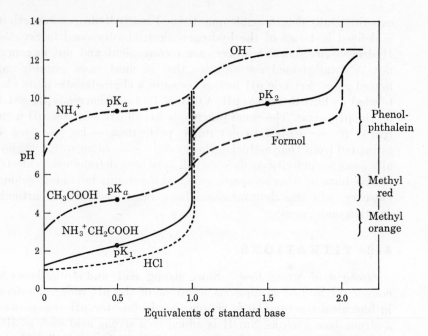

FIG. 4-1 Titration curves of 0.1 *N* solutions of acids with 0.1 *N* NaOH. Curve labeled formol is for titration of glycine in presence of formaldehyde. Regions of indicator changes are shown on the right.

than activities are used for HB and B$^-$, so that we are interested in a concentration-dependent constant:

$$K_a = \frac{(\text{H}^+)[\text{B}^-]}{[\text{HB}]} \tag{4-9}$$

where

$$K_a{}^o = \frac{K_a \gamma_{\text{B}^-}}{\gamma_{\text{HB}}} \tag{4-10}$$

We continue to express hydrogen ion in terms of activity because this quantity is nearer than concentration to what is read by the pH meter. K_a in Eq. (4-9) is, therefore, a hybrid constant composed of an activity term in hydrogen ion and concentration terms in acid and its conjugate base. If ionic strength and temperature are held constant, K_a should be independent of the [B$^-$]/[HB] ratio. Later we shall discuss the determination of $K_a{}^o$ from K_a values.

We can calculate the pH of a 0.10 *N* acetic acid solution, the point on the titration prior to the addition of base, by recalling that electroneutrality for the whole solution demands that

$$[H^+] = [B^-] + [OH^-]$$

and that the total molar concentration of acid in all its forms is

$$C_{HB} = [HB] + [B^-]$$

Substituting in Eq. (4-9), we obtain

$$K_a = (H^+) \frac{[H^+] - [OH^-]}{C_{HB} - \{[H^+] - [OH^-]\}} \tag{4-11}$$

Since the solution is acid, $[OH^-] \ll [H^+]$, and the last term in the numerator and denominator of Eq. (4-11) is negligible for purposes of addition and subtraction. Often, but not always, $[H^+] \ll C_{HB}$, so that the simpler expression (4-12) is obtained with the additional proviso that $[H^+]$ may be approximated by (H^+):

$$K_a = \frac{(H^+)^2}{C_{HB}} \tag{4-12}$$

For acetic acid $K_a = 2 \times 10^{-5}$. Since this number is quite small, Reaction (4-7) tends only slightly to the right, and the denominator of Eq. (4-11) may be approximated by C_{HB}. Therefore,

$$(H^+)^2 = 2 \times 10^{-5} \times 0.10$$

and pH = 2.85 for a 0.10 N solution of acetic acid. Higher concentrations of acid yield lower pH values. For an acid with an ionization constant greater than about 10^{-3}, the $[H^+]$ term in the denominator of Eq. (4-11) cannot be ignored, so that it is necessary to solve a quadratic equation.

Once we add NaOH to the solution of pure acetic acid, the electroneutrality equation is

$$[Na^+] + [H^+] = [B^-] + [OH^-] \tag{4-13}$$

and substitution in Eq. (4-9) yields

$$K_a = (H^+) \frac{[Na^+] + [H^+] - [OH^-]}{C_{HB} - \{[Na^+] + [H^+] - [OH^-]\}} \tag{4-14}$$

This equation is used for calculating the pH of all solutions in which the equivalents of base added are greater than zero and less than 1. Conversely, if all the quantities on the right-hand side of Eq. (4-14) are known, K_a may be evaluated. This method is often employed for determination of ionization constants.

From about 10 to 90% of the titration, it is frequently found that $[Na^+] \gg [H^+]$ and $[OH^-]$, and the following simpler equation is obtained:

$$K_a = (H^+) \frac{[Na^+]}{C_{HB} - [Na^+]} \tag{4-15}$$

Equation (4-15) is often used with little regard for the assumptions made in its derivation, although there is little additional work involved in using the full Eq. (4-14). If Eq. (4-15) is valid for a particular set of circumstances, use of the complete Eq. (4-14) only means that $[H^+]$ and $[OH^-]$ are so small compared with $[Na^+]$ that they are numerically insignificant. If $[H^+]$ or $[OH^-]$ is not negligible, Eq. (4-15) will yield an incorrect answer. Note that if Eq. (4-15) can be used, dilution of the solution during titration need not be considered, because (H^+) is determined on a pH meter, and the total quantity of solution appears in both numerator and denominator and hence cancels out. The result is thus independent of concentration when activity coefficients are neglected.

Finally, at the equivalence point, at which equal numbers of equivalents of acid and base are present, the situation is identical to that obtained by adding solid sodium acetate to water, so that its concentration is 0.05 M. The conjugate base interacts with the solvent,

$$H_2O + B^- \rightleftarrows HB + OH^- \tag{4-16}$$

for which the equilibrium constant is

$$K_b = \frac{(OH^-)[HB]}{[B^-]} \tag{4-17}$$

where K_b is the basic ionization constant of the weak base B^-. The product of the acid and basic ionization constants from Eqs. (4-9) and (4-17) $K_a K_b$ is equal to K_w, the ion-product constant of the solvent. This result is a general one and indicates that we need record only K_a or K_b; since K_w is known, we can always calculate the unrecorded ionization constant. For this reason only K_a values are used in this book.

For acetate ion, $K_b = K_w/K_a = 5 \times 10^{-10}$, the very small value indicating that Reaction (4-16) proceeds less to the right than did Eq. (4-7) for the solution of the conjugate acid in water. Therefore, to a very good approximation, $[B^-] = 0.05$, and if we take $[HB] = (OH^-)$, $(OH^-)^2 = 5 \times 10^{-10} \times 0.05$, from which pH = 8.70 for a 0.05 M solution of sodium acetate. This pH is also the equivalence point of the titration of 0.10 N acetic acid with 0.10 N NaOH. Thus the solution of a salt of a weak acid and a strong base is slightly basic. As in the case of the solution of acetic acid before the addition of base, the result just obtained is concentration-dependent.

Weak Base–Strong Acid. As already stated, a weak base such as NH_3 ionizes in water to yield the conjugate acid NH_4^+:

$$H_2O + NH_3 \rightleftarrows NH_4^+ + OH^-$$

from which the equilibrium constant is

$$K_b = \frac{(OH^-)[NH_4^+]}{[NH_3]} \tag{4-18}$$

which is identical with Eq. (4-17) except that NH_3 is a base of a different charge type than acetate ion. In the evaluation of quantities with the concentration-dependent ionization constant, differences in charge type are of no consequence. Therefore, the NH_3 problem and others like it are already solved.

For ammonia, $K_a = 5 \times 10^{-10}$, which is an acid ionization constant referring to the following reaction:

$$NH_4^+ + H_2O \rightleftarrows H_3O^+ + NH_3 \tag{4-19}$$

Since $K_b = K_w/K_a = 2 \times 10^{-5}$, the titration of NH_3 with a strong acid is a mirror image of results just obtained with acetic acid. A solution of pure NH_3 is analogous to one of acetate ion. At the end of a titration, the resulting solution of NH_4Cl formally presents the same problem as does a solution of acetic acid, because NH_4^+ and acetic acid are both weak acids differing only in acid strength. Figure 4-1 shows the titration curve of 0.1 N NH_4^+ with 0.1 N NaOH.

Our discussion of acid-base titrations in terms of the Brønsted concept has made it unnecessary to introduce the word hydrolysis. Acetate ion and NH_4^+ are often described as hydrolyzing in water. According to our view, acetate ion is a base in its reaction with water, and NH_4^+ an acid. Describing the reaction of acetate ion as hydrolysis is necessary in the old, classical definition of acids and bases, because acetate ion has no OH^- to donate. With the adoption of the Brønsted concept of a base as any substance that may accept a proton, hydrolysis becomes a superfluous idea contributing nothing but confusion.

Buffer Solutions. Inspection of the titration curves in Fig. 4-1 reveals flat portions at about pH 4.7 for acetic acid and pH 9.3 for ammonium ion. These regions, in which only a small change in pH occurs upon addition of a relatively large amount of base, are said to be *buffered.* Base added to a buffered solution reacts with the conjugate acid form,

$$HB + OH^- \rightleftharpoons H_2O + B^-$$

whereas added acid combines with the conjugate base,

$$H^+ + B^- \rightleftharpoons HB$$

Hence buffering efficiency is a maximum when [HB] = [B$^-$], for then the solution is equally resistant to added acid and base. From Eq. (4-9), K_a = (H$^+$) at the point of maximum buffering efficiency. Therefore, to select a buffer system in the desired pH range, a table of acid ionization constants should be consulted, and the acid-base system selected in which pH $\simeq$ pK_a, when pK_a is defined as $-$ log K_a. Thus an acetic acid–acetate solution buffers in the range 3.7 < pH < 5.7, and an ammonia–ammonium ion system buffers from 8.3 < pH < 10.3, but neither system is efficient at the limits of the range. Since no concentration term appears in the expression for maximum buffering efficiency, pH = pK_a, the point of maximum efficiency is independent of buffer concentration. However, the capacity of a buffer system is dependent upon concentration of buffer components, and for a given total concentration of components it is greatest when pH = pK_a. The greater the concentration of buffer components and the nearer pH to pK_a, the greater is the amount of added acid or base the buffer system can accommodate with relatively little change in pH.

Figure 4-1 also shows little change in the pH of the HCl-NaOH titration at pH values less than 2 and greater than 12. Though usually not called buffers, solutions with pH < 2 and pH > 12 have sufficiently high concentrations of hydrogen and hydroxide ions, respectively, so that their buffering capacity is significant.

Polybasic Acids. Ionization constants of most simple polybasic acids are sufficiently far apart so that the titration curve may be calculated as if only one acid were present in the system at a time. Phosphoric acid contains three ionizable protons, and three acid ionization constants may be defined:

$$H_3PO_4 \rightleftharpoons H^+ + H_2PO_4^- \qquad K_1 = \frac{(H^+)[H_2PO_4^-]}{[H_3PO_4]}$$

$$H_2PO_4^- \rightleftharpoons H^+ + HPO_4^= \qquad K_2 = \frac{(H^+)[HPO_4^=]}{[H_2PO_4^-]}$$

$$HPO_4^= \rightleftharpoons H^+ + PO_4^≡ \qquad K_3 = \frac{(H^+)[PO_4^≡]}{[HPO_4^=]}$$

Figure 4-2 shows the titration curve for addition of standard base to a

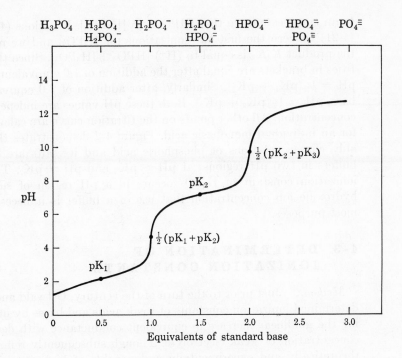

FIG. 4-2 Titration curve of 0.1 *N* H_3PO_4 with 0.1 *N* NaOH. Formulas at top of page indicate predominant species in solution at specified points along the titration curve.

solution containing H_3PO_4. Determination of pH for the initial solution and for points along the titration curve is the same as that already described for acetic acid, with the exception of H_3PO_4 solutions after addition of 1.0 and 2.0 equivalents of base. These exceptions reflect the fact that succeeding ionizations are about to take place. After addition of 1.0 equivalent of base to a solution containing H_3PO_4, $H_2PO_4^-$ is the predominant species in solution. It is amphoteric and may react in either of two ways: as an acid

$$H_2PO_4^- \rightleftarrows H^+ + HPO_4^= \tag{4-20}$$

or as a base

$$H^+ + H_2PO_4^- \rightleftarrows H_3PO_4 \tag{4-21}$$

In sufficient concentration and at pH values not too far removed from neutrality, we may assume that Reactions (4-20) and (4-21) occur to an equal extent, so that $[HPO_4^=] = [H_3PO_4]$. Reactions (4-20) and (4-21) concern the first two ionizations for H_3PO_4, and we note that the product K_1K_2 is equal to $(H^+)^2[HPO_4^=]/[H_3PO_4]$. Since the quantities in brackets are equal after the addition of 1.0 equivalent of base, $pH = \frac{1}{2}(pK_1 + pK_2)$. Similarly, after addition of 2.0 equivalents of base, $pH = \frac{1}{2}(pK_2 + pK_3)$. Both these pH values are independent of concentration. All other points on the titration curve are calculated as for an individual monobasic acid. Figure 4-2 demonstrates that suitably chosen solutions of phosphoric acid and its salts are effective buffers in two pH regions: at $pH \simeq pK_1$ and $pH \simeq pK_2$. The third ionization constant of H_3PO_4 occurs in a pH region of such high hydroxide ion concentration that use of a buffer is unnecessary for most purposes.

4-3 DETERMINATION OF IONIZATION CONSTANTS

Methods. Just prior to the turn of the century, Ostwald and others determined ionization constants of weak acids and bases by interpreting the nonlinear increase in equivalent conductance with decreasing concentration of weak electrolyte. Though subsequently refined both theoretically and experimentally and capable of high precision, the conductivity method is not commonly employed and is not considered further in this book.

Ionization constants are accurately determined by measuring the electromotive force of cells without transference, i.e., cells with no liquid junction due to the presence of two different liquid mixtures. Precision to 0.001 pK_a units is possible, and temperature coefficients are accurately obtainable. Theoretically less sound but more convenient for the purpose of biological mixtures is the electromotive determination of pK_a in cells with liquid junction. In particular, the glass-electrode pH meter is rapid and convenient, since metal ion interactions with the acid or base are minimal, and gas pressures may be accurately controlled. Liquid-junction potentials may be minimized by calibrating the pH meter with a buffer solution similar in composition, pH, and temperature to the solution to be tested. If these conditions are met, so that the solutions contain similar concentrations of ions of comparable mobilities, the liquid-junction potential cancels out. Equation (4-14) may be used for evaluating the acid ionization constant at several ratios of conjugate acid and base. A constant value of pK_a (± 0.01) obtained over a 1:7 to 7:1 ratio of conjugate acid to base at constant ionic strength and temperature provides a sensitive criterion of purity.

We may formulate this method in a slightly different way. Taking the negative logarithm of both sides of Eq. (4-9), we obtain

$$pK_a = pH - \log \frac{[B^-]}{[HB]} \tag{4-22}$$

where $pK_a = -\log K_a$. Define α as the fraction of acidic protons removed, $\alpha = [B^-]/\{[HB] + [B^-]\}$; then $1 - \alpha = [HB]/\{[HB] + [B^-]\}$, and

$$pK_a = pH - \log \frac{\alpha}{1 - \alpha} \tag{4-23}$$

For an initial solution of base to be titrated with standard acid, the definition of α is not changed. In the method just described, α is determined from the known initial concentration of acid (or base) and the known number of equivalents of strong base (or acid) added. Once $\alpha/(1 - \alpha)$ is evaluated, measurement of pH on a pH meter provides all the additional information needed for determination of pK_a, which should be constant over a range of α and pH values according to Eq. (4-23).

Other methods for evaluating the $\alpha/(1 - \alpha)$ ratio may be used in conjunction with pH measurements to provide the information necessary for determination of pK_a by Eq. (4-23). One of the most useful alternative methods is spectrophotometry, because the requisite measurements are conveniently made in very dilute solutions. The only requirements are that absorption of the conjugate acid and base differ significantly in an accessible region of the spectrum and that absorption of a species be proportional to its concentration (i.e., that Beer's law is valid). When the latter condition prevails, absorption of a species in 1-cm cells is given by $A_i = \epsilon_i C_i$, where C_i is the molar concentration, and ϵ_i the molar extinction coefficient.

In a solution containing a conjugate acid and its base, the total absorption A is the sum of the absorption A_A of the acid and A_B of the base forms:

$$A = A_A + A_B = \epsilon_A C_A + \epsilon_B C_B$$

Dividing through by the total molar concentration of acid in all its forms, $C = C_A + C_B$, we obtain

$$\epsilon = \frac{A}{C} = \epsilon_A(1 - \alpha) + \epsilon_B \alpha \tag{4-24}$$

where ϵ, the observed extinction coefficient for the mixture, is dependent upon α. Solving Eq. (4-24) for α yields

$$\alpha = \frac{\epsilon - \epsilon_A}{\epsilon_B - \epsilon_A} \qquad \text{from which} \qquad 1 - \alpha = \frac{\epsilon_B - \epsilon}{\epsilon_B - \epsilon_A}$$

and

$$\frac{\alpha}{1 - \alpha} = \frac{\epsilon - \epsilon_A}{\epsilon_B - \epsilon}$$

Substituting in Eq. (4-23) gives

$$pK_a = pH - \log \frac{\epsilon - \epsilon_A}{\epsilon_B - \epsilon} = pH - \log \frac{A - A_A}{A_B - A} \tag{4-25}$$

The last equality of Eq. (4-25) is valid because concentration cancels out in numerator and denominator. Therefore, concentration need not be known for determination of pK_a by the spectrophotometric method if known aliquots of an original stock solution are used. It is important that A_A and A_B be accurately known, because their values enter into each calculation for pK_a as pH and A are varied. Values of A midway between A_A and A_B yield the most reliable pK_a values, because the difference between two large numbers is avoided. In practice, solutions of the absorbing species are prepared in a suitable nonabsorbing buffer with an acid strength comparable to that of the unknown. The species under test usually is not used as its own buffer, because high dilutions, 10^{-4} M, are often required to have absorption readings in an appropriate range for reliable readings. It is frequently convenient to dilute some samples more than others in order to have absorption readings in the 0.2 to 1.0 range, where spectrophotometers give optimum relative accuracy. This dilution operation and the whole method depend upon the validity of Beer's law, which states that absorption is proportional to concentration.

Under conditions of unusual solvent composition such as in concentrated solutions of urea and sulfuric or other acids, changes in dielectric constant and other properties of the medium may cause spectral changes additional to those induced by uptake or release of protons. For nonpolar molecules in nonpolar solvents, a decrease in dielectric constant of the medium shifts the absorption band to shorter wavelengths. When two different nonpolar solutes are compared in the same solvents, the shift is proportional to the extinction coefficient. Other effects also occur for polar molecules, so that the shift may even be to the red.

If the spectra are sufficiently complex, an ionization constant may be more accurately estimated by simultaneous consideration of two wavelengths, one where absorption by the acidic form is predominant, and the other where absorption of the basic form is greater. The two wavelengths should be chosen so that the difference in absorption of the acidic and basic forms is as great as practicable at each wavelength. Let the extinction coefficients of the acid form be a_1 and a_2, and the extinction coefficients of the conjugate base form be b_1 and b_2, where the subscripts 1 and 2 refer to the two different wavelengths. Analogous to Eq. (4-24), we have, at the first and second wavelengths, respectively,

$$\epsilon_1 = a_1(1 - \alpha) + b_1\alpha$$
$$\epsilon_2 = a_2(1 - \alpha) + b_2\alpha$$

Define the difference $D = \epsilon_1 - \epsilon_2$, from which

$$D = (a_1 - a_2)(1 - \alpha) + (b_1 - b_2)\alpha$$

Solving for α, we obtain

$$\alpha = \frac{D - (a_1 - a_2)}{(b_1 - b_2) - (a_1 - a_2)}$$

and

$$\frac{\alpha}{1 - \alpha} = \frac{D - (a_1 - a_2)}{(b_1 - b_2) - D}$$

This result may be substituted into Eq. (4-23) to evaluate pK_a at several pH or H_0 (Hammett acidity function) values. When medium effects are pronounced, however, individual treatment, depending upon the nature of the particular spectra, is required. Some evidence suggests that in some cases use of the wavelength maximum at half conversion can lead to reliable results.

The spectrophotometric method is particularly valuable for analyzing overlapping ionization constants where only one of the ionizations gives rise to a spectrophotometric change. In this way the ammonium and sulfhydryl ionizations of cysteine, which occur in the same pH region, were distinguished (only the —SH ionization produces a change in absorption). Similarly, the overlapping ammonium and phenolic ionizations of tyrosine have been separated by using the fact that only the latter gives rise to a significant change in absorption. Later we shall see how application of this method to proteins can delineate the ionization of certain groups when others are also ionizing in the same pH range.

Ionization Constants at Zero Ionic Strength. For purposes of determining temperature coefficients, making theoretical calculations, and other comparisons, it is imperative to know the values of ionization constants at zero ionic strength. In methods which involve determination of $\alpha/(1 - \alpha)$ for evaluation of pK_a, the ionization constant is always determined at finite ionic strength, because addition of standard strong base to an acid or vice versa produces a mixture of conjugate acid and base, at least one of which must be charged. The ratio $\alpha/(1 - \alpha)$ is strictly a concentration term and does not include activity-coefficient corrections. Taking the negative logarithm of both sides of Eq. (4-10), we obtain

$$pK_a{}^o = pK_a - \log \frac{\gamma_{z-1}}{\gamma_z} \tag{4-26}$$

where the subscripts on the activity coefficients are generalized to indicate that the charge on the acid form z is one unit more positive than the charge on the conjugate base $z - 1$. As discussed in the previous chapter, activity coefficients of charged species are strongly dependent upon ionic strength, becoming unity only at zero ionic strength. One satisfactory method for evaluation of $pK_a{}^o$ is to plot pK_a values versus the square root of ionic strength. At low ionic strengths the straight line obtained may be extrapolated to zero ionic strength, yielding $pK_a{}^o$.

A less accurate method avoiding the determination of pK_a at several ionic strengths is to evaluate pK_a at one suitably low ionic strength and to apply the Debye-Hückel equation (3-11) for an estimation of the activity coefficients. Although originally formulated for strong electrolytes, there is no restriction in Debye-Hückel theory that prohibits its application to the ionized fraction of weak electrolytes. For the conjugate acid of charge z, Eq. (3-11) becomes

$$- \log \gamma_z = \frac{A z^2 \mu^{1/2}}{1 + B a \mu^{1/2}} - K_S \mu \tag{4-27}$$

For the conjugate base of charge $z - 1$, we obtain

$$- \log \gamma_{z-1} = \frac{A (z - 1)^2 \mu^{1/2}}{1 + B a \mu^{1/2}} - K_S \mu \tag{4-28}$$

Since the salting-out constant K_S is determined largely by the size of the particle, the same salting-out constant is used for both conjugate acid and base. The difference of one proton does not change the size appreciably. Combination of Eqs. (4-27) and (4-28) yields

$$- \log \frac{\gamma_{z-1}}{\gamma_z} = \frac{A (-2z + 1) \mu^{1/2}}{1 + B a \mu^{1/2}} \tag{4-29}$$

as the salting-out term drops out. Substitution of Eq. (4-29) into Eq. (4-26) gives

$$pK_a^o = pK_a - \frac{A(2z - 1)\mu^{1/2}}{1 + Ba\mu^{1/2}}$$ (4-30)

Equation (4-30) demonstrates that when the charge on the conjugate acid $z = +1$, as for ammonium ion, pK_a increases with increasing ionic strength; when $z = 0$, as for acetic acid, pK_a decreases with increasing ionic strength; when $z = -1$, as for the second ionization of phosphoric acid, pK_a decreases three times faster than in the acetic acid case with increasing square root of ionic strength.

According to the Debye-Hückel equation (4-27), the activity coefficient for an uncharged molecule should be independent of ionic strength. Since amino acids, though neutral overall, are dipolar ions, following the Kirkwood formulation of Sec. 3-4, we may write

$$- \log \gamma_d = (K_R - K_S)\mu$$ (4-31)

where γ_d is the activity coefficient of the dipolar ion, and K_R and K_S are salting-in and salting-out constants, respectively. Dipolar ions such as amino acids are special cases which must be considered separately. For the ionization of glycine cation,

$$NH_3^+CH_2COOH + H_2O \rightleftarrows H_3O^+ + NH_3^+CH_2COO^-$$

Application of Eq. (4-27) yields, for glycine cation,

$$- \log \gamma_+ = \frac{A\mu^{1/2}}{1 + Ba\mu^{1/2}} - K_S\mu$$ (4-32)

Combining Eqs. (4-31) and (4-32) yields

$$- \log \frac{\gamma_d}{\gamma_+} = \frac{- A\mu^{1/2}}{1 + Ba\mu^{1/2}} + K_R\mu$$ (4-33)

as the size-dependent salting-out term drops out. Isoelectric glycine ionizes further to yield the anion:

$$NH_3^+CH_2COO^- + H_2O \rightleftarrows H_3O^+ + NH_2CH_2COO^-$$

The activity coefficient for the anion, γ_-, is given by Eq. (4-32), since z^2 is the same for $z = +1$ or -1. Hence we obtain

$$- \log \frac{\gamma_-}{\gamma_d} = \frac{A\mu^{1/2}}{1 + Ba\mu^{1/2}} - K_R\mu$$ (4-34)

Equations (4-33) and (4-34) for dipolar ions differ from Eq. (4-29) for other ions by the inclusion of a salting-in term of first power in ionic

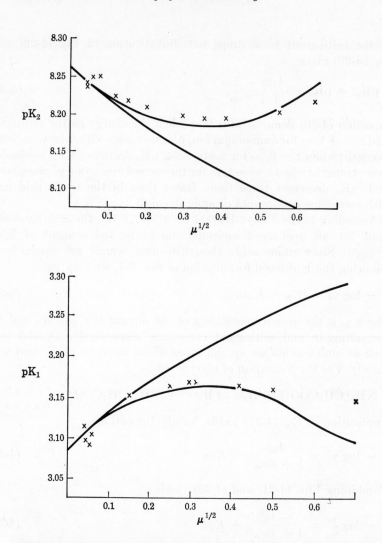

FIG. 4-3 pK_a versus square root of ionic strength for first and second ionizations of glycylglycine. Gently curved lines correspond to Eq. (4-30) with $Ba = 1$, and curves with pronounced curvature include a salting-in term $K_R = 0.4$. Crosses are experimental points. [After A. Neuberger, *Proc. Roy. Soc. London*, **A158**, 68 (1937).]

strength. The importance of this term is illustrated by some old data for glycylglycine ionizations in Fig. 4-3.

Summary of Ionization Constants.   Table 4-1 presents a summary of thermodynamic acid ionization constants for several acids of biological interest. Most of the values have been determined from potentials of electrochemical cells without transference over a range of temperatures; exceptions are imidazole and phenol, values for which are not as precise.

Comparing the pK_a^o values of propionic acid (CH_3CH_2COOH), 4.87, and glycine ($NH_3^+CH_2COOH$), 2.35, for the ionization of the carboxylic acid protons, we observe a decrease in pK_a^o or an increase in

TABLE 4-1 *Thermodynamic Acid Ionization Constants at 25°*

Substance	pK_a^o	ΔH^o, kcal/mole	ΔS^o, cal/deg mole
Water, pK_w	14.00	13.5	−18.7
Carboxylic acids			
Formic acid	3.75	−0.0	−17.6
Acetic acid	4.76	−0.1	−22.1
Propionic acid	4.87	−0.2	−22.8
Glycine, pK_1	2.35	1.0	−7.6
β-Alanine, pK_1	3.55	1.2	−12.3
Glycylglycine, pK_1	3.14	+0.0	−14.3
Carbonic acids			
Carbonic acid, pK_1	6.35	2.2	−21.6
Carbonic acid, pK_2	10.33	3.6	−35.2
Phosphoric acids			
Phosphoric acid, pK_1	2.15	−1.8	−16.0
Phosphoric acid, pK_2	7.20	1.0	−29.6
Phenol	9.98	5.6	−26.9
Ammonium ions			
Ammonium ion	9.25	12.4	−0.7
Glycine, pK_2	9.78	10.6	−9.4
β-Alanine, pK_2	10.24	12.6	−4.7
Glycylglycine, pK_2	8.25	10.6	−2.0
Imidazole	6.97	8	−5

acidity due to the presence of a positive charge on the glycine molecule. In β-alanine ($NH_3^+CH_2CH_2COOH$), 3.55, the decrease in pK_a^o is reduced because the positive charge is further removed from the acid center. This influence of the presence of a charge and its distance from an ionizing site elsewhere in the same molecule has been treated by electrostatic theory, which we shall discuss later in this chapter.

For all carboxylic acid ionizations, heat changes are nearly zero; hence the main contribution to free energy of ionization is made by the large negative entropy term, since for units of kcal/mole

$$1.36 \ pK_a^o = \Delta G^o = \Delta H^o - T \ \Delta S^o$$

When a carboxyl group ionizes, two charges are created where none existed previously:

$$RCOOH + H_2O \rightleftarrows H_3O^+ + RCOO^-$$

The appearance of charges in solution results in orientation, compression, and restrictions on internal rotations of solvent water molecules. Whereas the heat term may be considered as a property of the solute and mainly involves changes in covalent bonding, the entropy of ionization is composed largely of differences in solute-solvent interactions before and after ionization. Glycine, pK_1, exhibits a less negative entropy term than the other carboxylic acids because the solvent is already in a considerable state of organization due to the positive charge. This effect should decrease as the positive charge and the acid center become further separated, thus accounting for the intermediate entropy of ionization of β-alanine. Even larger negative entropies of ionization occur on the creation of a doubly charged ion, as in the pK_2 ionizations of carbonic and phosphoric acids. Carboxylic acid ionizations provide an example of the importance of entropy contributions to the free energy, since heat effects are negligible.

In contrast to the carboxylic acid ionizations, ammonium ions exhibit large positive heat changes. Entropy changes are less than with carboxylic acids, however, because no new charges are created; only proton transfer occurs.

$$RNH_3^+ + H_2O \rightleftarrows H_3O^+ + RNH_2$$

The entropy term displays a small negative value for the above process, owing to the greater effectiveness of the smaller H_3O^+ in organizing solvent, as compared to the often bulky RNH_3^+. Heat effects predominate in ammonium ionizations, and the pH of a buffer solution of ammonium ions and amines is strongly dependent upon temperature.

The first ionization constant of carbonic acid is complex and merits further discussion. Carbon dioxide CO_2 is not a Brønsted acid because it has no proton to donate. Unlike NH_4OH, for which no covalent structure can be drawn and which is an artificial creation of the classical theory of bases used to account for the basic properties of ammonia, carbonic acid H_2CO_3 is a distinct chemical species, even though it has never been isolated in a pure state. The hydration reaction

$$CO_2 + H_2O \rightleftarrows H_2CO_3 \tag{4-35}$$

is fast, but it is slower than the very rapid acid-base reaction

$$H_2CO_3 + H_2O \rightleftarrows H_3O^+ + HCO_3^- \tag{4-36}$$

For Eq. (4-36), the ionization constant is

$$K_{H_2CO_3} = \frac{(H^+)(HCO_3^-)}{(H_2CO_3)}$$

but K_1 of Table 4-1 is given by

$$K_1 = \frac{(H^+)(HCO_3^-)}{(H_2CO_3) + (CO_2)}$$

where the total concentration of CO_2, unhydrated and hydrated, appears in the denominator. Since equilibrium between HCO_3^- and both forms of CO_2 appearing in Reaction (4-35) is attained quickly, the constant K_1 is usually measured. Reaction (4-35) is faster in the reverse direction, so that $(H_2CO_3)/(CO_2) = 2.6 \times 10^{-3}$ at 25°, and hence $pK_{H_2CO_3}^o = 3.76$. This result indicates that carbonic acid is as strong as formic acid if only the hydrated form is considered. Though fast, Reaction (4-35) does not reach equilibrium rapidly enough for purposes of CO_2 transport in the body, and the presence of an enzyme, carbonic anhydrase, in red blood cells speeds the attainment of equilibrium. No complications occur for the pK_2 ionization of carbonic acid.

4-4 SMALL MULTIBASIC ACIDS

Amino Acids. Since amino acids are dibasic acids, for many years uncertainty prevailed over whether the form existing at neutral pH is a neutral molecule with no charges ($NH_2CHRCOOH$) or a dipolar ion with one negative and one positive charge ($NH_3^+CHRCOO^-$). Starting with the cation in acid solution, two paths are possible to the anion in basic solution:

$$NH_3^+CHRCOOH \underset{k_2}{\overset{k_1}{\rightleftharpoons}} \begin{matrix} NH_3^+CHRCOO^- \\ NH_2CHRCOOH \end{matrix} \underset{k_{21}}{\overset{k_{12}}{\rightleftharpoons}} NH_2CHRCOO^-$$

As there is now no doubt that the dipolar-ion form predominates in neutral solutions, we have already assumed this result in discussing amino acids. (The R group is considered to be neither acidic nor basic in this discussion.) Titration curves of several substances and glycine hydrochloride ($Cl^-NH_3^+CH_2COOH$) are compared in Fig. 4-1. The first ionization of glycine cation, $pK_1^o = 2.35$, occurs in more acidic solutions than the ionization of acetic acid, $pK_a^o = 4.76$. This difference is expected for an acetic acid molecule substituted with a positive charge, which facilitates the removal of the carboxylic acid proton in glycine. The second ionization constant of glycine is in the range of proton removal from an ammonium group, as Fig. 4-1 indicates.

These assignments, the first ionization of glycine cation to carboxylic acid proton and the second to the ammonium group, are substantiated by comparison of heats of ionization listed in Table 4-1. The first ionization of glycine cation exhibits a ΔH^o typical of carboxylic acid, $\Delta H^o \simeq 0$ kcal/mole, and the second ionization yields a value of $\Delta H^o \simeq 11$ kcal/mole, typical of proton removal from an ammonium group.

Additional evidence of the nature of the second ionization from glycine cation is gleaned by titration in the presence of formaldehyde, called *formol* titration. Formaldehyde reacts with the uncharged form of amines to yield hydroxymethyl derivatives:

$$RNH_2 + HCHO \rightleftarrows RNH(CH_2OH)$$
$$RNH(CH_2OH) + HCHO \rightleftarrows RN(CH_2OH)_2$$

The pK_a value of the final product is of the order of 8. As shown in Fig. 4-1 for the curve labeled formol, the second ionization of glycine is displaced to lower pH values in the presence of formaldehyde, so that phenolphthalein (indicating range $8 < pH < 10$) may be used as an indicator. Since only the pK_2 value is appreciably changed on addition of formaldehyde, the assignment of the ammonium group to this ionization gains additional support.

Several other forms of evidence favor the dipolar-ion structure for amino acids. As already noted in Sec. 3-2, neutral solutions of amino acids have high positive dielectric increments, the expected result for the dipolar-ion form. Dissolution of amino acids in water is accompanied by large negative volume changes, caused by compression of the water about charged groups of the dipolar ion. Amino acids exhibit a greater solubility in water than in nonpolar solvents, as do most ionic crystals. Raman spectra of amino acids in the solid state and in solution display a strong line at 1,740 cm^{-1}, a characteristic stretching frequency of unionized carboxylic acid groups, only in the cationic form. On the other hand, a pair of lines in the 3,350 cm^{-1} region, characteristic of uncharged amino groups, is present only in the anionic form of amino acids. Other frequencies could also be chosen to confirm the same interpretation. Finally, in the solid state, neutral amino acids yield high melting or decomposition points, typical of an infinite network of electrostatic binding, and x-ray analysis indicates a tetrahedral arrangement of bonds about nitrogen as in ammonium ion.

Microforms and Microconstants. Even though there is overwhelming evidence that neutral amino acids exist as dipolar ions in both solution and the solid state, it is advantageous for further application to formulate the problem quantitatively. Consider the complete ionization scheme for a dibasic acid

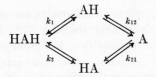

where no charges are specified on the four microforms since the only requirements are that the overall net charge be one positive unit less for A than for AH or HA and one positive unit less for the latter pair than for HAH. For constant ionic strength and temperature, we define the following microconstants:

$$k_1 = \frac{(H)[AH]}{[HAH]} \qquad k_2 = \frac{(H)[HA]}{[HAH]} \qquad k_{12} = \frac{(H)[A]}{[AH]} \qquad k_{21} = \frac{(H)[A]}{[HA]}$$

where subscript 1 indicates the ionization of the left-hand proton, and 2 the ionization of the right-hand proton. The macroconstants as determined by titration are

$$K_1 = \frac{(H)\{[AH] + [HA]\}}{[HAH]} = k_1 + k_2 \tag{4-37}$$

$$K_2 = \frac{(H)[A]}{[AH] + [HA]} = \frac{1}{1/k_{12} + 1/k_{21}} \tag{4-38}$$

from which $K_2^{-1} = k_{12}^{-1} + k_{21}^{-1}$. The second equalities in the expressions for K_1 and K_2 follow from substitution of the microconstant definitions. In addition, due to the properties of a cyclic system,

$$K_1 K_2 = k_1 k_{12} = k_2 k_{21} \tag{4-39}$$

Therefore, the four microconstants are not independent, since the determination of any three determines the fourth. However, titration only yields values of the macroconstants K_1 and K_2, so that we have two equations and three unknowns. It is thus necessary to evaluate one of the microconstants independently if the complete ionization scheme is to be worked out.

For the application to glycine, we may assume the pK_a of the methyl or ethyl ester equivalent to one of the microconstants, pk_2, where a proton leaves the ammonium group of glycine cation. This assumption is probably valid, since the dipole moments of fatty acids and their esters are nearly 1.8 Debye units (the corresponding amides have dipole moments of 3.6 Debye units). The pK_a values for the methyl and ethyl esters of glycine are 7.66 and 7.73, respectively, at 25°.

Taking $pk_2 = 7.70$ (the average), we find $pk_1 = 2.35$ from Eq. (4-37), and $pk_{12} = 9.78$ and $pk_{21} = 4.43$ from Eq. (4-39). The ratio

$$k_1/k_2 = \text{dipolar/uncharged} = 2.2 \times 10^5$$

justifies quantitatively our previous qualitative inferences concerning the predominance of the dipolar form. Note also, since $k_{21}/k_1 = k_{12}/k_2$ or $pk_{21} - pk_1 = pk_{12} - pk_2$, that, as exemplified by glycine, the reciprocal effects of ionized and unionized amino groups on carboxylic acid ionization are quantitatively the same as the effect of ionized and unionized carboxyl groups on the ammonium ionization.

In the case of glycine, in which the ratio of dipolar ion to uncharged isomer is high, for all practical purposes the carboxylic acid ionization takes place from glycine cation before a proton leaves the ammonium group. This result is generally the case for the carboxylic acid and ammonium groups of amino acids. When other acidic or basic groups are present in the R function of amino acids, ionizations become more competitive. The overlapping ionizations from the two carboxylic acid groups of glutamic acid have been resolved by comparing the ionization constants of both monoesters with those of the free acid. Resolution has also been achieved for the overlapping ammonium and sulfhydryl ionizations of cysteine, as well as the ammonium and phenolic ionizations of tyrosine. In both cysteine and tyrosine the carboxylic acid group ionizes before the subsequent two groups begin to ionize to any appreciable extent. In addition to the substitution of methyl groups for ionizable protons, the competitive ionizations have been analyzed spectrophotometrically. Spectrophotometric analysis is possible in each case because only one of the overlapping groups produces a change in ultraviolet absorption on ionization (sulfhydryl in cysteine and phenolic in tyrosine), even though the ammonium group loses a proton concurrently in both cases. A different kind of amino acid, the aminobenzoic acids, illustrates the importance of resolving overlapping ionizations. Ionization occurs predominantly from the carboxylic acid group in the meta cation yielding a dipolar ion, whereas the ortho and para derivatives are mainly uncharged molecules in the isoelectric pH region.

It is not possible to predict, a priori, the values of the microconstants k_1 and k_2 if the macroconstants K_1 and K_2 are known. If the latter are sufficiently alike, differing by about one pK unit or less, one may argue that k_1 and k_2 are competitive. This is not necessarily true, however, since instances are known in which the removal of the first proton facilitates the departure of the second. In such cases, K_1 and K_2 may have similar values, and yet either the k_1 or k_2 process will predominate in the first ionization. Thiamine (the diphosphate of which is the coenzyme vitamin B_1) has two titrable groups above pH 8 for which

$k_2 > 10k_1$, owing to the opening of the thiazole ring after the first ionization takes place. Molecular rearrangements, and even time factors, are frequently observed in cases such as that of thiamine. Conversely, even equal values of k_1 and k_2 do not imply similar values of K_1 and K_2. This fact is quickly demonstrated by consideration of H_2S or maleic acid, both of which are dibasic acids with equivalent acidic hydrogens, and hence for which $k_1 = k_2$. However, both acids display K_1/K_2 ratios greater than 5 powers of 10.

TABLE 4-2 *Microforms and Microconstants of Multibasic Acids*

Titrable groups	Microforms	Microconstants	Independent microconstants	Unknowns after titration
0	1	0	0	0
1	2	1	1	0
2	4	4	3	1
3	8	12	7	4
4	16	32	15	11
5	32	80	31	26
$\cdots$	$\cdots$	$\cdots$	$\cdots$	$\cdots$
n	2^n	$n2^{n-1}$	$2^n - 1$	$2^n - 1 - n$

Evaluation of microconstants for a tribasic acid is considerably more complicated than the dibasic-acid case discussed above. The complete scheme has been delineated for cysteine, tyrosine, glutamic, and citric acids (the center carboxylic acid group is the most acidic in the last named acid). Table 4-2 illustrates the increasing complexity as the number of titrable groups increases. The evaluation of the 32 microconstants for a case in which $n = 4$ would be a formidable task. Evidently, another approach is required for dealing with polyelectrolytes such as proteins and nucleic acids.

Evaluation of Overlapping Macroconstants. When two or more macroconstants have similar values, indicating that several groups titrate in the same pH range, use of Eq. (4-14) does not yield a constant pK_a value over a range of acid-to-base ratios because of concomitant ionization of other groups. Since this situation frequently arises, we shall describe one method for evaluating macroconstants of competitive ionizations. We are not now concerned with microconstants.

Starting with the acidic form and titrating with standard base, we define a quantity $\bar{h}$ as the mean number of protons removed per mole of acid originally present. For a dibasic acid, $0 \leq \bar{h} \leq 2$.

$$\bar{h} = \frac{[AH] + [HA] + 2[A]}{[HAH] + [AH] + [HA] + [A]} = \frac{K_1(H^+) + 2K_1K_2}{(H^+)^2 + K_1(H^+) + K_1K_2}$$

$$(4\text{-}40)$$

where the second equality results from substitution of Eqs. (4-37) and (4-38). The right-hand side is a function only of (H+) and the two macroconstants. Electroneutrality demands that at any point in the titration with NaOH,

$$[\text{Na}^+] + [\text{H}^+] = [\text{AH}^-] + [\text{HA}^-] + 2[\text{A}^=] + [\text{OH}^-]$$

where it is necessary to assign charges to the various acid species in order to write an electroneutrality equation. As the reader may verify for himself, however, Eq. (4-41) is always obtained from substitution of the electroneutrality equation into Eq. (4-40), regardless of the charge on the most acidic form considered.

$$\bar{h} = \frac{[\text{Na}^+] + [\text{H}^+] - [\text{OH}^-]}{C} \tag{4-41}$$

The denominator of Eq. (4-41) is the same as that of Eq. (4-40), where C is the total molar concentration of original acid in all its forms. From Eq. (4-41), $\bar{h}$ may be evaluated at any point in the titration. Note that brackets appear about H+ and OH−, and if their concentrations are not negligible compared with [Na+], they must be determined from the pH by use of an activity coefficient.

Perhaps the most convenient way to evaluate K_1 and K_2 is to define a function $M = (\text{H}^+)\bar{h}/(n - \bar{h})$, where n is the number of ionizable protons. For a monobasic acid, $\bar{h} = \alpha$, and $M = K_a$ is constant throughout the titration [compare Eq. (4-23)]. In a dibasic acid, $\bar{h} = 2\alpha$, and from Eq. (4-40) we obtain

$$M = \frac{(\text{H}^+)\bar{h}}{2 - \bar{h}} = \frac{K_1(\text{H}^+) + 2K_1K_2}{2(\text{H}^+) + K_1} \tag{4-42}$$

Data obtained during titration are used to plot $-\log M = \text{pM}$ versus $\bar{h}$. In the limit of $\bar{h} = 0$ or $(\text{H}^+) \to \infty$, $\text{pM} = \text{pK}_1 + \log 2$; in the limit of $\bar{h} = 2$ or $(\text{H}^+) \to 0$, $\text{pM} = \text{pK}_2 - \log 2$. Thus the values of pK_1 and pK_2 are obtained by extrapolation to the ordinate intercepts of the pM versus $\bar{h}$ plot. At the midpoint $\bar{h} = 1$, the value of pM is $(\text{pK}_1 + \text{pK}_2)/2$. The easily ascertained midpoint value of pM serves as a check on the pK_1 and pK_2 values obtained by extrapolation. The method of the pM versus $\bar{h}$ plot is more convenient than the solution of simultaneous equations to determine pK_1 and pK_2.

The shape of the pM versus $\bar{h}$ plot is determined only by the ratio K_1/K_2, and its position on the ordinate scale by the pK_1 and pK_2 values. To illustrate such plots, we remove their dependence on the particular pK_1 values by dividing both sides of Eq. (4-42) by K_1 to obtain

$$\frac{M}{K_1} = \frac{(H^+) + 2K_2}{2(H^+) + K_1} \tag{4-43}$$

From Eq. (4-43), a plot of $pM - pK_1$ versus $\bar{h}$ has a left-hand ordinate intercept $[(H^+) \to \infty]$ of $\log 2 = 0.30$ and is therefore a general plot independent of the particular pK_1 value of the system being considered. Plots of $pM - pK_1$ versus $\bar{h}$ for several ratios of K_1/K_2 are shown in Fig. 4-4. The family of curves fans out from the left-hand ordinate intercept of 0.30 with shapes dependent upon the K_1/K_2 ratios. From Eq. (4-43), the right-hand intercepts in Fig. 4-4 are $pK_2 - \log 2 - pK_1$, while the midpoint ($\bar{h} = 1.00$) values are $(pK_2 - pK_1)/2$.

For two equivalent and independent ionizing groups, all four micro-constants are equal and, from Eqs. (4-37) and (4-38), $K_1 = 4K_2$. Substitution of this result into Eq. (4-42) yields $M = K_1/2 = 2K_2$; therefore pM is a constant over the entire range of $\bar{h}$ as illustrated by the horizontal line in Fig. 4-4. The factor 4 is thus seen to arise from a statistical basis, since the most acidic form has two equivalent and independent protons to lose, and the most basic form has two equivalent and independent proton receptor sites. Monoesters of dicarboxylic acids have $K_a \simeq K_1/2$, because the free acids have two ionizable protons compared to only one for the monoesters. Equivalent and independent ionizing groups are seldom realized in practice because, after the initial ionization has taken place, the electrostatic effect of one less positive charge on the molecule retards the removal of the second proton. Table 4-3 shows that in the series of dicarboxylic acids the ratio K_1/K_2 approaches 4 as the electrostatic effect is diminished by increasing charge separation.

Often $K_1 \gg K_2$; in this case the pM versus $\bar{h}$ plot consists of two independent portions connected at $\bar{h} = 1$ by a nearly vertical line. This situation is illustrated by the uppermost curve in Fig. 4-4, where $K_1 = 1{,}024K_2$. Evidently such a plot is unnecessary for this situation; for all practical purposes the values of pK_1 and pK_2 may be evaluated independently of one another in the usual way for a monobasic acid. The method of evaluation outlined above is valuable for cases in which there is a distinct overlap of two ionization constants.

Extension to molecules with three or more ionizing protons is easily accomplished; however, the method yields precise values only for the first and last ionization constants determined by extrapolation to the ordinate intercepts. Intermediate pK_a values can be estimated from other points on the pM versus $\bar{h}$ plot after any necessary statistical corrections are made.

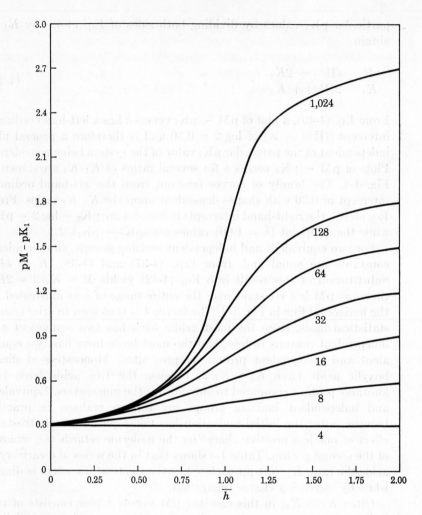

FIG. 4-4 Form of pM versus $\bar{h}$ plots for dibasic acids. To remove dependence on pK₁, pM − pK₁ is plotted against $\bar{h}$. The numbers on the contours correspond to K_1/K_2 ratios.

Intramolecular Electrostatic Effects. In several preceding sections we have noted the pronounced effect of intramolecular electrostatic interactions on the pK_a value of an ionizing group. Intramolecular electrostatic interactions are important in biological molecules, and we shall now discuss attempts to formulate the problem quantitatively. N. Bjerrum (1923) described the effect of a charged group on the acidity of a neighboring group in terms of simple electrostatic theory.

A charged group of valence z at a distance r from an acidic proton on a molecule in an ambient medium of dielectric constant ϵ contributes to the electrical potential ψ at the acidic proton $\psi = ze/\epsilon r$, where e is the protonic charge. The work required, on a molar basis, to remove the proton from a distance r to infinity from the charged group is expressed as follows:

$$W = Ne\psi = \frac{Nze^2}{\epsilon r}$$

The difference between the free energy of ionization of an acid containing a charged substituent and that of an acid of the same size lacking such a charge equals W, because ψ is zero in the uncharged case. More work is required to remove a proton from propionic acid (CH_3CH_2COOH, $pK_a^o = 4.87$) than from glycine ($NH_3^+CH_2COOH$, $pK_1^o = 2.35$) owing to charge repulsion in the latter acid:

$$W = \frac{Nze^2}{\epsilon r} = \Delta G_A{}^o - \Delta G_1{}^o = 2.3RT(pK_a{}^o - pK_1{}^o) = 2.3RT\,\Delta pK^o$$

At 25°, r in angstroms is

$$r = \frac{3.09}{\Delta pK^o} = \frac{3.09}{2.52} = 1.23 \text{ A}$$

Though of the right order of magnitude, this distance is shorter than the C—C single-bond distance of 1.54 A so that a simple electrostatic treatment yields too low a result in this case.

TABLE 4-3 *Dicarboxylic Acids* $HOOC(CH_2)_nCOOH$: *Distances between Acidic Protons*

Acid (1)	n (2)	$\Delta pK^o - \log 4$ (3)	Maximum, A (4)	Free rotation, A (5)	Bjerrum, A (6)	Kirkwood, A (7)
Oxalic	0	2.39	4.44	3.50	1.3	3.8
Malonic	1	2.24	4.87	4.12	1.4	4.1
Succinic	2	0.83	6.66	4.66	3.7	5.8
Glutaric	3	0.47	7.39	5.15	6.6	7.0
Adipic	4	0.39	9.02	5.59	7.9	7.6
Pimelic	5	0.34	9.91	6.00	9.1	8.3
Suberic	6	0.28	11.46	6.38	11.0	9.3
Azelaic	7	0.26	12.42	6.74	11.9	9.9

N. Bjerrum originally applied the simple electrostatic treatment to a series of dicarboxylic acids of the general formula $HOOC(CH_2)_nCOOH$. Table 4-3 lists dicarboxylic acids from $n = 0$ to 7. By comparing the first and second ionization constants, the inhibiting of departure of the second proton by a negative charge may be assessed. Values of ionization constants extrapolated to zero ionic strength must be used because the premises of the derivation are violated by the presence of salts which would alter electrostatic interactions and yield nonunity values of activity coefficients. In the third column, log 4 is subtracted from the difference of the two pK_a^o values for each dicarboxylic acid to eliminate the accidental symmetry of the most acidic and most basic forms which gives rise to the statistical factor of 4 discussed in the last section. For no electrostatic interaction, the figure in the third column would be zero. Columns 4 and 5 list the distances r between the center of negative charge and the acidic proton as calculated for maximum extension of the molecule and for an average value permitting free rotation about all bonds, respectively. Values of r calculated from the Bjerrum treatment are given in column 6. For glutaric and higher acids, the Bjerrum r values are reasonable, falling between the maximum and free-rotation figures, but the r values are low for the smaller acids, just as the value for glycine is too small.

Some assumptions made in the simple electrostatic picture of Bjerrum are not entirely applicable to molecular systems. Relative to a solute molecule, the solvent does not behave as a continuous medium characterized by a bulk dielectric constant. In addition, the solute molecule forms a cavity of low dielectric constant through which the electrostatic effect is transmitted more easily than through the medium of higher dielectric constant. The charged substituent exerts a greater effect than the high-dielectric-constant medium allows, and hence the r value will be too small, but less so as the length of the molecule is increased and more of the electrical interaction is transmitted through the solvent.

Kirkwood and Westheimer attempted to meet some of these objections in 1938. They assumed the dielectric constant of the solute cavity to be 2, the same as that of liquid paraffin hydrocarbons; however, the precise value is not critical. A continuous medium of dielectric constant 78 surrounds either a spherical or ellipsoidal solute cavity, depending upon which model best fits the molecule being considered. Their mathematical derivation yields a result which preserves the form of the Bjerrum equation, but an effective dielectric constant is calculated from the molecular volume and bond angles within the molecule. As shown in column 7 of Table 4-3, the r values obtained for the dicarboxylic acids are quite reasonable. Using an effective dielectric constant of 30 for glycine yields $r = 4.05$ A, slightly greater than the maximum value of 3.97 A. The theory has also been applied to dipolar substituents, but values obtained depend critically on assumed bond angles. In practice it is usually not possible to calculate ΔpK^o from

r values, even for charged substituents, because a small change in the assumed r value produces a large change in ΔpK^o. Instead, the r value is usually computed from the ΔpK^o and then checked to see if it is reasonable.

In 1957 Tanford extended the Kirkwood-Westheimer theory and found the results sensitive to a parameter d, which he describes as the distance of the charges beneath the surface of the low-dielectric-constant solute cavity. This additional parameter is not explicitly considered in the 1938 theory but is included in the r value. Since a low-dielectric-constant cavity would repel a charge, the latter must lie near the cavity surface. From calculations on dicarboxylic acids and other molecules, Tanford found that 1.0 A is a representative d value for charged groups. When this value is assumed along with the average of the free-rotation and maximum-extension values of r, the calculated ΔpK^o values are in good agreement with the experiment. Exceptions still appear, however, and additional explanations are required for some substances such as diethylmalonic acid even in this most recent theory. However, the theory is not sufficiently precise to ascribe the differences to inductive or other effects. Electrostatic (or coulombic) and inductive effects are quite different, but they are difficult to separate quantitatively.

SELECTED BIBLIOGRAPHY

1 J. T. Edsall and J. Wyman, "Biophysical Chemistry," chaps. 8 to 10, Academic Press Inc., New York, 1958.

2 R. A. Robinson, and R. H. Stokes, "Electrolyte Solutions," 2d ed., Butterworth Scientific Publications, London, 1959.

3 H. S. Harned and B. B. Owen, "The Physical Chemistry of Electrolytic Solutions," 3d ed., Reinhold Publishing Corporation, New York, 1958.

4 R. G. Bates, "Electrometric pH Determinations," John Wiley & Sons, Inc., New York, 1954.

QUESTIONS

4-1 Find the pH and pcH for solutions that are 2×10^{-4}, 2×10^{-3}, 0.02, 0.20, and 2.0 M in HCl.

4-2 What are the pH and pcH of 2×10^{-3} M HCl in the presence of (a) 0.018 M KCl and (b) 0.018 M $MgCl_2$?

4-3 Calculate the pH of each of the following acetic acid solutions: 1 M, 0.1 M, and 0.01 M.

4-4 What is the pH of a 0.1 M solution of glycine hydrochloride?

4-5 For the titration of 1.00 N acetic acid with 1.00 N NaOH, calculate the pH after the addition of 0.00, 0.25, 0.50, 0.75, 1.00, and 1.50 equiv of base.

4-6 For the titration of 0.100 N NH_3 with 0.100 N HCl, determine the pH after the addition of 0.00, 0.25, 0.50, 0.75, 1.00, and 1.50 equiv of acid.

4-7 What is the pH of a 0.10 M solution of glycine cation? Of a 0.10 M solution of glycine anion?

4-8   Contrast the efficiency with the capacity of a buffer solution.

4-9   Calculate the change in pH when 1-mmole of HCl is added to 100 ml of a solution containing NaCl, and compare this change with that produced by the addition of 1 mmole of HCl to 100 ml of a solution containing 10 mmoles of acetic acid and 10 mmoles of sodium acetate.

4-10   Evaluate the pH after the addition of 0.00, 0.05, 0.10, 0.15, 0.20, and 0.25 mole of NaOH to a 1.0-liter solution of 0.10 M carbonic acid. Draw the titration curve.

4-11   What are the slopes for Debye-Hückel extrapolations to zero ionic strength when pK_a is plotted against $\mu^{1/2}$ for ammonium ion, acetic acid, and the second ionization of phosphoric acid?

4-12   Write equations analogous to Eq. (4-30) for the first and second ionizations of an amino acid such as glycine.

4-13   Calculate the pK_a value at 0.16 ionic strength for all the acids of Table 4-1.

4-14   For the first acid in each group in Table 4-1, calculate the standard free-energy change from the pK_a^o value, and compare with the values obtained from the enthalpy and entropy values.

4-15   Calculate the pK_a value at 37° for the first acid in each group of Table 4-1.

4-16   We wish to select a buffer system with a pH near 10 and with as little dependence upon temperature as possible. Describe the buffer system in Table 4-1 that best satisfies this purpose.

4-17   Calculate ΔH^o and ΔS^o for the reaction $NH_3 + H_2O \rightleftarrows NH_4^+ + OH^-$. Rationalize the results.

4-18   At 25°, successive pK_a values for histidine are 1.82, 6.00, and 9.17, with heats of ionization of about 1.2, 6.9, and 9.4 kcal/mole, respectively. Sketch the titration curve. Match the groups in the molecule with the pK_a values.

4-19   Plot percentage dipolar ion versus pH in the range $0 < pH < 13$ for all forms of glycine.

4-20   The solubility of tyrosine is 0.147, 0.351, and 0.836 g per 100 g of water at 0°, 25°, and 50°, respectively. Calculate the heat of solution. At 25°, the pK_a values of tyrosine are 2.3, 9.1, and 10.3. What is the solubility of tyrosine at 25° and pH 12?

4-21   Show the relationships between all the microforms of tyrosine, and define all the requisite microconstants.

4-22   The successive pK_a^o values at 25° for citric acid are 3.13, 4.76, and 6.40. What are the relationships between the macroconstants and microconstants? How many microconstants are unknown? How might you evalute the unknown microconstants? By selecting the appropriate model acid from Table 4-3, predict the expected difference between the microscopic pk values for successive ionizations from the terminal carboxylic acid groups. The observed difference is 0.55.

4-23   Find K_1^o/K_2^o for the dicarboxylic acids of Table 4-3. Calculate the effective dielectric constants for each acid of Table 4-3 using the Kirkwood-Westheimer r values of column 7.

5 | Titrations of Proteins

5-1 THEORY

The development of exact methods for treating ionizations from individual groups presents a formidable problem with polyelectrolytes such as proteins containing up to 60 ionizable protons per 20,000 molecular weight. Table 5-1 lists the common acid-base centers in proteins with their normal ranges of ionization and the corresponding heats of ionization ΔH. The latter are useful for identification and for confirming assignments of groups but vary considerably and are a reliable

TABLE 5-1 *Acidic Groups Found in Proteins*

Group	Amino acid residue	pH range of normal ionization	ΔH, kcal/mole
α-COOH	C terminal	3.3–3.8	0
β,γ-COOH	Aspartic and glutamic acids	4.0–4.8	1
Imidazole	Histidine	6.4–7.4	7
α-NH$_3$$^+$	N terminal	7.4–7.9	11
ϵ-NH$_3$$^+$	Lysine	9.5–10.5	13
Phenolic	Tyrosine	9.5–10.5	6
Sulfhydryl	Cysteine	9–10	7
Guanidyl	Arginine	Greater than 12	12

guide only to ± 2 kcal/mole. Guanidine, the conjugate base of the guanidyl group in Table 5-1, is one of the few uncharged strong bases. A protein usually contains only a few imidazole and α-NH$_3$$^+$ groups, and hence the titration curve is strongly buffered from pH 3 to 5 and pH > 9 but weakly buffered in the intermediate range of pH 5 to 9.

For a monobasic acid,

$$\text{pH} = \text{p}K_a + \log \frac{\text{base}}{\text{acid}} = \text{p}K_a + \log \frac{\alpha}{1-\alpha} \qquad (5\text{-}1)$$

where α is the fraction of the acid form which has lost protons. Since many groups ionize in proteins, it is convenient to divide them into sets, depending upon the kind of group that is ionizing. For instance, all imidazole groups may belong to one set. The number of groups in a set is determined by titration or by amino acid analysis. Equation (5-1) may be applied to independently ionizing groups in a protein and to equivalent groups within each set if α is redefined as the fraction of all groups of a set which have lost protons. The ionization-constant term pK_a is then pk_{int}, where k_{int} is an intrinsic or microscopic ionization constant for a particular set and should correspond to one of the ranges of values listed in column 3 of Table 5-1.

Intrinsic constants are independent of the charge on the macromolecule, but apparent or observed ionization constants are charge-dependent. At low pH values, when the net charge on a protein is positive, protons will be repelled, and the observed pK_a value for a group will be less than otherwise expected. The reverse situation prevails at high pH, where comparatively high group pK_a values are measured. In both cases the magnitude of the shift depends upon the net charge on the protein and decreases with increasing ionic strength. Normally a pK_a value is not shifted by more than 1.5 units. The pH throughout a titration could be calculated by selecting an appropriate pk_{int} for the group in each set and superimposing the results for all sets if there were not an electrostatic effect due to the varying charge on the protein, which results in groups not ionizing independently. As it stands, Eq. (5-1) is incomplete, and some allowance must be made for the changing electrostatic effect of the charge on the protein as titration proceeds.

It has not been possible to derive a completely satisfactory account of a protein titration curve from theoretical principles alone. For computing a protein titration curve, the following equation is often applied:

$$pH = pk_{int} + \log \frac{\alpha}{1 - \alpha} - \frac{1}{2.3kT} \frac{\partial W}{\partial \bar{Z}} \qquad (5\text{-}2)$$

where k = Boltzmann's constant, R/N

$\bar{Z}$ = mean net charge on protein

W = electrostatic factor arising from Debye-Hückel theory

According to the theory, the total electrostatic free energy, or the work done in placing all the charges onto the surface of a rigid, non-polarizable, uniformly charged sphere of radius b, is

$$W = \bar{G}_e = \frac{\bar{Z}^2 e^2}{2\epsilon} \left(\frac{1}{b} - \frac{\kappa}{1 + \kappa a} \right) = kT\bar{Z}^2\omega \qquad (5\text{-}3)$$

where $\omega = \dfrac{e^2}{2\epsilon kT}\left(\dfrac{1}{b} - \dfrac{\kappa}{1 + \kappa a}\right) = 3.57\left(\dfrac{1}{b} - \dfrac{\kappa}{1 + \kappa a}\right)$

e = electronic charge

ϵ = dielectric constant of medium

a = distance of closest approach of a small ion and protein sphere, often taken as $b + 2.5$ A

κ = Debye-Hückel parameter (Sec. 3-3)

and 3.57 is the value of the collection of constants for aqueous systems at 25° when distances are measured in angstrom units. Since

$$\frac{\partial W}{\partial \bar{Z}} = 2\bar{Z}\omega kT$$

Eq. (5-2) becomes

$$\text{pH} = \text{pk}_{\text{int}} + \log\frac{\alpha}{1 - \alpha} - 0.868\omega\bar{Z} \tag{5-4}$$

Equation (5-4) indicates that the intrinsic ionization constant of a set of groups on a spherical macromolecule is modified by the presence of charge according to

$$\text{pk} = \text{pk}_{\text{int}} - 0.868\omega\bar{Z}$$

or

$$\text{k} = k_{\text{int}}e^{2\omega\bar{Z}}$$

Equation (5-4) is often employed in constructing titration curves of proteins. In aqueous solutions at 25°, κ is a function only of ionic strength μ ($\kappa = 0.33\mu^{1/2}$ A^{-1}), and the equation at the top of the page becomes

$$\omega = 3.57\left(\frac{1}{b} - \frac{0.33\mu^{1/2}}{1 + a0.33\mu^{1/2}}\right) \tag{5-5}$$

For a spherical protein with $b = 23.5$ A and $a = 26.0$ A, $\omega = 0.152$, 0.089, 0.052, 0.046, and 0.025 at ionic strengths 0.00, 0.01, 0.10, 0.15, and 1.00, respectively.

The effect of the ω term in Eq. (5-4) is to spread the titration curve on the pH axis. As ionic strength increases, interactions between charged groups decrease, and the titration curve shifts in the direction of more independently ionizing groups. If the ionic strength is increased while the amount of base is held constant, the pH shifts toward the isoelectric point. Since Eq. (5-4) may be only partially justified theoretically, ω is best considered as an empirical parameter which, when applied to protein titration curves, yields reasonable a and b values.

Even if the transition from theory to Eq. (5-4) were smooth, exact agreement would still not be expected because of the assumptions made in the theory. Most proteins only approximate spheres in solution. In addition, the assumption of a uniformly distributed charge near the protein surface is open to question. An acidic group buried inside the protein would lose a proton with much greater difficulty than a similar group at the surface. Charge fluctuations of microscopic forms tend to smear out the charges; yet these charges occur on amino acid side chains which have definite positions on the surface of the protein. If any electrolyte is added, polarization of the protein charge will occur on the approach of another ion. Once again the assumption of ϵ as the bulk dielectric constant of salt-free water is not correct. A microscopic dielectric constant less than one-tenth as great would be more accurate, but no independent method exists for ascertaining an appropriate value. The success of the model may be due to the compensating effects of overestimating the electrostatic interaction by the smeared-site approach and underestimating the interaction by use of the bulk dielectric constant. Analyses of titration curves of compact proteins indicate that they are impenetrable molecules which are not entered by ions. Associated water is either bound as water of hydration or occluded.

Tanford and Kirkwood have attempted to elucidate some of these points by elaborating the Kirkwood-Westheimer approach previously described for dicarboxylic acids. A protein is treated as a spherical cavity of dielectric constant 2 in which point charges are located at fixed positions near the surface. As with the dicarboxylic acids, it is necessary to place all charged groups about 1 A below the cavity surface in order to obtain agreement with experiment. This placement permits considerable variation in the titration curves to be accounted for by the distribution of acidic groups. Such a result is important because it means that some abnormalities in titration curves may be explained electrostatically, so that auxiliary postulates such as hydrogen bonding are not required, even though they are difficult to disprove. Electrostatic interaction energies are smallest for regular, uniform distributions, greater for random distributions, and greatest for nonuniform distributions. For instance, a crowding of carboxyl groups over a small region would tend to increase ω. Variations in pk_{int} may also be explained by the mode of charge distribution. In one of Tanford's models, the minimum of electrostatic interaction energy is not identical with the isoelectric point. This result at least qualitatively accounts for the observation that the region of maximum stability of some proteins is not at the isoelectric point. Only spherical models have been treated theoretically. Many proteins and nucleic acids are not spherical, and the model is not applicable to them. The mathematical difficulties inherent in the next least complicated model, an ellipsoid of revolution, are staggering.

We might expect that arguments based primarily on the electrostatic considerations just summarized cannot account for all features of titration curves. At least two other factors are important in some situations: effects of an apolar environment and hydrogen bonding. These two possibilities will be discussed in turn.

In carboxylic acid ionizations, as exemplified by acetic acid, two charges are created where none existed before:

$$CH_3COOH + H_2O \rightleftarrows CH_3COO^- + H_3O^+$$

In a low-dielectric-constant apolar environment such as might occur in the hydrophobic interior of a protein, the ionization of carboxylic acids would not proceed as far to the right as in water. We can estimate the magnitude of this effect by considering the energies required to charge a sphere in two media with different dielectric constants. Such a relation is derived from the ionic-strength-independent half of Eq. (5-3), from which we obtain

$$\Delta pK_a = 125 \left(\frac{1}{\epsilon_S} - \frac{1}{78.5} \right) \left(\frac{1}{b_1} + \frac{1}{b_2} \right) \tag{5-6}$$

for the difference between the acid ionization constants at 25° in water of dielectric constant 78.5 and in another solvent of dielectric constant ϵ_S. For the case of carboxylic acids, b_1 and b_2 are the radii in angstrom units of created cation and anion, respectively, considered as spheres. At 25° in 70% dioxane with dielectric constant 17.7, Eq. (5-6) indicates $\Delta pK_a = 3.6$ if both b_1 and b_2 are taken as about 3 A. The measured difference, ΔpK_a for acetic acid in aqueous dioxane solution and in water, is $8.32 - 4.76 = 3.56$ units, a result more in agreement with the calculated value than the crudeness of our model and our approximations deserves. A linear relation is not obtained, however, when pK_a for a single acid is plotted against $1/\epsilon$; the nonlinearity points up the inadequacy of our simple model. Nonetheless its usefulness has been demonstrated, and we expect that simple carboxylic acid, sulfhydryl, and phenolic ionizations will be markedly inhibited by transfer to an environment of lower dielectric constant.

In contrast to the results for carboxylic acids, various ammonium ions commonly show a small decrease in pK_a (ΔpK_a is negative) on being transferred from water to lower-dielectric-constant media. In these cases only a proton-transfer process is being described; no new charges are created or destroyed:

$$RNH_3^+ + H_2O \rightleftarrows RNH_2 + H_3O^+$$

Dielectric-constant changes are now much less important, and Eq. (5-6) must be modified so that only the reciprocal radii of the two charged ions contribute to our simple picture. This reciprocal-radii difference is smaller than the dielectric-constant effects for carboxylic acid and phenolic ionizations.

The second effect which may lead to abnormalities in titration curves is hydrogen bonding. If the acidic form of an acid is hydrogen-bonded, removal of the hydrogen will be inhibited, and the pK_a value increased. If the basic form of a conjugate acid-base system functions as a hydrogen-bond acceptor, it will be more difficult to add a proton to the base, resulting in a lowering of the pK_a. In order that either of these differences be describable with pK_a values, the titration curves must be reversible.

We have outlined three possible causes of the occurrence of abnormal pK_a values in titration curves. In practice it is often difficult to separate these three effects. Heat and entropy, in addition to free-energy data, are helpful. Once the charge on the molecule has been allowed for according to Eq. (5-4), groups that still appear to ionize abnormally may be in an apolar interior of the molecule or may be hydrogen-bonded. It is particularly difficult to separate these last two effects, and indeed they may often reinforce each other. If we picture a globular protein molecule as a hydrophobic core with most of the charged groups on the surface, an acidic group in the core may ionize at higher pH values than normal because of the low-dielectric-constant environment as well as hydrogen bonding. Since the group is removed from direct contact with a hydrogen-bonding solvent, it is more likely to be intramolecularly hydrogen-bonded if it is in the interior rather than on the surface of a molecule. Hydrogen bonding has frequently been invoked to account for abnormal ionizations in proteins. Recently a greater emphasis has been placed on the influence of the apolar interior. Carboxylic acid and tyrosine phenolic groups often titrate abnormally, and these are precisely the groups which our analysis has shown to be the most susceptible to a low-dielectric-constant environment. If charge on the molecule is an insufficient explanation, it is likely that hydrogen bonding is a cause of any abnormally ionizing ammonium groups.

5-2 RESULTS

In obtaining titration curves it is essential to check for reversibility by back titration. Only if the titration curve is reversible can an equilibrium constant be evaluated. The criterion of reversibility limits the curves to the region from about pH 2 to pH 11; however, there is much individual variation. Although it is often of interest to inquire into the changes taking place in the pH range in which irreversible denaturation occurs, this problem will not be considered here. The irreversible titration of DNA is mentioned in Sec. 18-3.

Polypeptides. Before considering titration curves in proteins, we shall illustrate some of the principles involved by describing titrations of polymers of single amino acids or copolymers composed of two different amino acids. Polypeptides differ from proteins in that they are *polydisperse;* not all the molecules are of the same molecular weight.

Poly-L-tyrosine averaging 30 residues per chain and hence about

FIG. 5-1 Spectrophotometric titrations of poly-L-tyrosine: pH versus fraction of phenolic groups ionized. Open circles are experimental points with 0.20 *M* NaCl; closed circles are experimental points with no added salt, extrapolated to zero ionic strength. The curves are calculated from Eq. (5-4). [From E. Katchalski and M. Sela, *J. Am. Chem. Soc.*, **75**, 5284 (1953).]

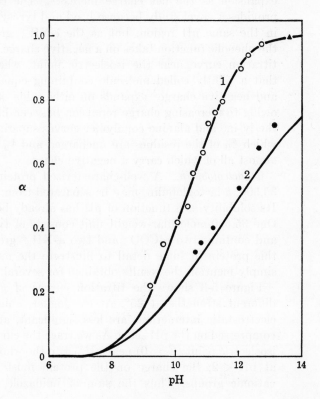

5,000 average molecular weight was titrated with base, and the course of the titration was followed spectrophotometrically since the ionized phenolic group absorbs strongly at 295 mμ, while the absorption of the acidic form is weak. If the fraction of phenolic groups ionized is α, the mean net charge is 30α. Figure 5-1 shows the experimental points and the titration curves computed by Eq. (5-4). ω values were calculated from Eq. (5-5) by taking $b = 17.5$ A and $a = 19.5$ A as inferred from the molecular weight. For the curve at 0.20 ionic strength, $\omega = 0.066$ and pk$_{int} = 9.5$ fit perfectly with the experimental points. Decreasing the ionic strength spreads the curve on the pH axis, as predicted from the greater electrostatic effect and larger ω value.

A study of three copolymers of tyrosine confirms the expectation that increasing positive charge on the molecule displaces the titration curve to lower pH values, as shown in Fig. 5-2. Conversely, because the negatively charged aspartic acid residues inhibit the removal of phenolic protons, the curve for this copolymer is displaced to higher pH values. Once again the curve is fitted with pk$_{int} = 9.5$, but $b = 15.4$ A because the polymer is smaller. For the alanine-tyrosine copolymer, ω is not constant but decreases as α increases, presumably owing to expansion as the net charge increases. The copolymer with lysine provides a novel study because lysyl and tyrosyl residues lose protons in the same pH region, but as the ϵ-NH$_3^+$ group becomes neutral, the phenolic function takes on a negative charge. A jump occurs in this titration curve near the isoelectric point, where $\bar{Z} = 0$, suggesting that a tightly coiled molecule containing equal numbers of positive and negative charges expands on either side of the isoelectric point owing to increasing charge repulsion between like charges. Note that the lysine and alanine copolymer curves superimpose in the region in which $\frac{8}{9}$ of the residues are uncharged and $\frac{1}{9}$ are phenolic residues, almost all of which carry a negative charge.

β-Lactoglobulin. A well-characterized protein of molecular weight 35,500, β-lactoglobulin, may be separated from milk in large crystals. Its solubility as a function of pH has already been shown in Fig. 3-4. One 35,500-molecular-weight unit consists of two polypeptide chains and contains two α-COO$^-$ and two α-NH$_3^+$ groups. We shall discuss this protein in some detail to illustrate the methods used and then simply mention the results obtained for several other proteins.

Figure 5-3 shows the titration curves of β-lactoglobulin at two different strengths at 25°. At the higher ionic strength of 0.15 M, electrostatic interactions are less significant, and the curve becomes compressed on the pH scale. As we trace the curve of Fig. 5-3 from the isoelectric point ($\bar{Z} = 0$) near pH 5.4 to the wholly protonated protein at pH < 2, the charge on the protein must equal the number of cationic groups. Thus the sum of imidazole, α- and ϵ-NH$_3^+$, and guanidyl groups is 40:

$$\Sigma(his^+) + \Sigma(\alpha\text{-}NH_3^+) + \Sigma(lys^+) + \Sigma(arg^+) = 40$$

A relatively unbuffered region occurs at pH 8.5, where $\bar{Z} = -19$, which charge must correspond to the difference between cationic and anionic groups at this pH. Inspection of Table 5-1 reveals that at pH 8.5 the cationic groups are lysyl and guanidyl, and the only anionic

FIG. 5-2 Spectrophotometric titration of copolymers of one part L-tyrosine and nine parts L-lysine, DL-alanine, and L-aspartic acid, respectively: pH versus fraction of phenol groups ionized. The average number of residues per molecule follows the letter n in the caption. Open points are forward titrations, and closed points back titrations to check the reversibility of the titration curve. [From M. Sela and E. Katchalski, *J. Am. Chem. Soc.*, **78**, 3986 (1956).]

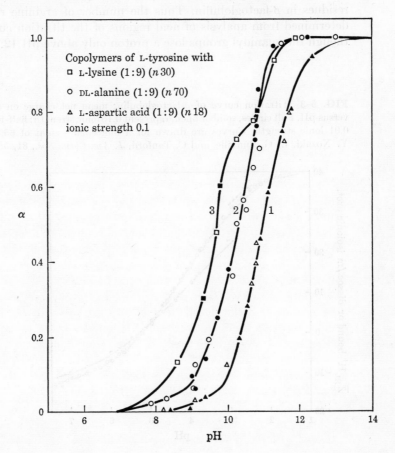

groups are carboxylate. Therefore,

$$\Sigma(\text{lys}^+) + \Sigma(\text{arg}^+) - \Sigma(\text{COO}^-) = -19$$

The number of lysyl groups may be estimated by means of the formol titration described in the preceding chapter. Addition of 0.3 M formaldehyde to the protein solution at pH 8.5 liberates protons, because the pK_a of the reactant lysyl residue is about 10, and that of the hydroxymethyl derivative of the order of 8. The amount of base required to bring the pH back to 8.5 is a measure of the number of lysyl residues. In β-lactoglobulin 28 lysyl residues are indicated by a formol titration.

A detailed analysis of Fig. 5-3 indicates that the best integral value for the number of carboxyl groups is 51, two of which are α-COO$^-$ while the others are β- and γ-COO$^-$. Two additional carboxylic acid groups titrate anomalously near pH 7.5. Combination of these results with those already presented implies six arginine and four histidine residues in β-lactoglobulin. Thus the number of arginine residues is determined from analysis of acid regions of the titration curve, even though the guanidyl groups lose a proton only above pH 12. That the

FIG. 5-3 Titration curve of β-lactoglobulin: mean net charge on the protein versus pH. Full circles, solid or open, represent 0.15 ionic strength; half-filled circles, 0.01 ionic strength. Curves are drawn for a molecular weight of 35,500. [From Y. Nozaki, L. G. Bunville, and C. Tanford, *J. Am. Chem. Soc.*, **81**, 5523 (1959).]

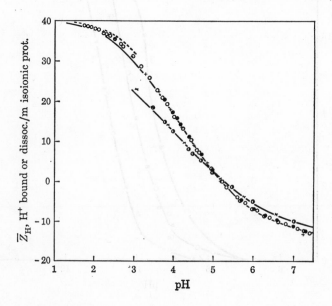

number of histidine residues is small is confirmed by Fig. 5-4, in which the apparent heat of ionization is plotted against the mean net charge. The curve changes abruptly from values characteristic of carboxylic acid ionizations to values corresponding to ammonium groups without pausing at the intermediate values of about 7 kcal/mole which are expected for imidazole groups as indicated in Table 5-1. In marked contrast, a similar curve for hemoglobin, in which almost 7 % of the amino acids are histidine, exhibits a broad plateau at about 7 kcal/mole. The apparent heat of ionization Q' is determined by measuring the change of pH with temperature in a solution of protein to which a specified amount of acid or base is added. From the van't Hoff isobar discussed in Sec. 2-1, $d(\ln K_a)/dT = Q'/RT^2$, we obtain

$$Q' = \frac{RT^2 d(\ln K_a)}{dT} = -2.3RT^2 \left[\frac{\partial(\mathrm{pH})}{\partial T}\right]_{\bar{h}}$$

since $\alpha/(1 - \alpha)$ is unchanged at constant $\bar{h}$ (the mean number of protons removed from the most acidic form). Occasionally unexpected Q' values are obtained, providing a clue to some special effect.

Finally, six tyrosyl residues are estimated from the increase in absorption at 295 mμ accompanying the ionization of phenolic groups.

FIG. 5-4 Heat of ionization in calories per mole for groups in β-lactoglobulin as a function of the mean net charge. [From R. K. Cannan, A. H. Palmer, and A. C. Kibrick, *J. Biol. Chem.*, **142**, 803 (1942).]

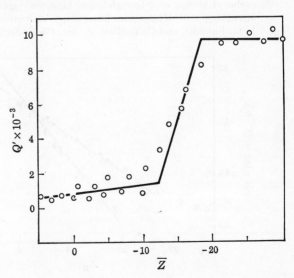

A change in conformation of the molecule takes place at pH 7.5, and two carboxylic acid groups previously hidden titrate reversibly in this pH region. Altogether, 53 carboxylic acid residues are present. Titration studies thus provide a probe for examining some aspects of protein transformations. Above pH 9.7, the protein is irreversibly denatured. At low pH, the protein dissociates into two 18,000 molecular weight units. The titration results agree to within one residue with amino acid analyses of the protein using conventional techniques.

When the number of acid and basic groups of each kind is known, we can proceed to the evaluation of pk_{int} and ω for side-chain carboxyl groups. Rearrangement of Eq. (5-4) yields

$$\text{pH} - \log \frac{\alpha}{1 - \alpha} = pk_{int} - 0.868\omega\bar{Z} \tag{5-7}$$

A plot of the left-hand side of Eq. (5-7) versus $\bar{Z}$ is shown in Fig. 5-5. A random coil molecule would show an almost horizontal slope at high $\bar{Z}$ values because charge repulsion extends the molecule and weakens electrostatic interactions. The straight, nonhorizontal lines of Fig. 5-5 are typical of a globular protein. At $\bar{Z} = 0$, the ordinate is pk_{int}, which is 4.69 at 0.15 M ionic strength and 4.75 at 0.01 M ionic strength. From the slopes, $\omega = 0.039$ and 0.072 at 0.15 and 0.01 ionic strengths, respectively. Unfortunately, the interpretation is complicated by

FIG. 5-5 Plot of the left-hand side of Eq. (5-7) versus $\bar{Z}$ for the side-chain carboxyl groups of β-lactoglobulin. Line with greater slope represents an ionic strength of 0.01 M; line with lesser slope, ionic strength of 0.15. [From Y. Nozaki, L. G. Bunville, and C. Tanford, *J. Am. Chem. Soc.*, **81**, 5523 (1959).]

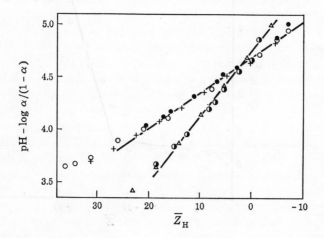

potassium-ion binding, but when this effect is taken into account, $pk_{int} = 4.87$ and 4.83, and $\omega = 0.058$ and 0.090, at ionic strengths 0.15 and 0.01 M, respectively. These values of pk_{int} are relatively high compared to the range of values listed in Table 5-1.

We may also estimate ω from the molecular weight ($35,500$) and the partial specific volume (0.75 cc/g). Many proteins have been found to bind about 0.2 g of water per gram of protein; therefore, 0.2 cc/g is added to the partial specific volume. The volume of one molecule is

$$V_m = \frac{35,500 \text{ g/mole} \times 0.95 \text{ cc/g}}{6.02 \times 10^{23} \text{ molecules/mole}} = 56 \times 10^{-21} \text{ cc/molecule}$$

If the molecule is considered as a sphere, the radius

$$b = \left(\frac{3V_m}{4\pi}\right)^{\frac{1}{3}} = 23.5 \text{ A}$$

This radius is the same as that already used to illustrate the calculation of ω by Eq. (5-5). For ionic strengths 0.15 and 0.01, ω is 0.046 and 0.089, respectively. Uneven distribution of carboxyl groups on the protein surface could account for the higher values of ω obtained from titration data, as well as the relatively high values of pk_{int}.

Ovalbumin. Ovalbumin, a protein of molecular weight $45,000$ obtained from eggs, is a typical albumin, since it is precipitated from solution by the addition of salt. The C-terminal group is proline, while the N terminus is acetylated, acetyl-gly-ser-. Such acetylation occurs only infrequently in proteins. Since it possesses carbohydrate groups, ovalbumin is a glycoprotein. It also contains one or two phosphoric acid groups, perhaps attached to alcoholic serine or threonine residues. The isoelectric point is near pH 4.9.

Ovalbumin exhibits a reversible titration curve in the range $2 < \text{pH} < 11.5$. An analysis similar to that described for β-lactoglobulin yields results in agreement with analytical data, including the presence of 14 guanidyl groups, if the above complications are considered. When allowance is made for a small amount of pH-independent salt binding, the entire titration curve can be represented as the superposition of three curves of the form of Eq. (5-4): 51 carboxylic acid groups of $pk_{int} = 4.29$, 5 imidazole groups of $pk_{int} = 6.75$, and 23 ammonium groups of $pk_{int} = 10.07$. In addition, all three groups yield the same value of ω. Up to an ionic strength of unity, this value of ω is 80% of the ω value calculated from the molecular weight and partial specific volume, assuming no hydration.

Analytical data indicate that ovalbumin contains about nine tyrosyl residues, which do not appear in the titration. Due to the large negative charge on the molecule in basic solutions, electrostatic effects in proteins with acid isoelectric points may displace $pk_{int} \simeq 10$ for phenolic groups to give an apparent $pk' \simeq 12$. Since only the anionic form of tyrosyl residues absorbs appreciably at 295 mμ, the ionization of phenolic groups can be distinguished from other groups that may be ionizing simultaneously. In ovalbumin the characteristic absorption of anionic phenolic groups does not appear until $pH > 12.5$, and then rapidly and irreversibly. Subsequent lowering of the pH yields a protein differing in conformation from the original. Irreversible denaturation may also be brought about by the addition of strong acid, concentrated urea, or heat. Tyrosyl residues, having little affinity for water, evidently are embedded in the hydrophobic, low-dielectric-constant interior of the molecule and hence are resistant to ionization. Hydrogen bonding may provide additional stabilization for some groups. Similar masked groups are observed in other proteins and with the sulfhydryl group of cysteine.

Ribonuclease (RNase). The second protein (after insulin with 51 amino acids) to have its complete amino acid sequence delineated, beef pancreas ribonuclease of molecular weight 13,683 consists of a single polypeptide chain of 124 amino acid residues. All eight cysteinyl residues are cross-linked to form four disulfide bridges, markedly reducing the possible spatial arrangements of the protein. Ribonuclease is an enzyme catalyzing the hydrolytic degradation of ribonucleic acid. Owing to a predominance of basic amino acids, the isoelectric point is high, about pH 9.7.

Agreement between analytical and titration data is perfect. The superposition of six curves of the form of Eq. (5-4) can account for the titration curve in the range $2 < pH < 11.5$. Of the six tyrosyl residues, three titrate normally and reversibly with $pk_{int} = 9.95$, and three ionize only above pH 12 and irreversibly as in ovalbumin. Titration of the latter also results in a loss of enzymatic activity. In the reverse titration or in the presence of sufficient urea, all six tyrosyl residues titrate together.

Serum Albumin. The main protein component of blood plasma, serum albumin has a molecular weight of about 65,000. Titration results agree well with the amino acid content obtained by analytical methods. Some anomalies appear, however. At about pH 4.2, the ω value (corrected for ion binding) drops sharply, though it is constant from pH 4.2 to pH 11. This drop implies a swelling of the molecule, confirmed by viscosity and light-scattering studies. Apparently the molecule rearranges into a form of lesser electrostatic energy to accommodate greater charge-repulsion effects. The situation is complicated, and other factors also affect it.

5-3   ISOELECTRIC AND ISOIONIC POINTS

Definitions and experimental measurements of isoelectric and isoionic points have associated with them the same difficulties that exist for pH. Definitions that have thermodynamic or theoretical significance are not experimentally measurable, and what is experimentally observed is difficult to interpret theoretically. As in the case of pH, the problem becomes one of narrowing the gap between what is useful theoretically and what is measured experimentally.

Isoelectric Point.   The isoelectric point may be defined theoretically as the pH at which the mean net charge of the molecules is zero, $\bar{Z} = 0$. The experimental or operational definition is that pH at which no net migration takes place in an electric field. Since the experiment must be conducted in buffered solutions containing salts, interacting flows (Sec. 9-4) may produce deviations, because even sugars migrate slightly in the presence of some salts. In most cases, however, the theoretical and experimental interpretations are nearly identical. Isoelectric points do not depend explicitly on protein concentration, but are dependent upon solvent composition.

Isoionic Point.   The theoretical definition of isoionic point is that pH at which the number of positive and negative groups arising exclusively from proton exchange are equal to each other. To determine the isoionic point experimentally, isoionic material is required. This material may be prepared by electrodialysis or, preferably, by a mixed-bed ion-exchange resin, so that all ions other than solute, hydrogen, and hydroxyl ions are removed. Given this isoionic solute, two experimental definitions of isoionic point are possible. The first is that pH of the solution which does not change on addition of more isoionic material. The second and more frequently used definition is simply the pH of a solution of isoionic material. These two experimental definitions are conflicting. For infinitely dilute solutions, the isoionic point according to the second operational definition is the same pH as pure water; that is, pH 7.00 at 25°. When the solution is very dilute, or if the isoionic point is far removed from pH 7, the first operational definition conforms more closely to the theoretical definition. However, if the solute concentration is not too small, nor the isoionic point too far removed from pH 7, the second experimental definition is nearly the same as the theoretical definition. When the preceding conditions are met and the solute strongly binds ions which are present in equivalent amounts, the second experimental definition more nearly approximates the theoretical.

Serum albumin binds anions much more avidly than cations. Since the addition of salt to isoionic protein causes the negative charge on the protein to increase, more positively charged protons are bound to

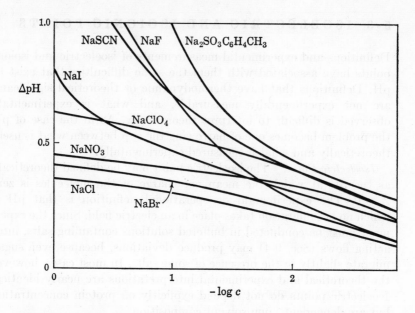

FIG. 5-6 Increase of pH of isoionic human serum albumin solutions on the addition of added salts. [From G. Scatchard and E. S. Black, *J. Phys. Colloid Chem.*, **53,** 88 (1949).]

albumin, owing to the greater electrostatic attraction. Since (H⁺) is small, and the albumin is too dilute to be an effective buffer, the binding of only a few protons markedly increases the pH, because the number of protons in solution decreases. Figure 5-6 shows the increase in pH of isoionic serum albumin solutions produced by the addition of various added neutral salts. At 0.1 ionic strength each additional bound univalent anion increases the pH about 0.03 units. The more strongly bound anions cause the greater displacement of pH. By the second operational definition of isoionic point, all the solutions of Fig. 5-6 are isoionic. In many of its properties serum albumin exhibits great conformational adaptability, producing indiscriminate binding of anions and the swelling previously referred to in the titration studies.

Comparison of Isoelectric and Isoionic Points. If the isoelectric point of a material is taken as that pH at which $\bar{Z} = 0$, the material cannot be isoelectric and isoionic unless the isoionic point is at pH 7. In an isoionic solution, electroneutrality requires that

$$[H^+] + [P]\bar{Z} = [OH^-] \tag{5-8}$$

where [P] is the molar concentration of protein. If the isoionic point is at pH 4 for a 1% solution of a protein of molecular weight 10^5, [OH$^-$] is negligible, and

$$\bar{Z} = -\frac{[\text{H}^+]}{[\text{P}]} = -\frac{10^{-4} \times 10^5}{10} = -1$$

which is clearly not isoelectric ($\bar{Z} = 0$). Since protons must be added to make $\bar{Z} = 0$, the isoionic pH is greater than the isoelectric pH. Conversely, for isoionic points on the alkaline side of neutrality, the isoionic pH is lower than the isoelectric pH.

Though the isoelectric point is not explicitly dependent upon the protein concentration, Eq. (5-8) demonstrates that the isoionic point is. The lower the concentration of protein, the greater the disparity between isoionic and isoelectric points. At moderate concentrations of protein, the difference between isoionic and isoelectric points is small as long as they fall between pH 3 and pH 11.

In the absence of salt, and for isoionic points near pH 7, the isoelectric and isoionic points are nearly the same. In the presence of salt, however, the difference between the two may become appreciable. Figure 5-6 shows that the isoionic point of serum albumin increases with the addition of salt, owing to anion binding. For the same reason the isoelectric point decreases, because protons must be added to neutralize the net negative charge on the molecule produced by the absorption of anions. For example, human serum albumin in the absence of salt has an isoionic point of 4.9 and an isoelectric point of 4.8. In the presence of 0.15 M NaCl, the isoionic point is 5.2, and the isoelectric point 4.4.

Estimation of Isoelectric Points. Isoelectric points of amino acids, proteins, and other molecules may be estimated rapidly if the number and pk$_{\text{int}}$ for each acid group is known. A four-step procedure is adequate.

1. List all the acidic groups in order of their increasing pk$_{\text{int}}$ values, noting the number of groups in each set.

2. Determine the number of cationic (positively charged) groups in the most acidic form.

3. To find the point at which $\bar{Z} = 0$, count off, in the list of step 1, the number of cationic groups in step 2.

4. Estimate the isoelectric point from the equation

$$\text{pH}_I = \text{pk}_{\text{int}} + \log [\alpha/(1 - \alpha)]$$

where α is the fraction of groups that are counted off in the last set of step 3, and pk$_{\text{int}}$ applies to the same set. If the countoff in step 3 results in the completion of one set but does not begin the next, take the average value of the two pk$_{\text{int}}$ for the sets under question.

For a hypothetical polypeptide containing three sets of groups, 30 carboxylic acid groups of $pk_{int} = 4.3$, 10 imidazole groups with $pk_{int} = 7.0$, and 15 lysyl residues with $pk_{int} = 10.0$, the number of cationic groups in the most acid form is $10 + 15 = 25$. Counting off as described in step 3, we find 25 ionized carboxylate groups and 5 unionized carboxylic acid residues; hence $\alpha = {}^{25}\!/_{30}$ for the carboxylic acid groups of the first set. The equation of step 4 yields

$$pH_I = 4.3 + \log 5 = 5.0$$

If the hypothetical peptide contained only 22 carboxylic acid residues in the first set, the countoff in step 3 would proceed through the first set into the second, where three cationic imidazole groups would be neutralized. Thus the equation of step 4 would become

$$pH_I = 7.0 + \log {}^{3}\!/_{7} = 6.6$$

Taking glycine as an example, we have one carboxylic acid group of $pk = 2.4$ and one ammonium group with $pk = 9.8$. The most acid form contains one cationic group; hence the countoff of step 3 falls between two sets of groups (in this case each set has one group). According to step 4, in this situation we take the average pk_{int}, and thus $pH_I = (2.4 + 9.8)/2 = 6.1$. In glycine, in which the pk values are widely separated, the isoelectric region is unusually broad. For the range $4.4 < pH < 7.8$, 99% or more of the amino acid molecules are in the isoelectric form.

In marked contrast to the case of glycine, only about 22% of all horse-hemoglobin molecules are isoelectric at any instant at the isoelectric point. Only the mean net charge is zero; due to charge fluctuations, 39% of the molecules are positively charged species, and 39% are negatively charged species at the isoelectric pH. All forms are in rapid equilibrium with each other. The positively and negatively charged species, listed in order of the number of molecules existing at any moment, are $\bar{Z} = \pm 1, \pm 2, \pm 3, \pm 4, \ldots$

SELECTED BIBLIOGRAPHY

1 C. Tanford, The Interpretation of Hydrogen Ion Titration Curves of Proteins, *Advan. Protein Chem.*, **17**, 69–165 (1962).

2 J. T. Edsall and J. Wyman, "Biophysical Chemistry," chap. 9, Academic Press Inc., New York, 1958.

3 C. Tanford, "Physical Chemistry of Macromolecules," chaps. 7 and 8, John Wiley & Sons, Inc., New York, 1961.

4 K. Linderstrøm-Lang and S. O. Nielsen, Acid-Base Equilibria of Proteins, in M. Bier (ed.), "Electrophoresis," Academic Press Inc., New York, 1959.

QUESTIONS

5-1 Evaluate ω according to Eq. (5-5) for $b = 30.0$ A and $a = 32.5$ A at 0.00, 0.01, 0.10, 0.15, and 1.00 ionic strengths.

5-2 Account for the numerical factor in Eq. (5-6).

5-3 Compare the values of ω for β-lactoglobulin calculated from the molecular weight and partial specific volume assuming no hydration with those obtained from titration.

5-4 What are the six groups ionizing in ribonuclease in the range $2 < \mathrm{pH} < 11.5$?

5-5 Compare the isoelectric and isoionic points in the presence and absence of salt for a protein with an alkaline isoelectric point that binds anions.

5-6 A hypothetical polypeptide contains four carboxylic acid groups with $\mathrm{pk}_{int} = 4.5$ and three ammonium groups of $\mathrm{pk}_{int} = 10.0$. What is the isoelectric pH? What would be the isoelectric pH if there were twice as many ammonium groups?

5-7 What difference would the introduction of two tyrosyl groups make in each case of Question 5-6?

5-8 Ribonuclease contains 11 carboxylic acid groups, 4 imidazole groups, 1 α-ammonium group, 10 ϵ-ammonium groups, 3 reversibly titrable phenolic groups, and 4 guanidyl groups. Starting with the imidazole groups, the pk_{int} values are 6.5, 7.8, 10.2, 10.0, and >12, respectively. Estimate the isoelectric point.

6 | Molecular Weights

One of the most important characteristics of a molecule is its mass. Special techniques must be employed for determining molecular weights of macromolecules. In this chapter we shall define the various molecular-weight averages and outline the methods available for molecular-weight determinations; physical methods will be considered in this and succeeding chapters. During the measurement of molecular weight, valuable additional information concerning molecular size and shape can often be obtained.

6-1 MOLECULAR - WEIGHT AVERAGES

Preparations consisting of a single kind of macromolecule should give identical molecular weights whatever physical method is used to determine them. When mixtures contain macromolecules of differing molecular weights, however, various physical methods will weight differently the several species present. Due to this difference in weighting, it is necessary to define precisely the molecular-weight average measured by each physical method.

Number Average $\bar{M}_n$

$$\bar{M}_n = \frac{n_1 M_1 + n_2 M_2 + n_3 M_3 + \cdots}{n_1 + n_2 + n_3 + \cdots} = \frac{\Sigma n_i M_i}{\Sigma n_i} \qquad (6\text{-}1)$$

where n is the number of moles of species of molecular weight M per unit volume, and the subscripts refer to the molecular species present. $\bar{M}_n$ is a "democratic" average because each molecule counts once, regardless of its weight. The weight concentration in grams per unit volume is $c = nM$; therefore, in terms of weight, $\bar{M}_n = \Sigma c_i / \Sigma (c_i / M_i)$.

The colligative properties of a solution are a function only of the number, and not the nature, of the molecules present. Colligative properties such as osmotic pressure thus determine a number-average molecular weight. Chemical end-group analysis also measures the number-average molecular weight.

Weight Average, $\bar{M}_w$

$$\bar{M}_w = \frac{c_1 M_1 + c_2 M_2 + c_3 M_3 + \cdots}{c_1 + c_2 + c_3 + \cdots} = \frac{\Sigma c_i M_i}{\Sigma c_i} = \frac{\Sigma n_i M_i^2}{\Sigma n_i M_i} \qquad (6\text{-}2)$$

The weight average gives more consideration to the heavier molecules. $\bar{M}_w$ is not as "democratic" as $\bar{M}_n$; all molecules are equal, but some are more equal than others. Light scattering and sedimentation measure weight-average molecular weights.

Z Average, $\bar{M}_Z$. The pattern already established may be extended to define

$$\bar{M}_Z = \frac{\Sigma c_i M_i^2}{\Sigma c_i M_i} = \frac{\Sigma n_i M_i^3}{\Sigma n_i M_i^2}$$

and generalized to

$$\bar{M}_{Z+n} = \frac{\Sigma n_i M_i^{3+n}}{\Sigma n_i M_i^{2+n}}$$

where $n = -1$ for weight-average molecular weights, and $n = -2$ for number-average molecular weights. Z and higher averages weight the larger molecules still more heavily. The Z-average molecular weight may be determined from sedimentation-equilibrium measurements.

For monodisperse systems, all the molecular weights are identical. The ratio $\bar{M}_w/\bar{M}_n$ is a measure of the degree of polydispersity. A polydisperse system is one with a continuous molecular-weight distribution such as occurs in synthetic polymers. A system containing several components is called paucidisperse; examples are an impure protein preparation and a mixture of two or more proteins such as the globulins of blood plasma.

Consider the paucidisperse system consisting of a solution containing equal *numbers* of molecules of molecular weights 50×10^3, 100×10^3, 200×10^3, and 400×10^3. In this system, $\bar{M}_n = 187.5 \times 10^3$, $\bar{M}_w = 284 \times 10^3$, and $\bar{M}_Z = 344 \times 10^3$, illustrating the progressive weighting of the heavier molecules. If the solution contained equal *weight* concentrations of the four species, the result would be $\bar{M}_n = 107 \times 10^3$, $\bar{M}_w = 187.5 \times 10^3$, and $\bar{M}_Z = 284 \times 10^3$. Thus it is apparent that $\bar{M}_{Z+n}$ (equal numbers) $= \bar{M}_{Z+n+1}$ (equal weights). This equality could have been established from the general formulations defined above.

6-2   METHODS OF MOLECULAR - WEIGHT DETERMINATION

I. Analytical Methods

   A. *End-group* analyses are often performed because terminal groups of a polymer are chemically different from internal groups. Caution must be exercised because a polymer may be branched or cyclic rather than single-stranded.

   B. *Amino acid* analysis can be used to calculate a minimum molecular weight of a protein or polypeptide by assuming that an amino acid must occur an integral number of times. Accurate values will be obtained only for amino acids of low occurrence. Human serum albumin gives a tryptophan content of only 0.7 residues per 69,000 molecular weight, the latter quantity known from other methods; therefore the protein cannot be homogeneous.

   C. *Combining weights* depend upon the availability of a chemical reagent specific for some group on the macromolecule. For example, sulfhydryl titration of human serum albumin by silver ion gives 0.7 equiv per 69,000 molecular weight. The protein must consist of at least two kinds of protein chains.

   D. *Elementary* analysis is particularly useful if a metal ion is present. Hemoglobin contains 0.335% iron. The number of grams of protein per mole of iron is

$$\frac{100 \text{ g protein}}{0.335 \text{ g Fe}} \times \frac{55.85 \text{ g Fe}}{1 \text{ mole Fe}} = 16,700 \frac{\text{g protein}}{\text{mole Fe}}$$

   This figure is a minimum molecular weight or an equivalent weight for each mole of iron. Since other methods yield a molecular weight of 67,000, there are four iron atoms per molecule.

II. Physical Methods

   A. Static Methods
      1. Osmotic pressure, $\bar{M}_n$ (Chap. 7)
      2. Light scattering, $\bar{M}_w$ (Chap. 8)
      3. X-rays, $\bar{M}_n$ (Chap. 13)
      4. Electron microscopy, $\bar{M}_n$ (Sec. 6-3)

   B. Dynamic methods
      Resistance to the motion of the macromolecule is characterized by a frictional coefficient which may be evaluated theoretically by assumption of a molecular model or eliminated by appropriate combination of two methods.

1. Diffusion (concentration gradient) (Chap. 9)
   a. Translational
   b. Rotational
      1. Flow birefringence
      2. Dielectric dispersion
      3. Depolarization of fluorescence
2. Sedimentation (centrifugal field), $\bar{M}_w$ (Chap. 10)
   a. Velocity
   b. Equilibrium
   c. Archibald
   d. Density gradient
3. Viscosity (hydrodynamic gradient), nearly $\bar{M}_w$ (Chap. 11)
4. Electrophoresis (electric field) (Chap. 12)

6-3 ELECTRON MICROSCOPY

Since electron microscopy is not considered in a separate chapter of this book, a brief discussion is included in this section.

The resolving power of an electron microscope is in the 10- to 30-A range, about two orders of magnitude greater than light microscopes. A beam of electrons incident on matter is scattered (not absorbed), depending upon the atomic number and density of the atoms, greater scattering occurring for heavier atoms. Thin samples are required; otherwise the entire beam is scattered. Constituent atoms of organic molecules have such similar atomic numbers that little differential scattering takes place. Materials are shadow-casted by a directed beam of an evaporating heavy metal such as platinum. Heavy-metal reagents such as osmium tetroxide can sometimes be selectively absorbed on part of a specimen. Since an electron beam exists only in a vacuum, all volatile materials such as water must be eliminated, or the sample encapsulated. Surprisingly meaningful results have been obtained from desiccated samples of biological materials normally associated with considerable quantities of water. Intricate techniques have been developed to minimize artifacts.

Molecular weights are determined by direct particle counting after the addition of a known number of foreign particles. Many precautions are necessary; impurities must be kept to a minimum. Spheres of polystyrene or other materials with a known diameter are added to aid focusing and to provide a standard for the shadow length-to-height ratio. Electron microscopy has important limitations. Diameters of spherical molecules are more accurately determined by other methods. The electron microscope reliably measures lengths, but not diameters, of asymmetric molecules. For certain purposes, however, the electron microscope is unexcelled. Unsuitable for complete analysis by other methods, a molecule such as fibrinogen, which consists of three beads linked by two filaments, readily reveals its makeup in the electron microscope. In collagen the electron microscope shows striations every 650 A, a longer-range level of organization than discussed in the molecular studies of following chapters.

SELECTED BIBLIOGRAPHY

1 J. T. Edsall, The Size, Shape and Hydration of Protein Molecules, in H. Neurath and K. Bailey (eds.), "The Proteins," vol. 1, part B, Academic Press Inc., New York, 1953.

2 P. Alexander and R. J. Block (eds.), "A Laboratory Manual of Analytical Methods of Protein Chemistry," vols. 2 and 3, Pergamon Press, New York, 1961.

3 R. W. G. Wyckoff, "The World of the Electron Microscope," Yale University Press, New Haven, Conn., 1958.

4 C. E. Hall and H. S. Slayter, The Fibrinogen Molecule: Its Size, Shape and Mode of Polymerization, *J. Biophys. Biochem. Cytology*, **5**, 11–16 (1959).

5 J. R. Warner, A. Rich, and C. E. Hall, Electron Microscope Studies of Ribosomal Clusters Synthesizing Hemoglobin, *Science*, **138**, 1399–1403 (1962).

QUESTIONS

6-1 Verify the molecular-weight averages calculated in this chapter.

6-2 Vitamin B_{12} contains 55.8% carbon, 6.6% hydrogen, 16.5% oxygen, 14.5% nitrogen, 2.3% phosphorus, and 4.35% cobalt. What is the minimum molecular weight?

6-3 Ribonuclease is 1.65% leucine (by weight) and 2.48% isoleucine. Both amino acids have molecular weights of 131. What is the minimum molecular weight of ribonuclease? How many moles of each amino acid are there per mole of protein?

6-4 A sample of ceruloplasmin, the copper-carrying protein of blood plasma, contains 0.29% copper and has a molecular weight of 151,000. How many copper atoms are in one molecule of the protein?

6-5 A protein sample consists of 90% by weight of 100,000 molecular weight material and 10% by weight of dimer of 200,000 molecular weight. What are the molecular weights as determined by light scattering and osmotic pressure?

7 | Osmotic Pressure

The colligative properties of a solution depend primarily upon the number, rather than the nature, of the molecules present. Of the four physical colligative properties of solutions—vapor-pressure lowering, boiling-point elevation, freezing-point depression, and osmotic pressure—only the last is accurately measurable in the case of large molecules. A 1% solution of a macromolecule of molecular weight 70×10^3 would depress the freezing point of water 0.0003°. This value is so small that it is difficult to obtain with precision. In contrast, the osmotic pressure of the same solution would be a conveniently measurable 3.6 cm of water.

Consider a membrane, permeable only to solvent molecules, separating a solvent from a solution. As the activity of solvent molecules will be less in solution than in pure solvent, the system will tend to compensate for this difference by the net passage of solvent molecules through the semipermeable membrane into the solution, a process called *osmosis*. The osmotic pressure II is the pressure it is necessary to apply to the solution to prevent osmosis.

Osmotic pressure is independent of the nature of the semipermeable membrane. If the osmotic pressure were dependent upon the nature of the membrane, it would be possible to construct a perpetual-motion machine by placing solution between two different membranes and letting the solvent on the outside develop a different pressure at each membrane. Such a machine is impossible according to the second law of thermodynamics.

In order to derive equations for the relationships between osmotic pressure and concentration of solute, we must consider further certain principles of thermodynamics which were introduced in Chap. 2.

7-1 PARTIAL MOLAR QUANTITIES

The volume of 1 mole of a pure compound in any single physical state is simply $V' = V/n$, the total volume divided by the number of moles contained by that volume. A single phase consisting of two components has a total volume

$$V = n_1 \left(\frac{\partial V}{\partial n_1} \right)_{n_2, T, P} + n_2 \left(\frac{\partial V}{\partial n_2} \right)_{n_1, T, P} = n_1 \bar{V}_1 + n_2 \bar{V}_2 \qquad (7\text{-}1)$$

where n represents the number of moles of a component. The quantities in parentheses are partial molar volumes $\bar{V}$ representing the change in total volume caused by the addition of an infinitesimal amount of one component to a given solution containing a fixed amount of the other component at constant temperature and pressure. In an ideal binary solution, the molar volume of the solution varies linearly as the composition, while the partial molar volumes are independent of concentration and have the same numerical values as the molar volumes V' of the pure components. The choice of symbol $\bar{V}$ commonly used for partial molar volume is unfortunate, because $\bar{V}$ is not an average quantity, as Eq. (7-1) demonstrates. Equation (7-1) can easily be extended to more than two components.

When 50 ml of ethanol are mixed with 50 ml of water, the volume of the mixture is only about 97 ml. In this case, the binary solution is nonideal, and the partial molar volumes are not identical to, but are less than, the molar volumes of the pure components. All the volumes we have mentioned so far have been on a molar basis. We can, however, divide all molar volumes by the molecular weight of the component to obtain the corresponding specific volume v in milliliters per gram. The reciprocal of the specific volume of a solution is the density, which may be determined in a pycnometer. Methods for the determination of partial molar volumes from density measurements are described in standard thermodynamics texts such as Refs. 2 and 3 of Chap. 2.

Another quantity, the apparent molar volume, often determined experimentally, is defined as

$$\Phi = \frac{V - n_1 V_1'}{n_2}$$

where the numerator is the difference between the total volume V and the volume of solvent (component 1) it contains. For a fixed quantity of solvent, such as 1 kg (which is convenient because then n_2 is the molality), we obtain, by differentiation of the preceding equation,

$$\bar{V}_2 = \Phi + n_2 \frac{\partial \Phi}{\partial n_2} \qquad (7\text{-}2)$$

from which $\bar{V}_2$ may be evaluated at any n_2. In the limit of dilute solutions, where n_2 approaches zero, the apparent molar volume assumes the value of the partial molar volume of the solute $\bar{V}_2$. Apparent molar volumes can also be determined from density measurements. Since apparent molar volumes have less thermodynamic utility than partial molar volumes, they are frequently converted to the latter. Standard thermodynamics texts describe methods for determination and manipulation of apparent molar volumes.

For many proteins the partial specific volume is about 0.75 cc/g. This figure represents the amount of solvent displaced by the solute, and not the volume actually occupied by the hydrated solute molecules, because of the possibilities of solute swelling, penetration of solute by solvent, and electrostriction of solvent about charged solutes.

The volume of a system is a property of the amount of material in the system. The partial molar volume, on the other hand, is a function only of the composition of the system at constant temperature and pressure and is independent of the size or extent of the system. Properties such as volume which depend on the extent of the system are called *extensive* properties; those properties which are independent of system size, such as the partial molar volume, are called *intensive* properties. It is convenient to define other partial molar quantities which are also intensive properties of a system.

Each of the several kinds of energy terms may be considered a product of a capacity and a potential factor. The capacity factor, a function of the size of the system, is called an extensive property of the system. The potential factor is independent of size and is termed an intensive property of the system. In Chap. 2 we considered thermal energy to be the product of the entropy (capacity factor) and temperature (potential factor). Electrical energy is the product of charge (extensive) and electrical potential (intensive) factors. Similarly, the free energy is the product of the number of moles (extensive) and chemical potential (intensive) terms. The electrochemical potential is the intensive factor of a free-energy change in the oxidation-reduction reactions of Sec. 2-6.

Since the capacity factor of the energy is a function of the size of the system, we can factor the size dependence so that the quotient will be independent of the extent of the system. For the free energy G, the capacity factor is the number of moles n, and the potential factor which results from factoring is called the *chemical potential* μ or *partial molar free energy* $\bar{G}$. Then, for substance 1,

$$\left(\frac{\partial G}{\partial n_1}\right)_{T,P,n_2,n_3,\ldots} = \mu_1 = \bar{G}_1 \tag{7-3}$$

Equation (7-3) defines the derivative of the total free energy G with respect to the number of moles of substance 1 at constant temperature, pressure, and number of moles of all other substances as the chemical potential μ or partial molar free energy $\bar{G}_1$ of substance 1. Similarly, for substance 2,

$$\left(\frac{\partial G}{\partial n_2}\right)_{T,P,n_1,n_3,\ldots} = \mu_2 = \bar{G}_2 \tag{7-4}$$

The chemical potential is not measured by any simple, direct experiment.

The total differential of the free energy in an open system of two components may be expressed as a function of temperature, pressure, and the moles of components 1 and 2:

$$dG = \left(\frac{\partial G}{\partial T}\right)_{P,n_1,n_2} dT + \left(\frac{\partial G}{\partial P}\right)_{T,n_1,n_2} dP + \left(\frac{\partial G}{\partial n_1}\right)_{T,P,n_2} dn_1$$
$$+ \left(\frac{\partial G}{\partial n_2}\right)_{T,P,n_1} dn_2$$

From the definition of the chemical potentials in Eqs. (7-3) and (7-4), we have

$$dG = \left(\frac{\partial G}{\partial T}\right)_{P,n_1,n_2} dT + \left(\frac{\partial G}{\partial P}\right)_{T,n_1,n_2} dP + \mu_1 \, dn_1 + \mu_2 \, dn_2$$

When temperature and pressure are held constant,

$$dG = \mu_1 \, dn_1 + \mu_2 \, dn_2 \tag{7-5}$$

At equilibrium,

$$dG = 0 = \mu_1 \, dn_1 + \mu_2 \, dn_2 \tag{7-6}$$

The latter equality is the thermodynamic criterion for equilibrium in a two-component system.

When component 1 exists in two different phases α and β, application of the equilibrium equation (7-6) yields $\mu_1{}^\alpha \, dn_1{}^\alpha + \mu_1{}^\beta \, dn_1{}^\beta = 0$, where $\mu_1{}^\alpha$ is the chemical potential of component 1 in phase α, and similarly for $\mu_1{}^\beta$. Since the number of moles gained or lost by phase α is equal to the number of moles lost or gained by phase β,

$$dn_1{}^\alpha = -dn_1{}^\beta$$

Therefore,

$$\mu_1{}^\alpha = \mu_1{}^\beta \qquad (7\text{-}7)$$

Equation (7-7) is the thermodynamic criterion for equilibrium between phases. At equilibrium the chemical potential of a diffusible substance is the same in all phases in which the substance can exist.

The total free energy is a homogeneous function of the number of moles. In a two-component system, $G = \mu_1 n_1 + \mu_2 n_2$. Differentiating, we obtain $dG = \mu_1 \, dn_1 + \mu_2 \, dn_2 + n_1 \, d\mu_1 + n_2 \, d\mu_2$. Comparing with Eq. (7-5), we have, at constant temperature and pressure,

$$n_1 \, d\mu_1 + n_2 \, d\mu_2 = 0 \qquad (7\text{-}8)$$

which is the Gibbs-Duhem equation as applied to a two-component system. Thus μ_2 may be calculated if μ_1 is known over a range of composition.

7-2 OSMOTIC PRESSURE

The thermodynamic expression relating the chemical potential and the activity is [compare Eq. (2-1)]

$$\mu = \mu^o(T,P) + RT \ln a \qquad (7\text{-}9)$$

where the parentheses indicate that μ^o is a function of temperature and pressure but is otherwise constant. Equation (7-9) may be taken as the definition of activity. In discussing osmotic pressure, we require an explicit term for the pressure variation of the chemical potential. From the thermodynamic relationship $dG = V \, dP - S \, dT$, we obtain $(\partial G/\partial P)_T = V$. Since the order of differentiation is immaterial, we also have $(\partial \bar{G}/\partial P)_T = (\partial \mu/\partial P)_T = \bar{V}$, where $\bar{V}$ is the partial molar volume [Eq. (7-1)]. Osmotic pressures are low enough so that the solvent may be considered incompressible, and Eq. (7-9) becomes, for component 1 (solvent),

$$\mu_1 = \mu_1{}^o(T) + P\bar{V}_1 + RT \ln a_1 \qquad (7\text{-}10)$$

The constant term $\mu_1{}^o(T)$ is now only a function of temperature.

We wish to compare the chemical potential of the solvent, μ_1, in the solution α and solvent β phases of an osmotic system. Application of Eq. (7-10) yields

$$\mu_1{}^\alpha = \mu_1{}^o(T) + P^\alpha \bar{V}_1 + RT \ln a_1$$
$$\mu_1{}^\beta = \mu_1{}^o(T) + P^\beta \bar{V}_1$$

The $RT \ln a_1$ term does not appear in the expression for μ_1^β because the activity of pure solvent is taken as unity. Combination with Eq. (7-7) gives, at equilibrium,

$$\Pi \bar{V}_1 = (P^\alpha - P^\beta)\bar{V}_1 = -RT \ln a_1 \tag{7-11}$$

where Π, the osmotic pressure, is defined as the additional pressure that must be applied to the solution (α) phase to maintain equilibrium.

In Eq. (7-11), a_1 is the activity of the solvent in the solution phase. Other expressions for the right-hand side of Eq. (7-11) may be derived from some of the equations developed earlier. Differentiating Eq. (7-9) at constant temperature and pressure yields

$$d\mu = RT \, d(\ln a)$$

Combining this result with the Gibbs-Duhem equation (7-8), we obtain

$$d(\ln a_1) = -\frac{n_2}{n_1} d(\ln a_2) \tag{7-12}$$

where the subscript 2 refers to the component which cannot diffuse through the semipermeable membrane. Differentiation of Eq. (7-11) for the osmotic pressure and combination with Eq. (7-12) give

$$\bar{V}_1 \, d\Pi = -RT \, d(\ln a_1) = RT \frac{n_2}{n_1} d(\ln a_2) \tag{7-13}$$

To express the osmotic pressure in terms of the experimentally measured quantities, we divide Eq. (7-13) by $\bar{V}_1$ and assign the product $n_1 \bar{V}_1$ as the volume of 1,000 g of water.

$$d\Pi = \frac{RT}{\bar{V}_1} \frac{n_2}{n_1} d(\ln a_2) = \frac{RTm_2}{V^o} d(\ln a_2) \tag{7-14}$$

The molality m_2 of the nondiffusible component is defined as the number of moles per 1,000 g of water, and V^o is the volume of solution containing 1,000 g of water. The activity of the nondiffusible component is given by $a_2 = m_2\gamma_2$, where γ_2 is the molal activity coefficient for component 2. Performing the indicated operations in Eq. (7-14) gives us

$$d\Pi = \frac{RTm_2}{V^o} \frac{d(m_2\gamma_2)}{m_2\gamma_2} = \frac{RT}{V^o} \frac{m_2 \, d\gamma_2 + \gamma_2 \, dm_2}{\gamma_2}$$

from which we obtain

$$\frac{d\Pi}{dm_2} = \frac{RT}{V^o}\left[1 + \frac{d(\ln \gamma_2)}{d(\ln m_2)}\right] \tag{7-15}$$

Since $\Pi = 0$ when $m_2 = 0$, integration at constant temperature yields

$$\Pi = \frac{RTm_2}{V^o}\left[1 + \frac{d(\ln \gamma_2)}{d(\ln m_2)}\right] = \frac{RTw_2}{V^oM_2}\left[1 + \frac{d(\ln \gamma_2)}{d(\ln m_2)}\right] \tag{7-16}$$

where w_2 is the number of grams of nondiffusible component of molecular weight M_2, per 1,000 g of water. The integration is valid only when $d(\ln \gamma_2)/d(\ln m_2)$ is a constant independent of m_2.

Expressing the osmotic pressure as in Eq. (7-16) has several advantages over other formulations. The use of molality (moles of solute per 1,000 g of water) means that the concentration term will be independent of temperature. This would not be the case if molarity (moles of solute per liter of solution) were used, because it is dependent upon the density of the solution. More important, solutions with high concentrations of a third component, e.g., urea, may easily be handled by an extension of Eq. (7-16) because m_2, w_2, and V^o have been carefully defined in terms of 1,000 g of water, and not in terms of volume of solution.

The foregoing derivation is strictly thermodynamic. As stated in Chap. 2, thermodynamics deals only with initial and final states, not with a particular path or mechanism. The mechanism of osmosis is not yet fully understood, but this deficiency is of no consequence for the thermodynamic result of Eq. (7-16).

For solutions exhibiting ideal behavior, the term in brackets in Eq. (7-16) is unity. We may also write

$$\lim_{w_2 \to 0} \frac{\Pi}{w_2} = \frac{RT}{V^oM_2}$$

from which the number-average molecular weight M_2 may be evaluated. According to this equation, the osmotic pressure is independent of the concentration of diffusible components and depends only upon the concentration, and not upon the nature, of the nondiffusible substance. As a result, osmotic pressure is a colligative property in the limiting case of ideal behavior or extrapolation to zero concentration of the nondiffusible component.

The concentration dependence of the osmotic pressure is often expressed on a volume-concentration basis, where $w_2/V^o = c_2$ is the number of grams of nondiffusible component per unit volume of solution. When the term in brackets in Eq. (7-16) is unity,

$$\Pi = \frac{c_2 RT}{M_2}$$

This is equivalent to an expression obtained by van't Hoff. Since $c_2/M_2 = n_2/V$, where n_2 is the number of moles of the macromolecule and V is the volume, $\Pi V = n_2 RT$. This formulation is analogous to the ideal gas equation, $PV = nRT$.

7-3 SECOND VIRIAL COEFFICIENT

According to the van't Hoff equation, a plot of Π/c_2 versus c_2 should be a straight horizontal line. The lines obtained experimentally are usually straight, with positive slopes as shown in Fig. 7-1. Extending the analogy with gases to the van der Waals equation for imperfect gases,

$$\left(P + \frac{a}{V^2}\right)(V - b) = RT$$

where V = volume of 1 mole

a = constant involving attractive forces of molecules

b = excluded volume due to finite size of molecules

Expanding the van der Waals equation, we obtain

$$PV + \frac{a}{V} - bP - \frac{ab}{V^2} = RT$$

The fourth term is negligible, since it contains the product of two small numbers a and b and is divided by the square of a large volume. Substituting the osmotic pressure Π for P, and M/c for V, yields

$$\frac{\Pi M}{c} = RT - \frac{ac}{M} + \frac{bRTc}{M}$$

The last term is obtained by substitution of RT/V for P in the $-bP$ term of the previous equation. Rearranging gives

$$\frac{\Pi}{RTc} = \frac{1}{M} + \frac{1}{M^2}\left(b - \frac{a}{RT}\right)c \tag{7-17}$$

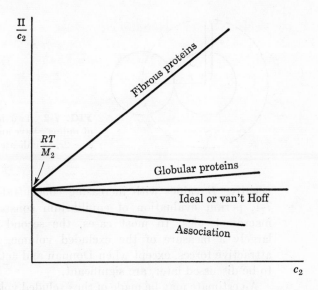

FIG. 7-1 Representative plots of Π/c_2 versus c_2 obtained from osmotic-pressure measurements, where c_2 is the concentration of the nondiffusible component.

Alternatively, we may consider the very general virial equation for describing the behavior of nonideal gases:

$$PV = RT\left[1 + \frac{B(T)}{V} + \frac{C(T)}{V^2} + \cdots\right] \tag{7-18}$$

where $B(T)$ and $C(T)$ are temperature-dependent constants. If we ignore the term containing $C(T)$ and all higher terms, the same substitutions as in the van der Waals case lead to

$$\frac{\Pi}{RTc} = \frac{1}{M} + \frac{Bc}{M^2} \tag{7-19}$$

Either Eq. (7-17) or Eq. (7-19) can account for the observed linear variation of Π/c_2 with c_2 shown in Fig. 7-1.

Comparison of Eqs. (7-17) and (7-19) indicates that the second virial coefficient B is approximated by $b - a/RT$ in the van der Waals formulation. This result agrees qualitatively with negative values of B at low temperatures, where the attractive forces between gas molecules predominate over the excluded-volume term b. In osmotic-pressure experiments, negative values of the second virial coefficient B are seldom observed, because usually $b \gg a/RT$; if this were not the case, phase separation (precipitation) might occur. Nonlinear variations of

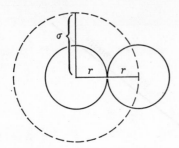

FIG. 7-2 Two identical spherical particles of radius r have an excluded volume of radius $\sigma = 2r$, as indicated by the dotted circle.

negative B values with increasing concentration, illustrated in Fig. 7-1, permit evaluation of equilibrium constants for association of macromolecules. In most cases, the second virial coefficient B is largely a measure of the excluded volume, somewhat reduced by attractive forces, except when Donnan and activity-coefficient effects, to be discussed later, are significant.

An estimate may be made of the excluded volume or van der Waals b term if the molecules are considered as hard spheres in a dilute gas or solution. Two identical spherical molecules of radius r exclude a volume of $4\pi\sigma^3/3$, where σ is the diameter of the particles or the radius of the excluded volume shown in Fig. 7-2. Since $\sigma = 2r$, the excluded volume per molecule is $\frac{1}{2} \times 4\pi\sigma^3/3 = 4 \times 4\pi r^3/3 = 4V_m$, where the factor $\frac{1}{2}$ is introduced because two molecules are considered in Fig. 7-2 while V_m is the volume of one molecule. Thus, for spherical molecules, the excluded volume per mole is $b_{\text{sphere}} = 4V_mN = 4V$, where N is Avogadro's number, and V is the molar volume.

For long, rigid rods, more complex considerations lead to an excluded volume per mole of $b_{\text{rod}} = N\pi dl^2/4$, where d is the diameter and l the length of the rod. In this case the molecular weight M is proportional to l; hence the second term on the right of Eq. (7-19) should be independent of the molecular weight. The volume of a mole of rods is $V = N\pi d^2l/4$; therefore the excluded volume per mole is $b_{\text{rod}} = Vl/d$. Since, for rods, $l/d > 4$, we see that $b_{\text{rod}} > b_{\text{sphere}}$. For a given molecular weight, the second term on the right of Eqs. (7-17) and (7-19) will be greater for rods than for spheres, and the slope of the Π/c_2 versus c_2 plot will be correspondingly greater for rods. Because fibrous proteins more nearly approximate rods, and globular proteins approximate spheres, the slope for fibrous proteins is greater than that for globular proteins in Fig. 7-1.

7-4   DONNAN EFFECT

Up to this point we have assumed that the nondiffusible component has no net charge. Macromolecules can acquire a net charge by addi-

tion or removal of protons and by binding of other ions. The charge
on the macromolecule must be counterbalanced by retention of additional diffusible ions on the solution side of the membrane. Thus the
concentrations of diffusible ions will not be the same on both sides
of the membrane. However, the thermodynamic equilibrium criterion
of Eq. (7-7) demands that the chemical potentials of all diffusible
components be the same on both sides of the membrane.

Let us consider a case in which NaCl furnishes the counterions to
balance a charge on the nondiffusible macromolecule. Equation (7-7)
yields

$$\mu_{(NaCl)} = \mu'_{(NaCl)}$$

where the primed term on the right stands for the chemical potential
of NaCl on the solvent side of the membrane. Application of Eq. (7-9)
to each ion on each side of the membrane gives

$$\mu^o_{(Na^+)} + RT \ln a_{(Na^+)} + \mu^o_{(Cl^-)} + RT \ln a_{(Cl^-)} = \mu^o_{(Na^+)} + RT \ln a'_{(Na^+)}$$
$$+ \mu^o_{(Cl^-)} + RT \ln a'_{(Cl^-)}$$

from which

$$a_{(Na^+)} a_{(Cl^-)} = a'_{(Na^+)} a'_{(Cl^-)}$$

Considering only the case of dilute solution, where concentrations
may be used in place of activities,

$$(Na^+)(Cl^-) = (Na^+)'(Cl^-)' \tag{7-20}$$

The concentrations include only the ions not bound to other molecules.
Equation (7-20) applies only to those ions which pass freely through
the membrane. The normal mammalian red cell membrane, for example, is nearly impermeable to cations except hydrogen ion.

Electroneutrality must apply to both sides of the membrane. We
shall assume that we are working with sufficient NaCl in a pH region
in which the concentrations of hydrogen and hydroxyl ions are negligible. On the solvent side of the membrane, $(Na^+)' = (Cl^-)'$; on the
solution side, $(Na^+) + Z_2 m_2 = (Cl^-)$, where Z_2 is the charge of nondiffusible component of molal concentration m_2. Substituting the
result on the solvent side of the membrane into Eq. (7-20) yields

$$(Na^+)(Cl^-) = [(Na^+)']^2 = [(Cl^-)']^2 \tag{7-21}$$

The results of Eqs. (7-20) and (7-21) are presented geometrically in
Fig. 7-3. The products of Eq. (7-20) are depicted as areas, with the

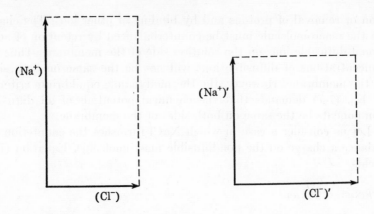

FIG. 7-3 The products of Eq. (7-20) depicted as equal areas. The sides of the area on the right, which refers to the solvent side of the membrane, are equal according to Eq. (7-21).

sodium- and chloride-ion concentrations as the sides of the areas. Since the products of the concentrations of the ions on the solution and solvent sides, of the membrane are equal, the areas must be equal. According to Eq. (7-21), the sides of the area that refer to the solvent (denoted by primes) are equal. Therefore, the primed area on the right in Fig. 7-3 is a square, whereas that on the left is a rectangle.

Application of Eq. (7-16), neglecting the nonideal term in brackets, yields

$$\frac{\Pi V^o}{RT} = m_2 + (Na^+) + (Cl^-) - (Na^+)' - (Cl^-)' \tag{7-22}$$

where the molal concentrations on the solvent side of the membrane are subtracted from those on the solution side. The last four terms of Eq. (7-22) are referred to collectively as the *Donnan* term. This term is always positive, because the perimeter of a rectangle is greater than the perimeter of a square of the same area (Fig. 7-3).

When appropriate substitutions and approximations are made, Eq. (7-22) may be written

$$\frac{\Pi}{w_2} = \frac{RT}{V^o M_2}\left[1 + \frac{Z_2^2 m_2}{4\mu}\right] \tag{7-23}$$

where μ is the ionic strength of the solution. The second term in brackets is the Donnan term. A plot of Π/w_2 versus w_2 should yield the reciprocal of M_2 on the ordinate, whatever the charge on the protein. The Donnan effect, which always increases osmotic pressure, may be diminished by working at high ionic strengths or near the isoelectric point of the protein. The latter is often difficult, because macromolecules are usually least soluble in the vicinity of their isoelectric points.

Variations of activity coefficients have been omitted so far in the discussion of the Donnan effect. A more complete equation than (7-23) is

$$\frac{\Pi}{w_2} = \frac{RT}{V^oM_2} + \frac{RTw_2}{2V^oM_2{}^2}\left[\frac{\partial(\ln\gamma_2)}{\partial m_2} + \frac{Z_2{}^2}{2\mu} - \frac{[\partial(\ln\gamma_2)/\partial m_3]^2\, m_3}{2 + 2\,\partial(\ln\gamma_3)/\partial(\ln m_3)}\right] \tag{7-24}$$

where the subscript 3 refers to salt components. Comparison of Eq. (7-24) with Eq. (7-19) indicates that the whole term in brackets in Eq. (7-24) is twice the second virial coefficient B. A plot of the B term versus Z_2 for bovine serum albumin is shown in Fig. 8-2.

The first term in brackets in Eq. (7-24) depends upon the variation of the activity coefficient of the macromolecule with its own concentration. For an isoionic macromolecule in a salt-free solution, this is the only term in the brackets that would not vanish. This term becomes large and positive for asymmetric molecules (and hence can give an indication of shape) and was the only one considered in the previous discussion relating B to the excluded volume.

That the second term in brackets is the Donnan term may be verified by comparison with Eq. (7-23). It is the only term which does not vanish when all the activity coefficients are unity. The Donnan term vanishes for zero net charge on the macromolecule and is decreased by increasing the ionic strength. Unless care is taken to work at high ionic strengths and near zero net charge on the macromolecule, the Donnan term greatly exceeds the first term in brackets, and excluded-volume effects are not apparent. Since $Z_2 = \bar{h}M_2/N$, where $\bar{h}$ is the mean number of protons taken up or given off per gram of the macromolecule, and N is Avogadro's number, the second term in brackets is independent of M_2. The last term in brackets is usually small, negative, and important only when the protein-salt interactions are unusually strong.

7-5 APPLICATIONS

The technique of osmometry is useful for studying molecules in the 3×10^3 to 100×10^3 molecular weight range. Smaller molecules leak through most membranes, and larger molecules give too small an effect for accurate results. New, very fine membranes are available for measurement of unusually small molecules. Experiments usually take at least several hours. Attainment of equilibrium should be as rapid as possible to avoid denaturation and bacterial growth. Increasing the membrane to capillary area promotes more rapid attainment of equilibrium. Organic liquids such as *n*-decane (density, 0.73 g/ml) perform better in capillaries and yield greater heights than water. Dynamic osmometers involving a flow rate have been developed.

Numerous osmotic-pressure measurements have been made for molecular weight and other determinations. For example, in 1925 the molecular weight of mammalian hemoglobin was established as 67,000, four times greater than the minimum value derived from the iron content. Later, careful work on bovine serum albumin gave results which could not be accounted for by Eq. (7-23); substantial chloride ion binding by the protein was indicated. Finally when the molecular weight of insulin was determined to be about 6,000 upon dilution in aqueous 6-molal guanidinium chloride solution, it was established by physical methods that the 12,000 molecular weight particle observed in most solutions is a dimer. Urea is less effective in producing insulin monomers.

SELECTED BIBLIOGRAPHY

1 D. W. Kupke, Osmotic Pressure, *Advan. Protein Chem.*, **15**, 57–130 (1960).

2 J. T. Edsall, Osmotic Pressure, in H. Neurath and K. Bailey (eds.), "The Proteins," vol. 1, part B, Academic Press Inc., New York, 1953.

3 G. Scatchard, Derivation of the Equations for Osmotic Pressure, *J. Am. Chem. Soc.*, **68**, 2315 (1946).

4 G. Scatchard, A. C. Batchelder, and A. Brown, Osmotic Equilibrium in Solutions of Serum Albumin and Sodium Chloride, *J. Am. Chem. Soc.*, **68**, 2320 (1946).

QUESTIONS

7-1 What term is used to describe the increase in volume of a very large amount of solution upon the addition of 1 g of a solute?

7-2 Verify Eq. (7-2).

7-3 In the following pairs of numbers, the first is the number of grams of human serum albumin per 100 g of solution, and the second is the corresponding specific volume in cubic centimeters per gram at 25°: 5.76, 0.9874; 2.30, 0.9967; 1.17, 0.9998; 0.00, 1.0029. Calculate the partial specific volume of serum albumin at infinite dilution. What is the corresponding partial molar volume if the molecular weight of the protein is 69,000?

7-4 Construct a perpetual-motion machine on the assumption that the osmotic pressure is dependent upon the nature of the semipermeable membrane.

7-5 Beginning with Eq. (7-16), show that all substitutions made to obtain the van't Hoff equation are consistent. Attach units to each physical quantity, and manipulate them appropriately.

7-6 Calculate the osmotic pressure in centimeters of water, boiling-point elevation, freezing-point depression, and vapor-pressure lowering of a 1% solution of a protein of molecular weight 100×10^3. The boiling-point elevation $\Delta T_b = K_b m$, and the freezing-point depression $\Delta T_f = K_f m$, where m is the molality of the protein, $K_b = 0.51$ deg/molal, and $K_f = 1.86$ deg/molal for water. According to Raoult's law, the partial pressure of the solvent in a solution is $P_1 = X_1 P_1{}^o$, where X_1 is the mole fraction of the solvent, and $P_1{}^o$ is the vapor pressure of the pure liquid at the same temperature. For a binary solution, show that $X_2 = 1 - X_1 = (P_1{}^o - P_1)/P_1$, where X_2 is the mole fraction of the solute, and $P_1{}^o - P_1$ is the vapor-pressure lowering.

7-7 What percentage impurity of molecular weight 100 would yield the same results as the pure protein in Question 7-3? What does this result indicate about the purity required for the measurement of physical colligative properties?

7-8 Human blood has an osmotic pressure of 7.7 atm at 40°. What is the total concentration of solutes in the blood? Find the freezing point of blood if the freezing-point depression is $\Delta T_f = K_f m$, where $K_f = 1.86$ deg/molal for aqueous solutions, and the molality m may be approximated by the concentration calculated in the first part of this question.

7-9 By differentiating Eq. (7-19), comparing with Eq. (7-15), and integrating, show that, in this case, $\ln \gamma_2 = 2Bc_2/M_2$.

7-10 Virial equations are often cast into forms other than that of Eq. (7-18). Compare the second virial coefficient B of Eq. (7-18) with the second virial coefficients in the following two equations:

$$PV = RT + B'P + C'P^2 + \cdots \quad \text{and} \quad PV = RT(1 + B''P + C''P^2 + \cdots)$$

Write Eq. (7-19) with B' and B''. What are the units of B, B', and B''?

7-11 Assuming the validity of van't Hoff's law, calculate the osmotic pressure in millimeters of water of a 1% solution of an isoelectric protein of molecular weight 50×10^3 at 4°C and at 37°C.

7-12 Ten equivalents of HCl are added to the solution in Question 7-11. Calculate the osmotic pressure at 37°, assuming no chloride-ion binding, in the presence of 10^{-3} and 10^{-1} M NaCl. Repeat the calculations for 20 equiv HCl and the same concentrations of NaCl.

7-13 Draw and explain a simple apparatus for the measurement of osmotic pressure.

7-14 When distilled water is added to a saline suspension of phage, the heads rupture, releasing the nucleic acid. What is the cause of this osmotic shock?

7-15 Explain why you might expect the cell-wall permeability to be less in an amoeba which can live in fairly fresh water than it is in a red blood cell.

8 | Light Scattering

8-1 SCATTERING FROM GASES

According to one report, Lord Rayleigh, while climbing in the Alps, noticed that even at great heights on clear days vision is limited. To account for this effect Rayleigh derived a formula for the scattering of light by a dilute gas of independent, nonabsorbing, isotropic particles smaller than one-twentieth the wavelength of the light. The decrease in intensity I with distance l is $-dI/dl = \tau I$, where the turbidity τ is a constant analogous to the extinction coefficient in absorption spectrophotometry. Integration yields $I/I_0 = e^{-\tau l}$, where I_0 is the incident intensity, and e is the base of the natural logarithms, about 2.72. For air, $\tau \simeq 10^{-7}$ cm^{-1}; hence 37% ($1/e$) of the initial light penetrates a distance of 100 km. Rayleigh thus accounted for his observation in quantitative terms.

The electric vector of an electromagnetic wave forces periodic vibrations in the electrons of matter, producing an oscillating electric moment of the same frequency as the incident light. The oscillating dipole thus formed serves as a secondary emitter giving rise to diffraction or scattering of light. If the scattered light is of the same wavelength as the incident light, *Rayleigh scattering* is said to occur. When vibrations or rotations of the molecule cause the scattered light to have a wavelength different from that of the exciting light, *Raman scattering* takes place. Raman scattering, several orders of magnitude weaker than Rayleigh scattering, will not be considered further here.

Rayleigh showed that the intensity of light i_θ scattered per unit volume at an angle θ from the incident beam relative to the incident intensity I_0 of an unpolarized light beam is

$$\frac{i_\theta}{I_0} = \frac{8\pi^4 \nu \alpha^2}{\lambda^4 r^2} (1 + \cos^2 \theta) \tag{8-1}$$

where ν = number of scattering centers per cubic centimeter

α = polarizability or induced dipole per unit field strength

r = distance from molecules to detector

The wavelength of light falling on the molecules is $\lambda = \lambda_0/n_0$, where λ_0 is the wavelength of light falling on the medium of refractive index n_0. Refractive index is the ratio of the velocity of light in vacuum to its velocity in a medium. For gases the medium is considered a vacuum. Scattering is strongly wavelength-dependent, as indicated by the inverse fourth-power dependence of the wavelength in Eq. (8-1). The greatest scattering occurs at the shortest wavelengths. Greater scattering of blue light than of other visible wavelengths accounts for the blue color of the sky.

Polarizability α cannot be determined directly, but from Maxwell's equations,

$$\alpha = \frac{\epsilon - \epsilon_0}{\epsilon_0 4\pi\nu} = \frac{n^2 - n_0^2}{n_0^2 4\pi\nu} = \frac{(n + n_0)(n - n_0)}{n_0^2 4\pi\nu} \cong \frac{n - n_0}{n_0 2\pi\nu}$$

where the dielectric constant of the medium is $\epsilon_0 = n_0^2$, and n_0 refers to the refractive index of the medium. The same symbols without subscripts refer to the mixture. For a gas the medium would be vacuum, and $\epsilon_0 = n_0 = 1$. The last equality holds for the case in which the refractive indices of medium and mixture are about unity.

Substituting for α in Eq. (8-1) yields

$$\frac{i_\theta r^2}{I_0} = \frac{2\pi^2 n_0^2(n - n_o)^2}{\lambda_o^4 \nu} (1 + \cos^2\theta) \tag{8-2}$$

The number of molecules per cubic centimeter ν can thus be determined from observable quantities. Since $\nu = Nc/M$, where c is in grams per cubic centimeter, either Avogadro's number N or the molecular weight M may be determined if the other is known. Avogadro's number has been determined from light-scattering measurements.

The ratio $R_\theta = i_\theta r^2/I_0$, called the *reduced intensity* or *Rayleigh ratio*, may be related to the turbidity τ by integrating i_θ over the surface of a sphere of radius r. The result is $\tau = 16\pi R_\theta/3(1 + \cos^2\theta)$, from which

$$\tau = \frac{8\pi}{3}\frac{i_0 r^2}{I_0} = \frac{8\pi}{3}R_0 = \frac{16\pi}{3}\frac{i_{90}r^2}{I_0} = \frac{16\pi}{3}R_{90}$$

Light scattered from small particles at 90° is always plane-polarized. For unpolarized incident light, the scattering at 0° is twice that at 90°. The polarization factor is taken into account by the $(1 + \cos^2\theta)$ term.

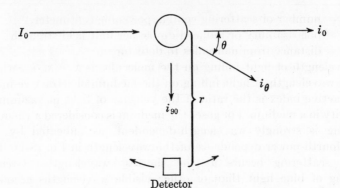

FIG. 8-1 Light-scattering apparatus. Monochromatic incident light I_0 is scattered by the sample. The phototube or other detector may be rotated around the sample to measure the scattered intensity i_θ as a function of the scattering angle θ. The light scattered at zero angle i_0 is more difficult to measure directly because of the large amount of unscattered light passing through most samples. A square cell may be used if only 90° scattering is required.

In most cases only a small fraction of the incident light is scattered, so that the turbidity, involving a difference between two large numbers, is more difficult to measure directly than the light scattered at some angle. Hence R_θ or, in particular, R_{90} is usually determined experimentally. A schematic diagram of a light-scattering apparatus is shown in Fig. 8-1.

8-2 SCATTERING FROM SOLUTIONS

P. Debye demonstrated that the Rayleigh equation (8-1) may be applied to solutions as a limiting relation for small, independent, isotropic particles, where ϵ and ϵ_0 apply to the dielectric constants of the solution and solvent, respectively. For most dilute solutions, the refractive-index increment $dn/dc = (n - n_0)/c$ (since $c_0 = 0$) is a constant independent of concentration and dependent upon wavelength and the nature of the solute. Substituting in Eq. (8-2) yields

$$R_\theta = \frac{2\pi^2 n_0^2 (dn/dc)^2 (1 + \cos^2 \theta)}{N\lambda_0^4} Mc = K_\theta Mc \qquad (8\text{-}3)$$

from which

$$\tau = \frac{32\pi^3 n_0^2 (dn/dc)^2}{3N\lambda_0^4} Mc = HMc \qquad (8\text{-}4)$$

The collections of constants K_θ and H are characteristic of a particular solution, and, once determined, they need not be reevaluated. Note that K_θ is dependent upon the angle, whereas H is not. When θ is 90° and $1 + \cos^2 \theta$ is therefore unity, we shall denote K_{90} simply as K. Since dn/dc appears as a square term in Eqs. (8-3) and (8-4), its accurate determination is more important than that of the light-scattering data.

Fluctuation Theory. The preceding considerations apply only to independent scattering centers, either in a dilute gas or as a limiting relation in solutions. In a perfect crystal, the periodic repeat of molecules or ions causes destructive interference, and no scattering occurs. In liquids, which are intermediate in randomness and order between gases and crystals, light is scattered from particles that are not wholly independent. Scattering from liquids is too complex to be treated by the methods outlined for dilute gases. Instead, statistical fluctuations of density and concentration are considered the causes of scattering from liquids. Since we are interested in scattering due to fluctuations in concentration of the solute, scattering due to the solvent is subtracted from that due to the solution. The result, due to M. Smoluchowski (1908) and A. Einstein (1910), is

$$R_\theta = \frac{\pi^2 R T c (\partial \epsilon / \partial c)^2 (1 + \cos^2 \theta)}{2 \lambda^4 N (\partial \Pi / \partial c)} \tag{8-5}$$

where Π is the osmotic pressure. The amount of scattering is governed by the osmotic work required to produce a concentration fluctuation. Since $\epsilon = n^2$, $\partial \epsilon / \partial c = 2n \, \partial n / \partial c$. For ideal solutions, the van't Hoff equation is $\partial \Pi / \partial c = RT/M$. Substituting these results in Eq. (8-5) yields Eq. (8-3), which is the Debye limiting equation for ideal solutions.

Combination of Eqs. (8-3) and (8-4) with Eq. (8-5) gives

$$\frac{K_\theta c}{R_\theta} = \frac{Hc}{\tau} = \frac{1}{RT} \frac{\partial \Pi}{\partial c}$$

A more realistic equation for the concentration dependence of osmotic pressure is Eq. (7-19). Differentiation of this expression yields

$$\frac{K_\theta c}{R_\theta} = \frac{Hc}{\tau} = \frac{1}{M} + \frac{2Bc}{M^2} \tag{8-6}$$

A plot of the left-hand side of Eq. (8-6) versus c has a slope of $2B/M^2$ and an intercept of $1/M$, where B is the second virial coefficient.

Equation (8-6) is strictly valid only in two-component systems. If the macromolecular component interacts preferentially in a multicomponent system, the effect must be taken into account if a reliable molecular weight is to be obtained.

Despite the similarity between intensity of scattered light and osmotic pressure, two different molecular-weight averages are obtained. From the van't Hoff equation for osmotic pressure, the ith component is

$$\frac{\Pi}{RTc_i} = \frac{1}{M_i} \quad \text{from which} \quad \frac{\Pi}{RT} = \sum_i \frac{c_i}{M_i}$$

This may be substituted in

$$\frac{\Pi}{RT\Sigma c_i} = \frac{\Sigma c_i / M_i}{\Sigma c_i} = \frac{1}{\bar{M}_n}$$

to yield the number-average molecular weight [Eq. (6-1)]. Adapting Eq. (8-6) with a negligible second-virial term, we have, for the ith component,

$$\frac{K_\theta c_i}{R_\theta} = \frac{1}{M_i} \quad \text{from which} \quad \frac{K_\theta}{R_\theta} = \frac{1}{\Sigma c_i M_i}$$

This may be substituted in

$$\frac{K_\theta \Sigma c_i}{R_\theta} = \frac{\Sigma c_i}{\Sigma c_i M_i} = \frac{1}{\bar{M}_w}$$

to yield the weight-average molecular weight [Eq. (6-2)]. Note that the concentration term is in the denominator of the osmotic-pressure equation and in the numerator of the light-scattering expression. In the case of a monodisperse solute, the molecular weights determined by the two methods are identical. In a polydisperse system the radio of the molecular weight determined by light scattering to that determined by osmotic pressure, $\bar{M}_w / \bar{M}_n$, is a measure of the polydispersity.

If the activity coefficients are not assumed to be unity when fluctuation theory is applied to a three-component system, the approximate result is

$$\frac{Kc_2}{R_{90}} = \frac{1}{M_2} + \frac{1}{M_2{}^2} \left\{ \frac{\partial(\ln \gamma_2)}{\partial m_2} + \frac{Z_2{}^2}{2\mu} - \frac{[\partial(\ln \gamma_2)/\partial m_3]^2 m_3}{2 + 2\,\partial(\ln \gamma_3)/\partial(\ln m_3)} \right\} c_2 \tag{8-7}$$

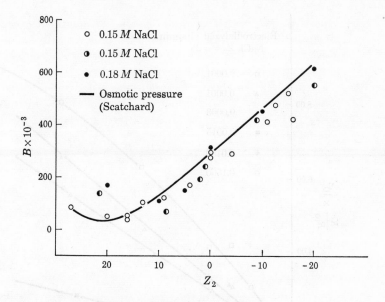

FIG. 8-2 Second virial coefficients B (cc/mole) from osmotic-pressure (solid line) and light-scattering measurements (points) versus net proton charge Z_2 of bovine serum albumin. The curve has a minimum at $Z_2 = +20$ rather than at zero, owing to chloride ion binding. (After Ref. 4.)

where the subscript 2 refers to the macromolecule, the subscript 3 to salt, m to molality, γ to molal activity coefficient, μ to ionic strength, and Z_2 to net proton charge on the macromolecule. The term in braces, equivalent to $2B$, is the same as that obtained for osmotic pressure [Eq. (7-24)], even to the inclusion of the Donnan (second) term. For a discussion of the terms in Eq. (8-7), see Sec. 7-4. The second virial coefficients B, determined from osmotic-pressure and light-scattering measurements on bovine serum albumin, are compared in Fig. 8-2. The agreement of these measurements is within the experimental error of the methods.

Figure 8-3 shows the values of Kc/R_{90} as a function of concentration of bovine serum albumin at $Z_2 = +25$ and several ionic strengths. The low value of the slope or B term at high ionic strengths indicates that, in this case, the Donnan term is the dominant factor in accounting for the slopes.

Figure 8-4 shows the variation of B with the charge Z_2 of bovine serum albumin. The curves exhibit the parabolic shape expected of a Donnan term in accordance with the second term in the braces of Eq. (8-7). The results support the conclusion of the preceding para-

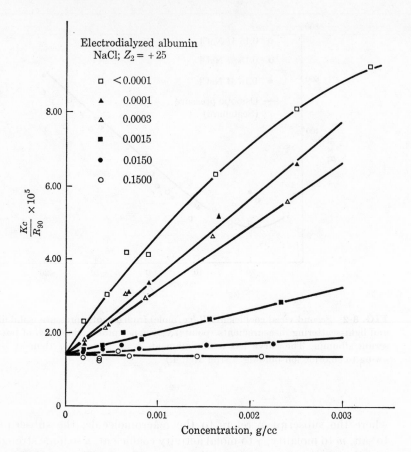

FIG. 8-3 Kc/R_{90} in moles per gram as a function of concentration for bovine serum albumin at net proton charge $Z_2 = +25$ and several ionic strengths. (After Ref. 4.)

graph that the Donnan term is the dominant of the terms in the braces of Eq. (8-7). Other effects do enter, however, and the progressive departure of the minima of the curves from the $Z_2 = 0$ position as ionic strength increases is due to chloride-ion binding.

8-3 INTERNAL INTERFERENCE

In the preceding discussion the particle size has been restricted to less than one-twentieth of the wavelength of the incident light, so that the scattering particles could be considered point dipoles. For larger macromolecules this restriction is not valid, and it is necessary to

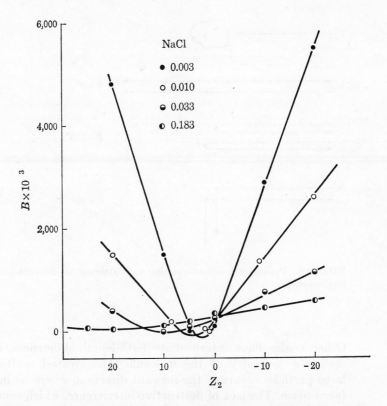

FIG. 8-4 Variation of the B term in cubic centimeters per mole for bovine serum albumin with net proton charge Z_2 on the protein, at several ionic strengths. (After Ref. 4.)

consider several independent dipole centers on one molecule. We still neglect the distortion of the electric field due to the difference in refractive index between scattering particles and medium. A formulation developed by Mie allows for this refractive-index difference in the case of spherical particles.

Destructive interference occurring between two or more scattering centers on one particle is illustrated in Fig. 8-5. At $\theta = 0°$, the path length for both scattering centers is the same, and no interference occurs. At $\theta = 180°$, the path length of scattered light is different for the various scattering centers of the particle, and destructive interference occurs when the separation between centers is greater than one-twentieth the wavelength of the incident light. Reinforcement can occur, however, if the path-length difference for two scattering centers happens to be an integral multiple of the wavelength.

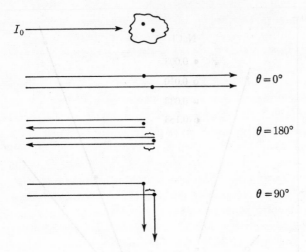

FIG. 8-5 Path-length differences due to scattering at different angles from a large particle.

Other angles have intermediate path-length differences, depending upon the geometry of the molecule. The greatest scattering from large particles occurs in the forward direction, where no interference takes place. The lack of destructive interference, which results in predominant scattering in the forward direction, may easily be verified by observing a shaft of light in a dusty atmosphere near $\theta = 0°$.

To allow for the angular dependence of the scattering from particles greater than one-twentieth of the wavelength of light, the particle-scattering factor $P(\theta)$ is introduced into Eq. (8-3) to yield

$$R_\theta = K_\theta P(\theta) Mc \qquad (8\text{-}8)$$

The particle-scattering factor $P(\theta)$ has been theoretically evaluated for molecules of various shapes. For molecules of all shapes, however, $P(\theta) = 1.0$ at $\theta = 0°$, because no interference occurs at $0°$. At angles greater than $0°$, $P(\theta) < 1.0$ when the particles are greater than one-twentieth of the wavelength of the light used. Thus, at $90°$, the apparent weight-average molecular weight determined by Eq. (8-3) will be less than the actual value in the case of larger particles. We shall discuss two of the methods for quantitatively evaluating the contribution of size and shape to the reduction in scattering.

The Debye dissymmetry method utilizes the fact that $P(\theta)$ is often a single-valued, continuous function of θ which decreases from a value of $P(\theta) = 1.0$ at $\theta = 0°$. The function $P(\theta)$ is therefore defined by the measurement of only two angles. If the two angles chosen are symmetrical about 90°, the $1 + \cos^2 \theta$ term in R_θ may be ignored. In particular, the dissymmetry Z is often taken as the ratio of the light scattered at 45° to that scattered at 135°: $R_{45}/R_{135} = Z$. The value of Z used in calculations should be extrapolated to zero concentration. When the particle size is less than one-twentieth of the wavelength of the incident light, the dissymmetry is nearly unity. The manner in which dissymmetry increases with particle size depends upon particle shape. Values of the dissymmetry expected for various shapes, such as rods, coils, and spheres, have been tabulated and plotted. Comparison of experimental dissymmetry values with those calculated on the basis of models frequently permits the approximate identification of a molecule with some standard shape. Other plots are available for correlating dissymmetry Z with $P(90)$, so that the approximate correction may be applied to Eq. (8-8) for molecular-weight determinations. For low values of Z the dissymmetry method is rapid and convenient; for high values of Z it suffers from a strong dependence on the assumed shape.

For molecules of all shapes, the particle-scattering factor $P(\theta)$ becomes independent of shape as θ approaches zero:

$$\lim_{\theta \to 0} P^{-1}(\theta) = 1 + \frac{16\pi^2 R^2 \sin^2 (\theta/2)}{3\lambda^2} \cdots \tag{8-9}$$

where R is the root mean square average radius of gyration of a molecule. The square of the radius of gyration is defined as the weight-average value of r_i^2 for all mass elements m_i located at distance r_i from the center of mass:

$$R^2 = \frac{\Sigma m_i r_i^2}{\Sigma m_i}$$

The radius of gyration or scattering radius is related to the dimensions of several geometric shapes capable of characterization in terms of a single parameter:

Spheres: $$R_S^2 = \frac{3r^2}{5} \tag{8-10}$$

Rods: $$R_R^2 = \frac{l^2}{12} \tag{8-11}$$

Random coils: $$R_C^2 = \frac{\overline{h^2}}{6} \tag{8-12}$$

where r is the radius of a sphere, l the length of a rod, and $(\overline{h^2})^{1/2}$ the

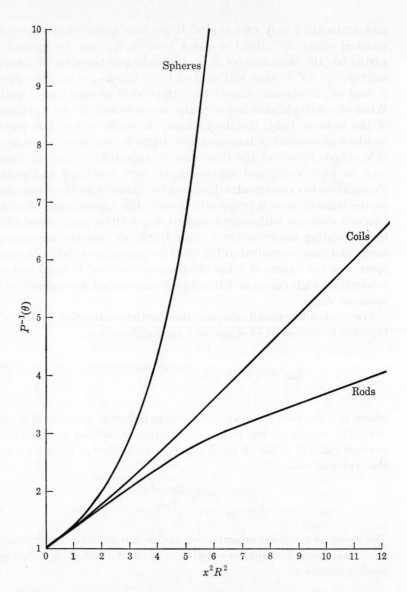

FIG. 8-6   Reciprocal of particle-scattering factor $P^{-1}(\theta)$ versus x^2R^2 for molecules of several shapes, where $x^2 = 16\pi^2 \sin^2(\theta/2)/\lambda^2$, and R is the radius of gyration. Note that for molecules of all shapes the initial slope is $\frac{1}{3}$. [After E. P. Geiduschek and A. Holtzer, *Advan. Biol. Med. Phys.*, **6**, 443 (1958).]

root mean square average distance between the ends of a coil. In the limit, where Eq. (8-9) can be applied, the radius of gyration may be evaluated independently of any assumption concerning shape. This independence of shape for R for low θ is illustrated in Fig. 8-6, where $P^{-1}(\theta)$ is plotted against x^2R^2, where $x^2 = 16\pi^2 \sin^2 (\theta/2)/\lambda^2$. Comparison with Eq. (8-9) shows that the initial slope in Fig. 8-6 for all shapes is $\frac{1}{3}$. The subsequent course of the curves is beyond the limits of Eq. (8-9) and is a characteristic of the particle shape.

For large particles, Eq. (8-6) is valid only at zero angle, where the diminution in scattered intensity due to internal interference vanishes. Eq. (8-8) is applicable only at low concentrations, where solute interactions disappear.

The second method for assessing the contribution of size and shape to scattering is that of the Zimm plot. In this method, a double extrapolation is performed by plotting $K_\theta c/R_\theta$ versus $\sin^2 (\theta/2) + kc$, where k is a constant selected so as to provide convenient spacing of the data. Figure 8-7 is a Zimm plot for collagen. The solid points at the bottom of the curve are extrapolated to zero angle and, according to Eq. (8-6), permit a determination of the molecular weight from the intercept, and of the second virial coefficient from the slope.

Combining Eqs. (8-8) and (8-9), we obtain

$$\frac{K_\theta c}{R_\theta} = \frac{1}{MP(\theta)} = \frac{1}{M}\left[1 + \frac{16\pi^2 R^2 \sin^2 (\theta/2)}{3\lambda^2} \cdots \right] \tag{8-13}$$

in the limit of low concentrations and small angles. The solid points at the left of Fig. 8-7 have been obtained by extrapolation to zero concentration. According to Eq. (8-13), a line drawn through these left-hand solid points will have an intercept of $1/M$, the same intercept obtained by extrapolation of the points at zero angle. Thus the double extrapolation should yield a common intercept which is the reciprocal of the weight-average molecular weight. The initial slope of a line drawn through the points at zero concentration divided by the intercept is, from Eq. (8-13), directly proportional to the square of the radius of gyration and inversely proportional to the square of the wavelength of light in the medium. For a given wavelength, the initial slope divided by the intercept is proportional only to the square of what turns out to be the Z-average radius of gyration. At greater angles the character of the slope is a function of the shape of the particle. Comparison of the entire left-hand slope of Fig. 8-7 with Fig. 8-6 indicates that collagen is best approximated as a rod.

Heat denaturation of collagen to yield gelatin, as followed by light

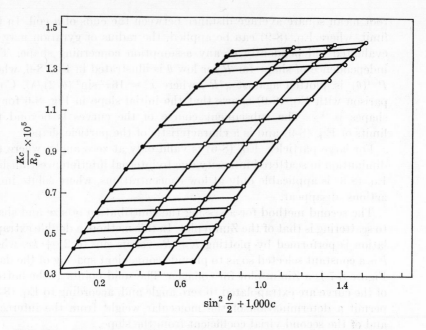

FIG. 8-7   Zimm plot of light scattering in collagen solutions at pH 3.7 and 15°. Open circles are experimental points; closed circles are values extrapolated to zero concentration (left) and zero angle (bottom). (From Ref. 5.)

scattering, is shown in Fig. 8-8. Initially, the curved line of solid circles is obtained. The downward curvature of the reciprocal envelope is interpreted as indicating a relatively stiff rodlike material (compare Fig. 8-6). Collagen consists of three polypeptide chains wound in a triple helix (Sec. 14-2). Heating for 5 min at 40° unwinds the triple helix and yields three single polypeptide chains in its place. Figure 8-8 shows that the straighter line of open circles, obtained after heating, exhibits almost three times the intercept, corresponding to nearly one-third the molecular weight of the initial material. The lesser slope of the denatured collagen indicates a smaller spatial extent, and the lack of curvature is typical of the random-coil conformation (Fig. 8-6) of single polypeptide chains.

More data are required for the Zimm plot than for the dissymmetry method, but the Zimm plot provides a more complete picture of the scattering, obtains a molecular weight independent of shape, and reveals highly aggregated material by intense scattering at low angles. For large, asymmetric molecules with large radii of gyration, such as DNA, to attain the limit at which Eq. (8-13) is applicable, it is necessary but difficult to take measurements at low angles (6 to 10°) in order to

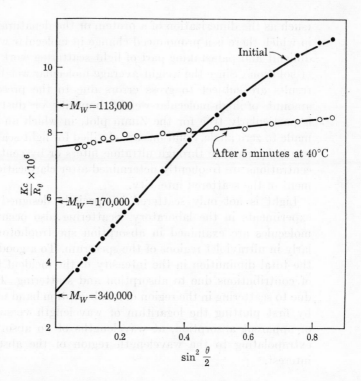

FIG. 8-8 Reciprocal scattering envelope of native (solid circles) and denatured (open circles) collagen at 2.6×10^{-4} g/cc. (From Ref. 5.)

obtain reliable extrapolations to zero angle without the additional assumption of a particular molecular model. At the other extreme, Fig. 8-6 shows that only small values of $P(\theta)$ are obtained for small spherical molecules, so that the exact value is difficult to determine. It is possible to increase precision in this region by decreasing the wavelength by use of x-rays.

Small-angle x-ray scattering has many similarities to light scattering. Due to the shorter wavelength of x-rays, particle dimensions of the order of hundreds of angstrom units may be estimated by this method, in contrast to dimensions of thousands of angstrom units estimated by light scattering. However, the techniques of small-angle x-ray scattering are more difficult to apply than those of light scattering; for instance, corrections must be made for scattering by the glass container.

Light-scattering measurements do not alter the system and may be performed rapidly. They are of value in following rates of reactions (such as the dimerization of a protein or the denaturation of collagen) in which there is a pronounced change in molecular weight. The most difficult and painstaking part of light-scattering work is the clarifying of solutions. Since the weight-average molecular weight is determined, results are subject to gross errors due to the presence of a small amount of high-molecular-weight impurity or dust particles. This is particularly true for the Zimm plot, in which an extrapolation is made to zero angle. Solutions are clarified for light-scattering measurements by passage through ultrafine filters or by centrifugation. Concentrations are frequently determined after clarification and measurement of the scattered intensity.

Light is not only scattered in specially designed light-scattering experiments in the laboratory. Scattering also occurs when macromolecules are examined in absorption spectrophotometers, particularly in ultraviolet regions of the spectrum. To a good approximation, the total diminution in the intensity of the incident beam is the sum of contributions due to absorption and scattering. The contribution due to scattering in the region of an absorption band may be estimated by first plotting the logarithm of wavelength versus the logarithm of apparent absorption, at wavelengths of no absorption, and then extrapolating to the wavelength region of the absorption band of interest.

SELECTED BIBLIOGRAPHY

1   K. A. Stacey, "Light Scattering in Physical Chemistry," Butterworth Scientific Publications, London, 1956.

2   P. Doty and J. T. Edsall, Light Scattering in Protein Solutions, *Advan. Protein Chem.*, **6**, 35–121 (1951).

3   G. Oster, The Scattering of Light and Its Applications to Chemistry, *Chem. Rev.*, **43**, 319–365 (1948).

4   J. T. Edsall, H. Edelhoch, R. Lontie, and P. R. Morrison, Light Scattering in Solutions of Serum Albumin: Effects of Charge and Ionic Strength, *J. Am. Chem. Soc.*, **72**, 4641–4656 (1950).

5   H. Boedtker and P. Doty, The Native and Denatured States of Soluble Collagen, *J. Am. Chem. Soc.*, **78**, 4267 (1956).

QUESTIONS

8-1   Light-scattering measurements made at 5,461 A and 4,358 A on very pure water gave R_{90} values of 1.05×10^{-6} and 2.89×10^{-6}, respectively. Account for the difference. What value would you predict for 3,650 A?

8-2   Draw and explain a simple apparatus for the determination of the light scattered from solutions at 90°. What modifications are necessary to obtain the data required for a Zimm plot?

8-3   Electron micrographs show that tobacco mosaic virus is a rodlike molecule about 3,000 A long. Calculate its radius of gyration.

8-4 Low-angle x-ray scattering indicates that spherical bushy stunt virus has a diameter of 310 A in solution. What is its radius of gyration?

8-5 You wish to determine as much information as possible about a sample of protein. You are equipped with an osmometer and a light-scattering apparatus. What information do you expect to obtain with the former apparatus and not with the latter, and vice versa? What information should you be able to obtain with both? What information that would have been unobtainable with either apparatus alone should you be able to derive because you have used both?

9 | Diffusion

So far this book has been concerned with only static methods for the determination of the size and shape of macromolecules. But all the dynamic methods outlined in Chap. 6, except viscosity, involve a study of diffusion. Diffusion is the process whereby concentration gradients in a solution spontaneously decrease until a homogeneous system is attained. The molecules of a fluid are in continual random Brownian movement owing to their thermal energy. The term diffusion is applied to the macroscopic flow of components due to concentration differences, rather than the microscopic random movements of individual molecules through the solution after macroscopic homogeneity has been reached. A knowledge of diffusion is basic to the understanding of transport cells and diffusion across cell membranes. Translational diffusion will be considered first; then rotational diffusion and relaxation times.

9-1 TRANSLATIONAL DIFFUSION

Consider a system with solvent carefully layered upon a solution in a negligible gravitational field at constant temperature and pressure. The vector flow J is defined as the mass (grams or moles) passing through an area of A cm² per second, dm/dt, as follows:

$$\frac{dm}{dt}\frac{1}{A} \equiv J = -D\frac{dc}{dx} \tag{9-1}$$

Assuming an analogy with the conduction of heat, A. Fick (1855) formulated that in a two-component system in which there is no volume change on mixing, the flow is proportional to the gradient of concentration, dc/dx, expressed as grams or moles per cm⁴. The second equality of Eq. (9-1) is Fick's first law of diffusion, where D

is the diffusion coefficient in square centimeters per second. The minus sign indicates that the flow always occurs in the direction of decreasing concentration.

In a two-component system, we may write Fick's first law for solvent and solute, respectively, as

$$J_0 = -D_0 \frac{\partial c_0}{\partial x} \qquad J_1 = -D_1 \frac{\partial c_1}{\partial x} \tag{9-2}$$

When there is no volume change on mixing, the volume of ascending solute must equal the volume of descending solvent, or

$$\bar{v}_0 J_0 + \bar{v}_1 J_1 = 0 \tag{9-3}$$

where $\bar{v}$ is the partial specific volume in cubic centimeters per gram. Substitution of Eqs. (9-2) into (9-3) yields

$$\bar{v}_0 D_0 \frac{\partial c_0}{\partial x} + \bar{v}_1 D_1 \frac{\partial c_1}{\partial x} = 0 \tag{9-4}$$

The total volume of the solution is

$$V = \bar{v}_0 g_0 + \bar{v}_1 g_1$$

where g is the number of grams. Dividing by V, we obtain

$$\bar{v}_0 c_0 + \bar{v}_1 c_1 = 1 \tag{9-5}$$

because $g/V = c$, the concentration in grams per cubic centimeter. When there is no volume change on mixing, $\bar{v}$ is independent of concentration and hence of x. Differentiating Eq. (9-5) yields

$$\bar{v}_0 \frac{\partial c_0}{\partial x} + \bar{v}_1 \frac{\partial c_1}{\partial x} = 0 \tag{9-6}$$

By substituting Eq. (9-6) in Eq. (9-4), we find that $D_0 = D_1$. Thus the diffusion coefficients for solvent and solute are equal in a two-component system when no volume change occurs on mixing.

For a system with more than two components, Fick's first law may be written for each component separately as

$$J_i = -D_i \frac{\partial c_i}{\partial x} \qquad i = 1, 2, \cdots, n \text{ solutes}$$

The solvent flow may then be obtained by difference from the generalization of Eq. (9-3):

$$\sum_{i=0}^{n} \bar{v}_i J_i = 0$$

The simplest method for determining the diffusion coefficient depends only upon Fick's first law. A sintered glass disk containing holes larger than any molecule present is placed between a solution and its solvent. Stirring maintains uniform compositions on both sides of the disk. Analyses are performed initially and after a period of time, and the relative concentrations are compared. After a time Δt, there is a small change in concentration, $\Delta c = kDc\,\Delta t$, where k is a proportionality constant dependent upon the area and characteristics of the glass disk. The value of k is determined by measuring a substance of known D. Once k is determined, many solutes may be tested, and the equation may be solved for D. This method gives only relative values for D. Diffusion coefficients of molecules absorbed on the sintered glass cannot usually be determined by this technique.

Fick's first law describes only the steady-state condition for diffusion. Conservation of mass is expressed in the continuity equation

$$\left(\frac{\partial c_i}{\partial t}\right)_x = -\frac{1}{A}\left[\frac{\partial(A J_i)}{\partial x}\right]_t \tag{9-7}$$

The change in concentration of component i per unit time in a unit volume is equal to the difference between the flows into and out of that volume. Equation (9-7) applies for any number of components, even if the flows interact, provided no chemical reactions occur. For flows in one dimension, A is a constant and cancels out. Substitution of Fick's first law, Eq. (9-1), into Eq. (9-7) yields

$$\frac{\partial c_i}{\partial t} = \frac{\partial}{\partial x}\left(D\,\frac{\partial c_i}{\partial x}\right) \qquad i = 0, 1$$

If D is independent of concentration and hence of x, we have

$$\frac{\partial c_i}{\partial t} = D\,\frac{\partial^2 c_i}{\partial x^2} \qquad i = 0, 1 \tag{9-8}$$

which is Fick's second law of diffusion, derived here from his first law. If there is no interaction of flows, Fick's second law may be generalized to more than two components such that $i = 0, 1, \ldots, n$ in Eq. (9-8).

Equation (9-8) of Fick's second law is analogous to the heat-conduction equation, which has been solved for many boundary conditions. We shall apply only one such solution, that for a tube of infinite length, a condition which is satisfied in diffusion if the concentrations at the ends of the tube do not change during the experiment. In practice the solvent is layered upon the solution.

Figure 9-1a is a diffusion cell meeting the above stipulation and rotated through an angle of $-90°$ from the experimental condition. If x is measured from the position of the sharp initial boundary, we

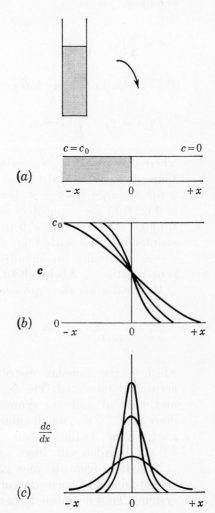

FIG. 9-1 Relative concentration and gradient of concentration for a diffusion experiment, rotated through an angle of $-90°$, compared with an experimental cell.

have

$$c = \begin{cases} c_0 & \text{for } x < 0 \\ 0 & \text{for } x > 0 \end{cases} \quad \text{at } t = 0$$

but as the boundary becomes blurred, we have

$$c \rightarrow \begin{cases} c_0 & \text{for } x \rightarrow -\infty \\ 0 & \text{for } x \rightarrow +\infty \end{cases} \quad \text{at } t > 0$$

Integration of Fick's second law, Eq. (9-8), between these boundary conditions yields

$$c = \frac{c_0}{2} [1 - P(y)]$$

$P(y)$ is the probability integral,

$$P(y) = 2\pi^{-\frac{1}{2}} \int_0^y e^{-y^2} \, dy$$

where $y = x/(4Dt)^{\frac{1}{2}}$. Numerical values of $P(y)$ appear in many collections of mathematical tables; it varies from -1 through 0 to $+1$ as y (or x) varies from $-\infty$ through 0 to $+\infty$. The c versus x curves of Fig. 9-1b are sigmoid in shape, passing from $c = c_0$ at $x = -\infty$ through $c = c_0/2$ at $x = 0$ to $c = 0$ at $x = +\infty$. The curve rotates counterclockwise with time about the point of inflection at $x = 0$, $c = c_0/2$. Finally, at infinite time, the cell is homogeneous, with concentration $c_0/2$ throughout.

Differentiating the expression for c, we obtain

$$\frac{dc}{dx} = \frac{-c_0}{(4\pi Dt)^{\frac{1}{2}}} e^{-x^2/4Dt}$$

which is the gaussian distribution function, also well known and accurately tabulated. The dc/dx versus x curves of Fig. 9-1c have a maximum at and are symmetrical about $x = 0$, irrespective of t. Since $[\Delta c]_{x \to -\infty}^{x \to +\infty}$ is c_0 for all values of t, the areas under the peaked curves are the same. As the c versus x curves rotate, the dc/dx versus x curves fall and broaden with time.

Deviations from the pure gaussian curves may occur in two ways. Heightening and narrowing of the curves takes place in polydisperse systems. Thus deviation from a pure gaussian curve indicates that the solute is not pure. The method is not sensitive enough, however, to be used as a criterion of purity. Skewing of the pure gaussian curves is caused by intermolecular interactions. Unfortunately, extrapolation to zero concentration is more complex for D than for most other concentration-dependent properties, such as osmotic pressure and light scattering.

At the maximum in the dc/dx versus x curves, we have

$$\left(\frac{dc}{dx}\right)_{\text{max}} = -\frac{c_0}{(4\pi Dt)^{1/2}}$$

The refractive index of a two-component system is usually a linear function of the solute concentration, $\Delta n = c_0 \, dn/dc$, where Δn is the difference between the refractive indices of solution at c_0 and solvent. Therefore, at the maximum, $(dn/dx)_{\text{max}} = -\Delta n/(4\pi Dt)^{1/2}$, from which $D = (\Delta n)^2/4\pi t(dn/dx)^2_{\text{max}}$. This equation provides one method for determining D. It is not necessary to know c_0, as only refractive-index differences are required. A nonlinear dependence of the refractive index on concentration would introduce skewing, which can be taken into account.

One apparatus for determining diffusion coefficients consists of a two-armed vessel placed in an accurately thermostatted bath. Ethylene glycol is added to the bath water to give a refractive index similar to that of the solution under study. One arm of the vessel contains only the solution, but the other has a sharp solution-solvent boundary. The solvent contains all the components of the solution, including the buffer and any inert salt except the compound whose D is being determined. The solution also contains about 1% (by weight) of the molecule under consideration.

Advances in the application of optical techniques to refractive-index gradients have been revolutionary. The quantitative study of diffusion, electrophoresis, and sedimentation is possible in high-quality commercial instruments. The ingenious optical systems used are too complex to be described in detail here.

The Schlieren optical system utilizes a diagonal knife-edge and a cylindrical lens to convert the variation of refractive index in the cell to a differential dn/dx versus x plot. Results of about 1% accuracy are obtainable by this method.

In a modified Rayleigh interferometer, the number and spacing of photographically recorded fringes as a function of time yield the shape of the n versus x curve directly. (Fringes are lines of constant refractive index.) Results accurate up to 0.1% (as well as the variation of D with concentration) can be obtained. Relatively simple absorption optics is also used for strongly absorbing substances such as nucleic acids, because the sensitivity permits analysis at low concentrations of these very asymmetric molecules.

Some representative values of $D \times 10^7$, obtained in aqueous solutions at 20 or 25°, in square centimeters per second are: water, 250; glycine, 106; diglycine, 79; triglycine, 67; ribonuclease, 11; β-lactoglobulin, 7.6; bovine plasma albumin, 6.7; bovine fibrinogen, 2.0. In general, D decreases with increasing molecular weight.

9-2 INTERPRETATIONS OF D

Kinetic. Diffusion may be related to Brownian movement. Thermal energy causes a particle to undergo successive random displacements in solution. The most probable displacement after an interval of time with respect to any one axis is zero. The mean square displacement along the x axis, $\overline{x^2}$, is the sum of many displacements after a time t, the values of which are squared and then averaged. The mean square displacement must be a positive number. A. Einstein (1906) showed that in dilute solutions $\overline{x^2} = 2Dt$. This relation cannot be tested precisely, because the measurements of Brownian motion in the ultramicroscope are of limited accuracy.

As might be expected, the mean square displacement is reduced as the friction on the solute molecule increases and is increased as the thermal energy kT (where k is Boltzmann's constant) increases. Einstein also showed that $\overline{x^2} = 2kTt/f$, where f is the frictional coefficient of a solute particle in grams per molecule. Combination of the equations derived by Einstein yields $D = kT/f = RT/Nf$, since $R = Nk$, where R is the universal gas constant, and N is Avogadro's number. This formula relates the macroscopic and microscopic aspects of diffusion. Considering the statistical nature of the discussion, it is not surprising to recall that the probability integral arose in a solution to a diffusion problem.

Thermodynamic. The velocity v of a solute particle is equal to the force on the particle, F/N, divided by the frictional resistance: $v = F/Nf$. The force may also be related to the chemical potential μ as follows, where C is molar concentration:

$$F = -\frac{d\mu}{dx} = -\frac{d\mu}{dC} \cdot \frac{dC}{dx}$$

By Fick's first law, the flow is $vC = J = -D\, dC/dx$, from which

$$F = \frac{d\mu}{dC} \frac{vC}{D}$$

Substituting for v yields

$$\frac{d\mu}{dC} = \frac{NfD}{C} \tag{9-9}$$

The thermodynamic relation between the chemical potential and the activity a is

$$\mu = \mu_0 + RT \ln a = \mu_0 + RT \ln C\gamma$$

where the activity may be replaced by the concentration and the appropriate activity coefficient γ. Differentiation with respect to concentration at constant temperature and pressure yields

$$\frac{d\mu}{dC} = \frac{RT}{C} \left[1 + \frac{d(\ln \gamma)}{d(\ln C)} \right] \tag{9-10}$$

Combining Eqs. (9-9) and (9-10), we obtain

$$D = \frac{RT}{Nf} \left[1 + \frac{d(\ln \gamma)}{d(\ln C)} \right] \tag{9-11}$$

As $C \to 0$ or in the case of ideal solutions, where there is a value of unity for the activity coefficient, Eq. (9-11) becomes $D = RT/Nf$, identical with the result obtained by kinetic arguments. Since the frictional coefficient is also concentration-dependent, the variation of D with concentration is nonlinear and complex.

9-3 FRICTIONAL COEFFICIENT

For rigid solute spheres with radius r large compared with the radius of the solvent molecules, so that the solvent appears as a continuous medium to the solute, G. G. Stokes (1851) derived the frictional coefficient $f = 6\pi\eta r$, where η is the coefficient of viscosity of the medium. Thus, for spheres in the limit of dilute solutions, $D = RT/N6\pi\eta r$. This equation indicates that for large, rigid spheres in dilute solutions D should vary directly as the temperature and inversely as the viscosity. Though it is not an exact description, the equation is useful in comparing diffusion coefficients obtained under different conditions. Since the molecular weight varies as the cube of the radius, the product $DM^{1/3}$ should be approximately constant for different spherical molecules measured at the same temperature. This relation is obeyed fairly well for spherical molecules with molecular weights M greater than 10^3; smaller molecules tend to give a constant $DM^{1/2}$ product.

The molecular volume V_m of an anhydrous spherical solute in solution may be expressed in two ways. In the first, $V_m = 4\pi r_0^3/3$, where r_0 is the radius of the spherical, anhydrous protein molecule. Since the partial specific volume $\bar{v}$ refers to the nonsolvated solute, we also have $V_m = \bar{v}M/N$, where M is the molecular weight, and N Avogadro's number. The two equations for V_m may be combined to yield $r_0 = (3\bar{v}M/4\pi N)^{1/3}$.

The corresponding frictional coefficient for the anhydrous spherical solute is $f_0 = 6\pi\eta r_0$. If the molecular weight is known from other measurements, f_0 may be computed and compared with the experimental value of f obtained from a determination of D: $f = RT/ND$. The frictional ratio f/f_0 is always greater than unity, owing to solvation of the protein or deviation from a spherical shape. A frictional ratio near unity would indicate a sphere with little hydration.

In the absence of additional information, the frictional ratio may be interpreted by a division into two parts, one due to hydration and the other to asymmetry:

$$\frac{f}{f_0} = \left(\frac{f}{f_0}\right)_{\text{hyd}} \left(\frac{f}{f_0}\right)_{\text{asym}}$$

We shall first estimate the contribution of hydration to the frictional ratio. The water of hydration is bound to or trapped by the solute; titration studies at varying ionic strengths indicate that the solvent does not move through the molecule. If 1 gram of solute binds w grams of water of the same density ρ as the solvent, then the molar volume V of the hydrated solute may be considered to be the sum of the contributions of anhydrous solute and water of hydration:

$$V = M\bar{v} + \frac{Mw}{\rho_0} = M\bar{v}\left(1 + \frac{w}{\bar{v}\rho_0}\right)$$

The radius of the sphere of the hydrated solute is $r = (3V/4\pi N)^{1/3}$, and since $(f/f_0)_{\text{hyd}} = r/r_0$, we have

$$\left(\frac{f}{f_0}\right)_{\text{hyd}} = \left(1 + \frac{w}{\bar{v}\rho_0}\right)^{1/3} \tag{9-12}$$

Many proteins bind about 0.25 g of water per gram of protein. If a representative value $\bar{v} = 0.75$ cc/g is selected, then $(f/f_0)_{\text{hyd}} = 1.10$. Experimental values of the frictional ratio range from 1.1 for ribonuclease to values greater than 2 for fibrinogen and some other proteins. High frictional ratios are not easily accounted for by hydration; they indicate that the solute is not spherical.

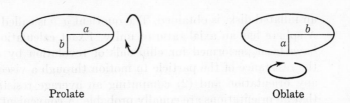

Prolate   Oblate

FIG. 9-2 Ellipses from which the two classes of ellipsoids of revolution may be generated; a is the semiaxis of rotation, and b the equatorial semiaxis.

The contribution to the frictional ratio due to deviations from sphericity has been computed only for rigid, impenetrable ellipsoids of revolution, as even the case of general ellipsoids is very complex. There are two classes of ellipsoids of revolution, as indicated in Fig. 9-2. Let a be the semiaxis of rotation, and b the equatorial semiaxis. Then for $a > b$ the ellipsoid is termed *prolate* and is similar to an inflated American football, while for $b > a$ an *oblate* ellipsoid, which resembles

FIG. 9-3 Contour plots of the frictional ratio f/f_0. [From J. L. Oncley, *Ann. N. Y. Acad. Sci.*, **41,** 121 (1941).]

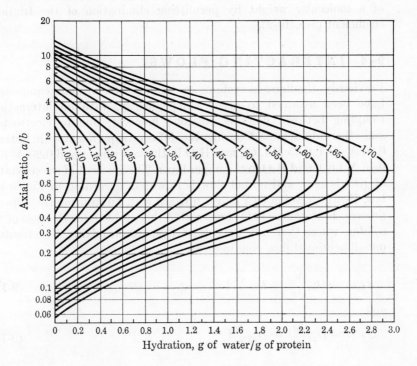

an inflated disk, is obtained. The quotient a/b is called the *axial ratio*. A sphere has an axial ratio of unity. Exact calculations of $(f/f_0)_{asym}$ have been performed for ellipsoids of revolution by (1) considering the resistance of the particle to motion through a viscous medium for any orientation and (2) computing an average resistance, assuming that all orientations are equally probable. A convenient way to express the results is shown in Fig. 9-3. The experimental value of the frictional ratio f/f_0 is found on the contours. For most values of the water of hydration, two values of the axial ratio are possible, depending upon whether a prolate or oblate ellipsoid of revolution is assumed. Since the water of hydration is also unknown, a double ambiguity exists.

A rigid, impenetrable ellipsoid of revolution may be a poor model for the system under study. The only virtue of the ellipsoid of revolution is that it is the sole nonspherical model that has received an exact treatment. At best, it approximates some native globular proteins. An alternative interpretation of frictional coefficients, possible when other hydrodynamic properties are also considered, is discussed in Sec. 11-2.

Diffusion results are most commonly used in conjunction with one of the other hydrodynamic methods, such as sedimentation-velocity experiments in the ultracentrifuge, to determine molecular weights. Combining the results of these two techniques allows the calculation of a molecular weight by permitting elimination of the frictional coefficient (Sec. 10-2).

9-4 INTERACTING FLOWS

Previously, the flows in systems containing three or more components have been assumed to occur independently, with no interactions. Coupling between flows is possible, however, due to electrostatic and other interactions. Consider the diffusion experiment with, initially, $0.20 \, N$ KCl, $0.35 \, N$ LiCl, and H_2O in the lower layer and $0.20 \, N$ KCl, $0.15 \, N$ LiCl, and H_2O in the upper layer. The gradient of concentration of KCl is zero, and no net flow is expected, according to Fick's first law. However, some KCl moves upward with LiCl during the diffusion process. L. Onsager (1945) has treated this problem for the case of two solutes, where there are no volume changes on mixing. The resulting one-dimensional flow equations are

$$J_1 = -D_{11} \frac{\partial c_1}{\partial x} - D_{12} \frac{\partial c_2}{\partial x} \tag{9-13a}$$

and

$$J_2 = -D_{21} \frac{\partial c_1}{\partial x} - D_{22} \frac{\partial c_2}{\partial x} \tag{9-13b}$$

where D_{11} and D_{22} are called *main* diffusion coefficients, and D_{12} and D_{21} *cross-term* diffusion coefficients. In general, $D_{12} \neq D_{21}$, but if both are equal to zero, Eqs. (9-13) reduce to equations of noninteracting flows in accordance with Fick's first law.

Values of the four diffusion coefficients, for the initial system described in the preceding paragraph and for a similar system with NaCl replacing KCl, are listed in Table 9-1. The results show that under the experimental conditions LiCl is about one-tenth as effective in moving KCl as is a concentration gradient of KCl, with the result that Li+ and Cl− move KCl against its own concentration gradient. Thus, diffusing ions produce a gradient of potential as well as of concentration, and the potential gradient can cause diffusion of other species in solution.

TABLE 9-1 *Diffusion Coefficients in square centimeters per second* $\times 10^5$ *at* $25°$ (*Component* 1 *is* LiCl, *component* 2 *is* KCl *or* NaCl)†

	LiCl-KCl-H₂O	LiCl-NaCl-H₂O
D_{11}	1.14	1.10
D_{12}	0.00	0.09
D_{21}	0.20	0.19
D_{22}	1.81	1.36

† From H. Fujita and L. J. Gosting, *J. Am. Chem. Soc.*, **78**, 1099 (1956).

The values of D_{11} for LiCl differ only slightly for the two systems. The zero value of D_{12} in the KCl system was predictable because of the nearly identical ionic conductances of K+ and Cl−. For the same reason the value of D_{22} in the KCl system is close to the value of 1.85×10^{-5} for pure KCl in water.

Diffusion measurements of macromolecules are usually made in the presence of excess inert electrolyte to suppress the charge effect. In this situation interacting flows may not be negligible. Though difficult to evaluate, interacting flows may be significant, and their contribution should always be considered. More experimental work is needed in this field.

Since a biological system consists of more than three components, interacting flows may occur. Knowledge in this field is so meager that the importance of interacting flows is difficult to assess. Their influence may be important in transport across cell membranes and in the maintenance of the potentials of cells and nerve fibers, among other situations.

9-5 ROTATIONAL DIFFUSION AND RELAXATION TIMES

In addition to the translational diffusion just discussed, solute molecules have a random orientation due to their rotational Brownian movement. The randomness of the orientation may be destroyed by the application of an external force. If the applied force is suddenly removed, the return to random orientation is characterized by a rotational diffusion coefficient θ. For rotation in two dimensions,

$$\frac{\partial \rho(\phi)}{\partial t} = \theta \frac{\partial^2 \rho(\phi)}{\partial \phi^2} \qquad (9\text{-}14)$$

where $\rho(\phi)$ is an angular distribution function of ϕ, the angle through which the solute molecule has rotated away from the axis of the external field. Equation (9-14) is analogous to Fick's second law for translational diffusion. The dimensions of the diffusion coefficients differ, however, D being in $l^2 t^{-1}$ while θ has units of t^{-1}, usually per second.

A. Einstein showed that, analogous to translational diffusion, $\theta = \overline{\phi^2}/2t$. In addition, like D, θ is directly proportional to the thermal energy of the molecules and inversely proportional to the rotational frictional coefficient: $\theta = kT/\zeta$. The rotational frictional coefficient ζ is a measure of the torque required to rotate the molecule with unit angular velocity and is dependent upon the viscosity η of the medium and the size and shape of the solute molecule. For large spheres of radius r, Stokes showed that $\zeta = 8\pi\eta r^3$.

The relaxation time τ is defined as the time required for the mean value of $\cos \phi$ for all the molecules to fall to $1/e$ of its original value, where e is the base of the natural logarithms, about 2.72. For spheres, Einstein derived

$$\tau = \frac{1}{2\theta} = \frac{4\pi\eta r^3}{kT}$$

This equation was verified by J. Perrin (1909), who followed the rotational motion of spherical colloidal mastic particles of 6.5×10^{-4} cm radius by observing, in a microscope, small enclosures of impurities on their surfaces. For spherical, unsolvated molecules, calculated values of θ_0 and τ_0 are greater and less, respectively, than observed values. As in the case of translational diffusion, the difference is due to solvation and/or nonspherical shapes.

Extension of the discussion to ellipsoids requires the definition of three relaxation times, one for each axis. It is found that

$$\tau_a = \frac{1}{\theta_b + \theta_c} \qquad \tau_b = \frac{1}{\theta_a + \theta_c} \qquad \tau_c = \frac{1}{\theta_a + \theta_b}$$

The corresponding rotational frictional coefficients ζ_a, ζ_b, and ζ_c are functions of the axial ratios. The general equations are complicated, but they may be simplified by considering ellipsoids of revolution of axial ratio a/b. The values of θ_0 and τ_0 for a sphere of the same volume as the ellipsoid of revolution are related by

$$\tau_0 = \frac{1}{2\theta_0} = \frac{4\pi\eta ab^2}{kT}$$

Detailed analyses relating τ_a and τ_b to the axial ratios have been performed for both prolate and oblate ellipsoids of revolution.

Experimental Methods. Flow birefringence is the orientation of highly elongated particles of length greater than 200 A in a velocity gradient produced by a mechanical shearing force. External force is applied by rotating the outer of two concentric cylinders between which the solution is placed. The field between the cylinders is observed with light directed parallel to the cylinder axis passing through crossed polarizers. Application of the external field produces four dark regions, in the shape of a cross (cross of isocline), on an otherwise bright field. In the regions of the cross, the plane of vibration of the light transmitted by either the polarizer or analyzer is parallel to the optic axis of the solution. Observations of the angle between the planes of the polarizers and the arms of the cross allow evaluation of θ and τ.

This method is useful for the study of asymmetric, rodlike molecules such as fibrous proteins with relaxation times from 10^{-4} to 1 sec. Rotation rates of globular proteins are so great that little orientation occurs.

The method of *dielectric dispersion*, the variation of dielectric constant with the frequency of the applied field, is the most versatile method for the determination of rotational diffusion coefficients. The dielectric constant increases as the dipole moment of the molecule increases, and it displays a nearly linear dependence on concentration (Sec. 3-2). The ability of molecules to keep pace with the alternations of the imposed electric field allows a calculation of their relaxation times. Spheres exhibit a single relaxation time. It is possible to determine two relaxation times for an asymmetrical molecule if components of dipole moment lie along both axes. Dielectric dispersion has been used for measurement of short relaxation times of the order of 10^{-8} sec but is limited to solutions of low conductivity.

Figure 9-4 gives results of measurements of the dielectric constant ϵ in an electric field alternating with frequency ν. In the low-frequency range, less than 10^5 cps, all molecules in the solution rotate in synchronization with the alternating field, yielding a value of ϵ_1 for the dielectric constant of the solution. For solutes more polar than the solvent, $\epsilon_1 > \epsilon_0$, where ϵ_0 is the dielectric constant of pure solvent.

In the 10^5 to 10^7 cps range, large solute molecules begin to lag; they finally appear unaffected by the field, because the alternations become comparable to and then surpass the relaxation time of the solute. At frequencies greater than 10^7 cps, the solute no longer contributes to the dielectric constant of the solution, but rather it acts as a nonpolar diluent to the solvent; hence $\epsilon_2 < \epsilon_0$. If ν_c is the frequency at $(\epsilon_1 + \epsilon_2)/2$, then, for a simple solute particle, $\tau^{-1} = 2\pi\nu_c$. Axial ratios and molecular

FIG. 9-4 Dielectric constant ϵ of a solution as a function of the logarithm of the frequency ν, in cycles per second, of an alternating electric field.

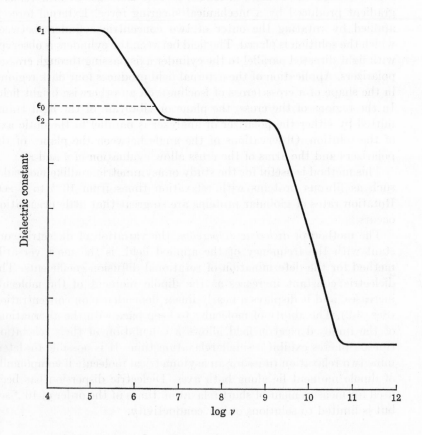

lengths may also be estimated. In the 10^{10} cps region, the field frequency is comparable to the relaxation time of the solvent molecules.

Dielectric-dispersion studies on globular proteins yield results which require the assumption of two different relaxation times for their interpretation. These two relaxation times, of the order of 10^{-7} sec, may be related to the axial ratios of an ellipsoid of revolution. Analysis is complicated, however, by the fluctuations of mobile protons on the protein surface. By dielectric-dispersion measurements in the 10^{10} cps range, information can also be obtained about the irrotationally bound water, to give an estimate of one kind of hydration.

Depolarization of Fluorescence. The absorption of light at one wavelength and its reemission at another is called *fluorescence*. Reemission of the light at the second wavelength occurs about 10^{-8} sec after absorption. When the exciting light is plane-polarized, the fluorescent light will also be polarized if little rotational Brownian movement occurs while the molecule is in the excited state. However, small molecules will undergo many random orientations while in the excited state, and the fluorescent light will be depolarized. The amount of depolarization of fluorescence may be related to the relaxation time and hence to molecular size and shape, as already indicated. Macromolecules not naturally fluorescent may be rendered so by the attachment of dye molecules.

Spin-resonance Techniques. Organic free radicals and paramagnetic ions contain electrons with unpaired spins. In the presence of an external magnetic field (even the magnetic field of the earth), the unpaired electrons assume positions either parallel with or opposite to the field direction. The unpaired electrons are almost equally divided between these two alignments of unequal energy. When electromagnetic energy corresponding to a precise frequency, usually in the microwave (10^9 sec^{-1}) region, is simultaneously applied, the free electron can flip between the two energy states, and a resonance condition exists. Because the local magnetic fields about free electrons differ, their exact resonance frequencies vary, and a probe exists for characterizing free-electron environments.

Electron spin resonance also provides a sensitive detection method for free radicals, down to 10^{-9} M in favorable cases, though the absolute value is difficult to assess. Free radicals have been detected in oxidation-reduction reactions in biological systems and in illuminated chloroplasts. By studying the variation in the resonance signal with the angle of myoglobin or hemoglobin crystals, the angle of the heme groups has been accurately defined. The planar heme group contains a paramagnetic iron atom whose unpaired electrons are subjected to varying magnetic fields, depending upon the angle the imposed external magnetic field makes with the local fields in the asymmetric heme.

Since the reciprocal of the frequency for many electron spin-resonance experiments is of the order of 10^{-9} sec, reference to Fig. 9-4 shows that small molecules, but not proteins, will have tumbled about many times during this period. The effect of this tumbling is to average the environment of unpaired electrons in many molecules and sharpen the spectra. Large molecules such as proteins do not undergo this averaging, so that if a comparison is to be made with small molecules, solids or frozen solutions of both kinds of molecule are required. In contrast to molecules containing paramagnetic ions discussed above, free radicals undergo relaxation by a different mechanism and yield well-defined spectra at room temperature.

Protons are also characterized by two spins, and in a magnetic field a splitting into two energy levels occurs. The splitting for protons is only about 0.1% of that of electrons, and radio-wave radiation of about 10^7 sec^{-1} is usually required for proton magnetic resonance. Local magnetic fields produce varying environments for the different kinds of hydrogen nuclei present, and an accurate count of nuclei in each type of environment is frequently possible. Assignment of nuclei to a particular environment is aided by spin-spin interactions between neighboring nuclei. Concentrations of at least 10^{-2} M in hydrogen nuclei are required. Figure 9-4 shows that most proteins cannot quite keep up with the radio-wave field oscillations of 10^7 sec^{-1}, and the proton magnetic-resonance spectra of proteins are broad. On denaturation, however, groups in proteins are less restrained by intramolecular interactions and are better able to tumble about during the lifetime of a spin state; hence they experience a more homogeneous magnetic field, which results in a sharpening of the proton magnetic-resonance spectrum.

SELECTED BIBLIOGRAPHY

1 L. J. Gosting, Measurement and Interpretation of Diffusion Coefficients of Proteins, *Advan. Protein Chem.*, **11**, 429–554 (1956).

2 A. Einstein, "Investigations on the Theory of the Brownian Movement," Dover Publications, Inc., New York, 1956. Reprint in English of five papers.

3 W. Jost, "Diffusion in Solids, Liquids and Gases," Academic Press Inc., New York, 1952.

4 K. G. Denbigh, "The Thermodynamics of the Steady State," Methuen & Co., Ltd., London, 1951.

5 R. Cerf and H. A. Scheraga, Flow Birefringence in Solutions of Macromolecules, *Chem. Rev.*, **51**, 185–261 (1952).

QUESTIONS

9-1 Verify Eq. (9-12).

9-2 Predict how the diffusion coefficient depends on the molecular weight of spheres.

9-3 Calculate the frictional ratios from the diffusion coefficients given in this chapter, given the following proteins and molecular weights: ribonuclease, 13,683; albumin, 69,000; fibrinogen, 330,000.

9-4 For frictional ratios of 1.10, 1.40, and 1.70, determine (*a*) axial ratios, assuming no hydration, (*b*) hydration, assuming spherical particles, and (*c*) axial ratios, assuming 0.2 g of water per gram of protein.

9-5 Fick's first law has been modified to relate the flow to the gradient of chemical potential, $J = L(-\partial\mu/\partial x)$, where L is the diffusional mobility. What are the units of L? What is the relation between L and D?

10 | Ultracentrifugation

Simple diffusion produces a condition of maximum entropy, a random distribution of components throughout a solution. A force applied to this solution unequally in different directions tends to drive or orient the particles in a particular manner. At any given time the state of the system depends upon the intensity of the force, the frictional resistance of the medium, and the rate of the opposing diffusion process, which reduces concentration gradients. One such force, the gravitational field of the earth, has been used to investigate properties of some large colloidal particles. For many molecules of biological interest, however, centrifugal acceleration provides a greater and more conveniently measured effect.

In 1923 T. Svedberg developed the first ultracentrifuge, for which he received a Nobel prize in 1926. Advancements and refinements have led from the early oil- and air-driven rotors to the more recent electrical drives. Present-day duraluminum rotors are ellipsoidal in shape to reduce mass and localization of stresses at cell holes. Speeds up to 60,000 rpm are routine. The sector-shaped cell used in the modern ultracentrifuge minimizes convection of sedimenting material, which is greater in a rectangular cell because sedimenting material strikes the cell walls.

The rate of flow of solute at concentration c across an area A in a centrifugal field is $-dm'/dt = Ac\,dr/dt$, where m' is the mass of solute in grams, and r is the distance of the molecule from the center of the rotor. The flow J' due to centrifugation is

$$- \frac{dm'}{dt} \frac{1}{A} = J' = c \frac{dr}{dt}$$

According to Sec. 9-1, the flow J'' due to diffusion is

$$\frac{dm''}{dt} \frac{1}{A} = J'' = -D \frac{dc}{dr}$$

The net flow J is

$$-\frac{dm}{dt}\frac{1}{A} = J' + J'' = J = c\frac{dr}{dt} - D\frac{dc}{dr} \tag{10-1}$$

However,

$$\frac{dr}{dt} = s\omega^2 r \tag{10-2}$$

where ω = angular velocity, radians/sec

$\omega^2 r$ = centrifugal acceleration

s = proportionality constant, called *sedimentation coefficient*, sec

Sedimentation coefficients are reported in units of Svedbergs, S, where $1 \text{ S} = 10^{-13}$ sec.

Centrifugal flow occurs along radii in two dimensions. The continuity equation expressing conservation of mass, for use in the ultracentrifuge, is found from Eq. (9-7) by noting that in the sector-shaped cell A is proportional to r:

$$\left(\frac{\partial c}{\partial t}\right)_r = -\frac{1}{r}\left(\frac{\partial(rJ)}{\partial r}\right)_t \tag{10-3}$$

Substituting Eqs. (10-1) and (10-2) into Eq. (10-3), we obtain

$$\left(\frac{\partial c}{\partial t}\right)_r = \frac{-1}{r}\frac{\partial}{\partial r}\left(r^2 cs\omega^2 - rD\frac{\partial c}{\partial r}\right)_t \tag{10-4}$$

Equation (10-4) is a fundamental equation of ultracentrifugation. If s and D are assumed to be independent of r and hence also of c, then

$$\frac{dc}{dt} = D\left(\frac{d^2c}{dr^2} + \frac{1}{r}\frac{dc}{dr}\right) - s\omega^2\left(r\frac{dc}{dr} + 2c\right) \tag{10-5}$$

10-1 SEDIMENTATION VELOCITY

In this method, high speeds up to 60,000 rpm are applied to an originally homogeneous solution. Heavy solute molecules settle quickly, leaving a region consisting only of solvent and more slowly sedimenting components separated from the solution by a boundary. This boundary is observed by one or more of several optical systems: absorption, Schlieren, or Rayleigh optics. Figure 10-1 depicts the variation of concentration and concentration gradient of a macromolecular solute with distance. A detailed analysis shows that the square root of the second moment of the gradient curve indicates the position of the boundary. For many systems the use of the maximum in the gradient curve does not introduce appreciable errors.

Ahead of the boundary in the plateau region of the concentration curves of Fig. 10-1a, $dc/dr = d^2c/dr^2 = 0$. Hence, Eq. (10-5) becomes

FIG. 10-1 Sedimentation-velocity experiment. Concentration (a) and concentration gradient (b) as functions of distance in the cell. Starting at the left, each succeeding curve refers to a later time, with equal time intervals between the curves. (From Ref. 1.)

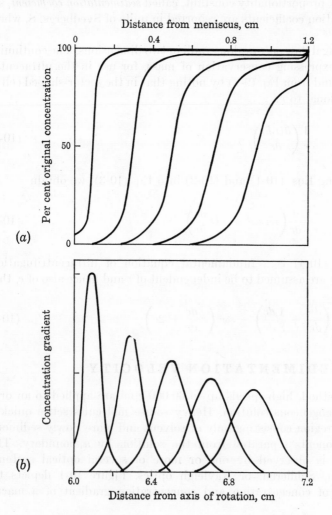

Distance from meniscus, cm

(a)

(b)

Distance from axis of rotation, cm

$dc/dt = -2s\omega^2 c$, which on integration yields $\ln (c_0/c_b) = 2s\omega^2 t$, where c_b is the concentration ahead of the boundary, and c_0 is the original concentration throughout the cell at zero time. Equation (10-2) may be integrated between the boundary position at zero time r_0 (the air-liquid meniscus) and the position at a later time r_b to give $\ln (r_b/r_0) = s\omega^2 t$. Combination with the previous result yields $\ln (c_b/c_0) = -2 \ln (r_b/r_0)$. This radial-dilution equation expresses the dilution of sedimenting components with distance.

The sedimentation coefficient is evaluated by plotting $\ln r$ versus time for the moving boundary. The slope of the plot is $s\omega^2$, as required by Eq. (10-2). Since ω^2 is known, s may be evaluated. The value of s so determined corresponds to the concentration in the plateau region in the cell ahead of the boundary. The concentration dependence of s has not yet been adequately formulated, but the empirical equation $s = s^0/(1 + kc)$ has been found to fit many situations. Thus the sedimentation coefficient at zero concentration s^0 may be determined from the intercept of a $1/s$ versus c plot. The constant k, determined from the slope, is always positive and is greater for synthetic polymers than for globular proteins. As indicated by positive k values, s^0 is greater than s at any concentration.

The value of s^0 obtained above is usually converted to the value that would be obtained in a solvent having the viscosity and density of water at 20° by the equation

$$s_{20,w}^0 = s^0 \frac{\eta_T}{\eta_{T,w}} \frac{\eta_{T,w}}{\eta_{20,w}} \frac{(1 - \bar{v}_2\rho)_{20,w}}{(1 - \bar{v}_2\rho)}$$

where η = coefficient of viscosity
ρ = density
$\bar{v}_2$ = partial specific volume of solute
The partial specific volume changes little with temperature. However, this equation has not been verified experimentally in any exhaustive study and is valid as derived only for two-component systems.

Typical sedimentation coefficients are as follows: 1.6 S for ribonuclease, 2.8 S for β-lactoglobulin, 4.3 S for hemoglobin and serum albumin, 7.9 S for fibrinogen, and over 100 S for small viruses.

Boundary Analysis. Four factors control the shape of the boundary in a sedimentation-velocity experiment.

1. Diffusion resulting from the concentration gradient produced by the centrifugal field yields a broadening of the boundary. Careful measurements of the broadening can give values of D compatible with those obtained directly from diffusion measurements. Special synthetic boundary cells permit the layering of solvent onto the solution during a run so that even a sucrose boundary may be observed.

2. Broadening of the boundary is also caused by polydispersity in the solute as the faster- and slower-moving components become separated. Boundary spreading due to diffusion is proportional to $t^{1/2}$; spreading due to separation of macromolecules is proportional to t. Extrapolation to infinite time renders the former negligible, and separation of the effects is possible though difficult.

3. Opposing the first two effects is a boundary sharpening due to the dependence of s on concentration. At the trailing or solvent side of the boundary, the concentration is much lower than on the solution side. The solute molecules which have diffused to a position behind the boundary are in a region of lower concentration. Since s varies inversely as c, the correspondingly higher sedimentation coefficients result in the overtaking of the boundary by the laggard solute molecules. The resulting boundary-sharpening effect may produce a false sense of homogeneity. The high concentration dependence of s on c for synthetic polymers and other asymmetric molecules results in sharp peaks for inhomogeneous samples. The boundary-sharpening effect must be either rendered negligible or taken into account in any quantitative evaluation of boundary-spreading effects.

4. The Johnston-Ogston effect occurs in mixtures of two or more solutes in which the sedimentation coefficient is strongly dependent on concentration. The ratio of apparent concentrations of slow to fast components decreases as the total concentration is reduced, eventually becoming constant at sufficiently low total concentrations. Johnston and Ogston accounted for this in 1946, when they noted that some molecules of the slow component sediment in the presence of the fast component, while other molecules of the slow component sediment behind the boundary of the fast component. The two categories of slow molecules have different s values. Mixtures of components whose s values differ only slightly produce larger effects than mixtures of components with widely separated s values. The Johnston-Ogston effect may be taken into account quantitatively in analyzing mixtures.

10-2 SVEDBERG EQUATION

The movement of the boundary in a centrifugal field is directly proportional to the centrifugal force and inversely proportional to the frictional coefficient: $dr/dt = \phi/f$. If ω is the angular velocity in radians per second (1 rev = 2π rad), and r is the distance from the center of the rotor, the centrifugal acceleration is $\omega^2 r$. Centrifugal force ϕ is the acceleration multiplied by the effective mass of the sedimenting particles. Effective mass is the actual mass minus a buoyancy correction to allow for the mass of solvent displaced. If m is the mass of the particle, the buoyancy correction is $m\bar{v}_2\rho$, where $\bar{v}_2$ is the partial specific volume of the solute, and ρ is the density of the solution. The equation for calculating the centrifugal force is $\phi = m\omega^2 r(1 - \bar{v}_2\rho)$. For organic compounds of high molecular weight, it is not usually necessary to apply corrections to $\bar{v}_2$ for compressibility in a centrifugal field. The frictional coefficient may be obtained from a separate diffusion experiment.

Introducing Eq. (9-11), we obtain

$$\frac{dr}{dt} = \frac{\phi}{f} = \frac{Nm\omega^2 r(1 - \bar{v}_2\rho)D}{RT[1 + d(\ln \gamma)/d(\ln C)]}$$

The product of Avogadro's number and the mass of a molecule is identical with the molecular weight of the solute: $Nm = M$. Solving for M, we obtain

$$M = \frac{RT[1 + d(\ln \gamma)/d\,(\ln C)]}{D(1 - \bar{v}_2\rho)} \frac{dr/dt}{\omega^2 r} = \frac{RTs[1 + d(\ln \gamma)/d(\ln C)]}{D(1 - \bar{v}_2\rho)}$$

$$(10\text{-}6)$$

The last equality results from the substitution of Eq. (10-2). For ideal solutions, or upon extrapolation to zero concentration in two-component systems, $d \ln \gamma/d \ln C$ is zero, and the result is the Svedberg equation. From it, the molecular weight of a substance may be determined by measurements of s, D, and $\bar{v}_2$, all made at the same temperature. For many protein solutes the partial specific volume $\bar{v}_2$ is about 0.75, so that a 1% error in $\bar{v}_2$ results in about a 3% error in $1/(1 - \bar{v}_2\rho)$. When its value is to be used in the Svedberg equation, $\bar{v}_2$ must be determined as accurately as possible.

The molecular weight determined by Eq. (10-6) is not a simple average molecular weight, partly because of the division of s by D. In polydisperse systems in which a more or less continuous weight distribution exists, the sedimentation-velocity method should be avoided and one of the other ultracentrifugal methods, to be described later, should be used, because the calculated molecular weight is a complex average of the molecular weights of the solute components. In the case of homogeneous solutes or paucidisperse mixtures containing several discrete kinds of molecules, the sedimentation-velocity method, in conjunction with diffusion measurements, can yield a meaningful molecular weight for each macromolecular component. The resolution of paucidisperse protein mixtures in the ultracentrifuge is historically significant because it indicates that proteins are discrete molecular species and not indiscriminate conglomerates of smaller molecules.

In two-component systems at infinite dilution, even though s and D are determined in solution on solvated solutes, the molecular weight is that of the anhydrous solute, because the partial specific volume refers to the nonsolvated solute. In multicomponent systems the molecular weight obtained will not be that of the anhydrous solute if preferential reactions of some solution components occur with the macromolecular solute. Small amounts of carefully chosen buffer components and inert electrolytes probably cause no complications in most cases. High concentrations of a third component such as urea may cause large errors if either water or urea reacts preferentially with the solute. Corrections can be made by independently determining the extent of selective interactions and allowing for them. Interactions may be minimized for denaturation studies by choosing detergents such as sodium dodecyl sulfate, since they are effective at lower concentrations and increase the density of the solution less than do either urea or guanidinium salts.

Electrostatic effects of charged solutes in ultracentrifugation are rendered almost negligible by the addition of inert electrolyte. If inert electrolyte is not added, the Svedberg equation must be modified. This modification is achieved by the introduction of electroneutrality throughout the solution. Macromolecules are under a greater centrifugal force, but the more slowly sedimenting counter ions decrease the sedimentation rate of a charged macromolecule as compared to its unchanged counterpart of the same size, shape, and partial specific volume. The opposite effect takes place in diffusion, because the more rapidly diffusing counter ions tend to pull the slower-moving charged macromolecules, so that the latter diffuse faster than their uncharged counterparts. It is the usual practice to minimize these electrolytic effects by the addition of inert electrolyte, even though this may introduce complications due to the preferential interactions discussed above.

10-3 SEDIMENTATION EQUILIBRIUM

While the sedimentation-velocity method requires observation of the position of a boundary in the cell as a function of time, the sedimentation-equilibrium technique requires a knowledge of the concentration distribution in the cell when the opposing forces of sedimentation and diffusion have been equilibrated. To avoid the eventual accumulation of all heavy material at the bottom of the cell, low speeds of the order of 10^3 to 10^4 rpm are required.

The time course of events in a sedimentation-equilibrium run is shown in Fig. 10-2. Solute concentration decreases at the meniscus and increases at the cell bottom, but, in contrast to a sedimentation-velocity experiment, no part of the solution is ever devoid of solute. The gradient curves do not exhibit maxima. In an ideal sedimentation-equilibrium experiment, the equilibrium concentration of solute at the meniscus is one-half the original concentration, which in turn is one-half the equilibrium concentration at the cell bottom. The curves of Fig. 10-2 show that one position of the cell maintains the initial concentration of solute throughout the run.

When equilibrium is achieved, there is no net flow ($J = 0$); hence Eq. (10-1) becomes $c\, dr/dt = D\, dc/dr$. Substituting from the first equality of the Svedberg equation (10-6) for dr/dt and rearranging, we

FIG. 10-2 Sedimentation-equilibrium experiment. Concentration (a) and concentration gradient (b) as functions of distance. The higher the number near the curve, the later the time during the course of the run. (From Ref. 1.)

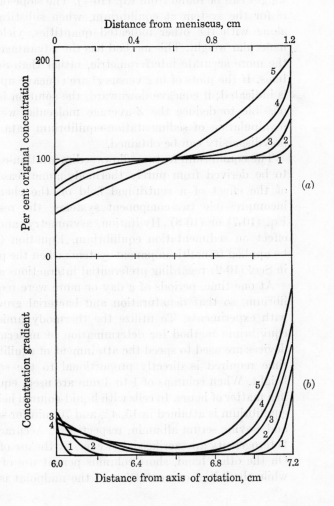

obtain

$$M = \frac{RT[1 + d(\ln \gamma)/d(\ln C)]}{\omega^2(1 - \bar{v}_2\rho)} \frac{1}{rc} \frac{dc}{dr} \tag{10-7}$$

or

$$M = \frac{RT[1 + d(\ln \gamma)/d(\ln C)]}{\omega^2(1 - \bar{v}_2\rho)} \frac{2\, d(\ln c)}{d(r^2)} \tag{10-8}$$

The term in brackets in the numerator approaches unity at infinite dilution in two-component systems. Since the diffusion coefficient has canceled out, the molecular weight may be evaluated directly from sedimentation data. If dc/dr is determined at the hinge point (midpoint in Fig. 10-2a), c is simply the initial concentration, and the molecular weight can be found from Eq. (10-7). The slope of a plot of $\ln c$ versus r^2 for the system at equilibrium, when substituted into Eq. (10-8) along with the other indicated quantities, yields a weight-average molecular weight. This method has the advantage of directly utilizing the more accurate interferometric, rather than Schlieren, optical systems. If the plots of $\ln c$ versus r^2 are concave upward, polydispersity is indicated; if concave downward, the solution is not ideal. It is also possible to deduce the Z-average molecular weight by appropriate manipulation of sedimentation-equilibrium data. Thus a measure of polydispersity can be obtained.

The equilibrium feature allows sedimentation-equilibrium equations to be derived from purely thermodynamic reasoning by evaluation of the effect of a centrifugal field on the chemical potential. For incompressible two-component systems, the result is the same as Eq. (10-7) or (10-8). Hydration, asymmetry, and cell shape have no effect on sedimentation equilibrium. Equation (10-7) or (10-8) may be applied to multicomponent systems when the precautions discussed in Sec. (10-2) regarding preferential interactions are observed.

At one time, periods of a day or more were required to reach equilibrium, so that denaturation and bacterial growth often interfered with experiments. To utilize the thermodynamic advantages of the equilibrium method for determination of molecular weights, various devices are used to speed the attainment of equilibrium. The length of time required is directly proportional to the square of the column height. When columns of 1 to 3 mm are used, equilibrium is achieved in a matter of hours. In cells with liquid-column heights of only 0.8 mm, equilibrium is attained in 15, 45, and 70 min for sucrose, ribonuclease, and bovine serum albumin, respectively. Accuracy and sensitivity to heterogeneity are sacrificed, however, by the use of such short columns. On the other hand, short columns permit use of higher rotor speeds while the initial concentration at the midpoint is maintained. Multichannel cells permit the simultaneous determination of several concentrations at an identical temperature. Initial overspeeding and subsequent reduction in speed of the rotor in a prescribed manner facilitate attainment of equilibrium. Concentration may be determined by counting Rayleigh fringes, and the molecular weight is evaluated by analysis of the concentration gradient at the hinge point (midpoint in Fig. 10-2a) of the column. The constant speeds used in some sedimentation-equilibrium experiments are best maintained with a magnetic suspension of a steel rotor in a high vacuum. Once brought to an appropriate speed, the rotor coasts, losing only 1 rps in 1 day.

10-4 ARCHIBALD METHOD

Before the advent of special techniques to reduce the time for attainment of equilibrium in the sedimentation-equilibrium method, considerable effort was expended on the analysis of intermediate stages before equilibrium is reached. W. J. Archibald, who developed the approach-to-equilibrium or transient-state method in 1947, noted that no material flows through the meniscus or through the bottom of the cell: $J_m = J_b = 0$, where the subscript m refers to meniscus, and b to bottom. Combining Eqs. (10-1) and (10-2), we obtain

$$c_m s \omega^2 r_m = D \left(\frac{dc}{dr} \right)_m \quad \text{and} \quad c_b s \omega^2 r_b = D \left(\frac{dc}{dr} \right)_b \tag{10-9}$$

which may be combined to give, for homogeneous material,

$$\frac{1}{c_m r_m} \left(\frac{dc}{dr} \right)_m = \frac{\omega^2 s}{D} = \frac{1}{c_b r_b} \left(\frac{dc}{dr} \right)_b$$

Combining Eqs. (10-9) with the Svedberg equation (10-6) yields

$$M_m = \frac{RT[1 + d(\ln \gamma)/d(\ln C)]}{(1 - \bar{v}_2 \rho)\omega^2} \frac{(dc/dr)_m}{c_m r_m}$$

and

$$M_b = \frac{RT[1 + d(\ln \gamma)/d(\ln C)]}{(1 - \bar{v}_2 \rho)\omega^2} \frac{(dc/dr)_b}{c_b r_b} \tag{10-10}$$

Weight-average molecular weights calculated at the meniscus (M_m) and the cell bottom (M_b) are not usually identical for homogeneous material, because the concentrations and hence the activity-coefficient terms are not the same at both ends of the cell. In polydisperse systems,

$M_b > M_m$. Archibald runs are performed at low speeds, and data corresponding to curve 1 of Fig. 10-2 are taken at the very beginning of a run, often within an hour. Shlieren optics may be used for the concentration-gradient terms of Eqs. (10-9), and the Rayleigh interferometer for the determination of concentration. Commercial instruments record both kinds of optical measurements simultaneously. The Archibald approach-to-equilibrium technique is useful for molecular-weight determinations to about 5% for molecules as small as peptides and as large as viruses. Compared to the sedimentation-equilibrium method, some precision is lost in extrapolation to the ends of the cell.

10-5 SEDIMENTATION EQUILIBRIUM IN A DENSITY GRADIENT

If a fairly concentrated solution of low-molecular-weight salt is spun in the ultracentrifuge, a density gradient forms, with the densest part of the solution at the cell bottom. An appropriate concentration of a suitable salt may be chosen so that the density near the center of the cell corresponds to that of some molecule of interest. An initially homogeneous aqueous solution of deoxyribonucleic acid (DNA) and 7.7 M cesium chloride forms a band near the center of the cell upon spinning in the ultracentrifuge, as indicated by ultraviolet absorption optics. In a typical experiment at equilibrium in 7.7 M CsCl, the density ranges from about 1.64 to 1.76 g/ml in a liquid column 1 cm high.

A molecule bands at the position in the density gradient corresponding to the density of the molecule and all associated solution components. The bandwidth is determined by the diffusion of the molecules and the polydispersity of the material. For monodisperse material, the molecular weight may be estimated from bandwidth and shape. For heterogeneous material such as DNA, the calculated molecular weight will be low. The estimated molecular weight is that of the molecule and all associated ions because the value of the partial specific volume, as determined from the position of the band, corresponds to the solvated complex. In addition to water of hydration, the number of associated ions may be large in the concentrated salt solutions used. Preferential interactions of solution components complicate the estimation of molecular weights.

This method has been used to separate N^{15} DNA from N^{14} DNA in two distinct bands; the difference in density was only 0.014 g/cc. Ultraviolet absorption optics allowed determination of the relative amounts of each form from the intensity of the darkening on photographic plates. DNA samples from multiple sources exhibit a wide range of base contents. Samples high in guanine and cytosine base pairs band at a higher density than those with high adenine and thymine contents. DNA samples prepared from a single bacterium exhibit little spreading. The significance of these experiments will be discussed in Secs. 18-3 and 18-4. Application of the technique to proteins is difficult because proteins, having molecular weights of only 1% of those of nucleic acids, form bands 10 times as broad in the same density gradient and may fill the entire cell. Inducing precipitation of proteins by the introduction of a small quantity of ammonium sulfate markedly sharpens the bands.

SELECTED BIBLIOGRAPHY

1 H. K. Schachman, "Ultracentrifugation in Biochemistry," Academic Press Inc., New York, 1959.

2 J. W. Williams, K. E. van Holde, R. L. Baldwin, and H. Fujita, The Theory of Sedimentation Analysis, *Chem. Rev.*, **58**, 715–806 (1958).

3 T. Svedberg and K. O. Pederson, "The Ultracentrifuge," Oxford University Press, Fair Lawn, N.J., 1940.

4 M. Meselson, F. W. Stahl, and J. Vinograd, Equilibrium Sedimentation of Macromolecules in Density Gradients, *Proc. Natl. Acad. Sci. U.S.*, **43**, 581–588 (1957). See also *Proc. Natl. Acad. Sci. U.S.*, **44**, 671–682 (1958).

5 J. W. Williams, ed., "Ultracentrifugal Analysis in Theory and Experiment," Academic Press Inc., New York, 1963.

QUESTIONS

10-1 For a cell placed 6.5 cm from the axis of rotation and spun at 60,000 rpm, show that the acceleration is 2.6×10^5 times the acceleration due to gravity.

10-2 Verify the substitutions leading to Eq. (10-5).

10-3 Show that the equation $f = M(1 - \bar{v}_2 \rho)/Ns$ may be derived from the Svedberg equation. How might you determine M so that this equation could be applied?

10-4 Verify Eqs. (10-7) and (10-8).

10-5 A sample of bovine serum albumin gave a sedimentation coefficient of 4.29 S when corrected to water at 20°, a diffusion coefficient of 6.1×10^{-7} cm^2 sec^{-1} at the same temperature, and a partial specific volume of 0.734 cc/g. What is the molecular weight of the sample?

10-6 Some alteration in conditions causes a macromolecule to have twice its original S value. What are the possible explanations of this change? What additional information do you need to make a decision as to the specific alteration responsible?

11 | Viscosity

Compared to other physical methods for the characterization of macromolecules, measurements of viscosity are simply performed on inexpensive apparatus. Unfortunately, the theoretical interpretation of viscosity measurements is more complicated. Nevertheless, viscosities are frequently determined and are useful for detecting changes in a system or for yielding more definite information if one of the empirical correlations may be applied to the case at hand.

11-1 VISCOSITY

We shall consider only streamlined, laminar or newtonian flow as distinct from turbulent or nonnewtonian flow, even though recent theoretical developments relative to the latter have made it a tool for the characterization of macromolecules. The force required to produce a shearing stress in a fluid may be derived from reference to Fig. 11-1. The separation between the parallel planes normal to the direction of flow is dl; the force F required to pass one plane past the other at a net rate dv is proportional to the area of contact A between the planes and to dv/dl: $F = \eta A \, dv/dl$. This equation expresses Newton's law of viscous flow. The constant of proportionality η, called the *coefficient of viscosity*, is a measure of the resistance of a fluid to a

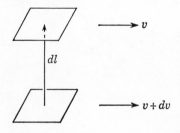

FIG. 11-1 Representation of viscosity in a fluid as the rate of slippage of a plane in the fluid past another parallel plane, the planes being separated by the distance dl normal to the direction of flow.

shearing stress. The units of η are $ml^{-1}t^{-1}$, and 1 dyne cm^{-2} sec is called a *poise*, in honor of the French physician Poiseuille, who studied blood flow in narrow blood vessels. Water at 20° has a viscosity of almost exactly 0.0100 poise or 1.00 centipoise.

Viscosities are frequently determined by measuring the rate of flow of a fluid through a capillary. The velocity is maximum at the center of the capillary and falls to zero at the walls. For laminar flow the velocity at any two points on a given circle concentric with the capillary must be the same. This condition is observed for solutions of all but the most asymmetric molecules if the rate of flow is not too great.

Very asymmetric molecules align themselves in the field of flow of the capillary viscometer, causing η to decrease with an increase in gradient. Unlike the interactions of solute molecules, which disappear on extrapolation to infinite dilution, the orientation of the solute molecules persists to zero concentration. Either the results obtained with the capillary viscometer on very asymmetric molecules must be extrapolated to zero shearing stress, or an alternative form of viscometer must be used. The Couette viscometer consists of two concentric cylinders between which the liquid is placed. The torque transferred through the liquid to the suspended inner cylinder when the outer cylinder is rotated at constant speed is a measure of the viscosity of the liquid. This type of viscometer may be operated at very low gradients.

In a capillary-tube viscometer the liquid flows through the capillary under its own head of pressure; therefore $\eta \sim \rho t$, where ρ is the density of the fluid, and t is the time for passage between two fixed points on the viscometer. If the times are compared for equal volumes of solution and solvent, the ratio of the coefficient of viscosity of the solution to that of the solvent is called the *viscosity ratio* or *relative viscosity* η_r.

$$\eta_r = \frac{\eta}{\eta_0} = \frac{\rho t}{\rho_0 t_0}$$

Except for some electrolytes, this ratio is greater than unity, because the presence of a solute disturbs the streamlines of a liquid. The *specific viscosity* η_{sp} is defined as

$$\eta_{sp} = \frac{\eta - \eta_0}{\eta_0} = \frac{\eta}{\eta_0} - 1 = \eta_r - 1$$

The *viscosity number* or *reduced viscosity* is given by

$$\frac{\eta/\eta_0 - 1}{c} = \frac{\eta_{sp}}{c}$$

where c is the concentration in grams per 100 ml. Extrapolation to infinite dilution yields the *limiting viscosity number* or *intrinsic viscosity* $[\eta]$.

$$[\eta] = \lim_{c \to 0} \frac{\eta/\eta_0 - 1}{c} = \lim_{c \to 0} \frac{\eta_{sp}}{c}$$

The limiting viscosity number is the quantity of interest, because intermolecular solute interactions have been eliminated. Since the ratio η/η_0 may be near unity, great care and temperature control are required if meaningful values of $[\eta]$ are to be obtained.

A. Einstein (1906) used hydrodynamics to show that $\eta/\eta_0 = 1 + 2.5\phi$ for large, rigid, impenetrable, solvent-adhering spheres in dilute solution, where ϕ is the volume fraction of the solute. Hence the viscosity ratio depends only upon the volume fraction of the solute and not directly upon the number or size of the solute molecules. The extrapolated value of $(\eta/\eta_0 - 1)/\phi$, derived from a plot of this quantity versus ϕ at $\phi = 0$ is ν, the viscosity increment. For unsolvated spheres with the properties just described, $\nu = 2.5$. Higher values of ν indicate solvation and/or asymmetry, similar to the interpretations of frictional ratios f/f_0 greater than unity in Sec. 9-3. A figure similar to Fig. 9-3 has been developed for viscosity; it correlates ν values with the water of hydration and the axial ratio of ellipsoids of revolution. Once again an ambiguity exists because the water of hydration is unknown. An alternative interpretation of viscosity measurements is presented in Sec. 11-2.

Macromolecules, due to their large volume, markedly increase the viscosity of a solution, even at low concentrations. The more asymmetric the molecule, the greater the increase in viscosity. For the larger molecules the viscosity increment ν is an approximate indication of the ratio of the volume occupied by a molecule in solution to its volume in the dry state. Some typical values of the viscosity increment are 3 to 10 for globular proteins, 10 to 1,000 for asymmetric proteins, 1,200 for collagen, and about 7,000 for some samples of DNA.

Molecular weights cannot be determined directly from viscosity measurements without some additional information. The limiting viscosity number $[\eta]$, which has been shown independent of molecular weight M for spheres, varies as $M^{0.5}$ to $M^{0.8}$ for random coils, about $M^{1.1}$ for stiff coils or somewhat flexible rods, and $M^{1.8}$ for rigid rods. When the exponent of M is 1.0, a weight-average molecular weight is obtained. Intrinsic viscosities of the α-helical synthetic polypeptide poly-γ-benzyl-L-glutamate display $M^{1.7}$-dependence, while those of collagen exhibit $M^{1.8}$-dependence. The nucleic acid RNA from tobacco mosaic virus exhibits an intrinsic viscosity dependent upon $M^{0.5}$. For native DNA the intrinsic viscosity is proportional to $M^{1.1}$, while for denatured DNA $[\eta]$ is proportional to $M^{0.7}$.

Viscosity measurements often yield information concerning intramolecular interactions. Figure 11-2a shows the viscosity number versus deoxyribonucleic acid (DNA) concentration at several salt

FIG. 11-2 Viscosity number versus concentration of macromolecule at various salt concentrations, 25°, and 0.25 sec^{-1} shear rate for (a) DNA, (b) polyvinylbutylpyridinium bromide, and (c) RNA. [a, b, C. L. Sadron, in E. Chargaff and J. N. Davidson (eds.), "Nucleic Acids," vol. 3, p. 18, Academic Press Inc., New York, 1960; c, U. Z. Littauer and H. Eisenberg, *Biochim. Biophys. Acta,* **32,** 320 (1959).]

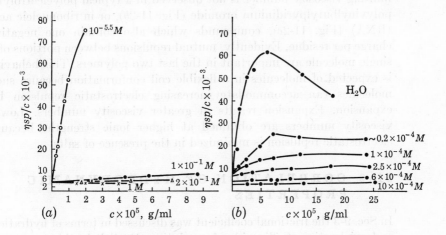

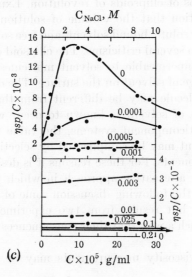

concentrations. Because of the phosphate group, DNA contains a negative charge on each nucleotide residue. At $10^{-5.5}$ M salt, two DNA molecules are forced to share the same ionic atmosphere, which varies inversely as the square root of ionic strength (Sec. 3-3), thereby interacting to a greater extent and increasing their apparent effective hydrodynamic volumes. At low ionic strengths, very low concentrations of charged macromolecule are required to eliminate this effect. The limiting viscosity number, as determined from the ordinate intercept, has the same value, however, regardless of the salt concentration, indicating that the conformation of DNA is the same in solutions of varying ionic strength and is independent of intramolecular electrostatic repulsions. Independence of salt concentration for the limiting viscosity number is not observed in a typical polyelectrolyte, polyvinylbutylpyridinium bromide (Fig. 11-2b), or in ribonucleic acid (RNA) (Fig. 11-2c), compounds which also contain one negative charge per residue. Evidently, mutual repulsions between portions of a single molecule are important in the last two polymers. This behavior is expected of molecules in a flexible coil conformation because such molecules can accommodate increasing electrostatic repulsion by expansion. Expansion results in greater viscosity numbers. Lower viscosity numbers are obtained at higher ionic strengths because electrostatic repulsion is minimized in the presence of salts.

11-2 CORRELATION OF HYDRODYNAMIC PROPERTIES

In Sec. 9-3 the frictional coefficient was discussed in terms of hydration and axial ratios of ellipsoids of revolution. Explicit in this treatment is the assumption that the volume of solution may be considered a function of dry solute, bound solvent, and free solvent. This assumption is vulnerable to several criticisms. The ellipsoid of revolution is treated as rigid and impermeable to solvent molecules of much smaller size with no slippage of solvent on the surface. The density of water bound to a macromolecule may be different from that of unbound water; electrostriction of solvent is known to occur when electrolytes bind water. In multicomponent systems, the value to use for the density of bound solvent may be complicated by selective adsorption of some solution components. For these reasons it is desirable and informative to consider an alternative approach in which the criticisms are not important. In the following discussion some of the same assumptions will be made, but results from two experimental methods will be combined in such a way that their consequences will, to a large extent, cancel.

Results of viscosity measurements may be combined with other results to obtain information without assumptions regarding hydration. In the limit of dilute solutions, specific viscosity η_{sp} may be expressed as the product of the number of solute particles per milliliter n, the effective volume of a hydrodynamic ellipsoid of revolution V_e, and the viscosity increment ν, a function only of the axial ratio:

$$\eta_{sp} = nV_e\nu = \frac{cN}{100M} V_e\nu$$

where c is the solute concentration in grams per 100 ml. Then

$$[\eta] = \lim_{c \to 0} \frac{\eta_{sp}}{c} = \frac{N\nu}{100} \frac{V_e}{M} \tag{11-1}$$

Equation (11-1) illustrates that the limiting viscosity number is a function of both the shape and the volume of an equivalent hydrodynamic ellipsoid of revolution. Values of ν have been tabulated as a function of axial ratio.

Like the viscosity, the frictional coefficient f may also be expressed as a function of V_e and shape. Here, as in Sec. 9-3, this shape is expressed in terms of the axial ratio a/b. Since two unknowns, volume and shape, exist in hydrodynamic measurements, the ambiguities of Sec. 9-3 can be removed if it is assumed that the equivalent hydrodynamic ellipsoids of two hydrodynamic properties of the solute in solution are identical.

We shall combine limiting viscosity number with frictional coefficient. The frictional coefficient may be expressed as

$$f = 6\pi\eta_0 \frac{a}{F} \tag{11-2}$$

where η_0 is the coefficient of viscosity of the solvent, and a is the radius of a sphere having the same volume V_e as the equivalent hydrodynamic ellipsoid of revolution, which can be characterized by a shape factor F dependent only upon the axial ratio. Like the viscosity shape factor ν, F has been tabulated as a function of axial ratio for ellipsoids of revolution. For spheres, $1/F = 1.00$; it increases for both prolate and oblate ellipsoids. Substitution of $V_e = 4\pi a^3/3$ into Eq. (11-2) yields

$$f = 6\pi\eta_0 \left(\frac{3V_e}{4\pi}\right)^{1/3} \frac{1}{F} \tag{11-3}$$

Equations (11-1) and (11-3) may be combined to eliminate V_e, yielding

$$\beta \equiv \frac{M^{1/3}[\eta]^{1/3}\eta_0}{f} = \left(\frac{N}{75\pi^2}\right)^{1/3}\frac{\nu^{1/3}F}{6} \qquad (11-4)$$

The frictional coefficient in dilute solution is obtainable from diffusion ($f = RT/ND$) or sedimentation-velocity [$f = M(1 - \bar{v}_2\rho)/Ns$] experiments to yield

$$\beta = \frac{DNM^{1/3}[\eta]^{1/3}\eta_0}{RT} \qquad (11-5)$$

and

$$\beta = \frac{sN[\eta]^{1/3}\eta_0}{M^{2/3}(1 - \bar{v}_2\rho)} \qquad (11-6)$$

Equation (11-5) for diffusion measurements has the advantage that $\bar{v}_2$ need not be determined. On the other hand, sedimentation coefficients are usually known with considerably more accuracy than diffusion coefficients.

Since ν and F in Eq. (11-4) are both functions only of the axial ratio, values of β may be calculated theoretically. Results of such computations are presented graphically in Fig. 11-3. For axial ratios p less than unity, the horizontal curve demonstrates the insensitivity of β to axial ratio for oblate ellipsoids of revolution. An experimental value of $\beta > 2.2 \times 10^6$ indicates that the particle cannot be represented by an oblate ellipsoid of revolution. The minimum value of $\beta = 2.11 \times 10^6$ is obtained for spheres.† In the region where $p > 6$, $10^{-6}\beta = 0.81 \log p + 1.60$. Unfortunately, even in the ascending straight-line portion of Fig. 11-3, a tenfold change in axial ratio is accompanied by only a 25% change in β. Accurate measurements are required if meaningful axial ratios are to be obtained for prolate ellipsoids of revolution. Once the axial ratio is known, V_e may be calculated from Eq. (11-1) or (11-3). Combination of the axial ratio with V_e allows the determination of a and b.

When $\beta \simeq 2.15 \times 10^6$, the axial ratio is not determinable from β. Other physical quantities such as intrinsic viscosity and rotational frictional coefficient (Sec. 9-5) may be combined to yield the axial ratio in this region. These other possible combinations are omitted from this discussion. Though individual hydrodynamic methods are quite sensitive to particle size and shape, the result obtained by the

† The minimum value given in Ref. 3 and elsewhere, $\beta = 2.12 \times 10^6$, requires the assumption of an unusual value for Avogadro's number N. For $N = 6.023 \times 10^{23}$, the minimum value of $\beta = 2.112 \times 10^6$.

elimination of particle size between two such methods is frequently discouragingly insensitive to shape. The insensitivity of β up to an axial ratio a/b of 3 permits a representative value of β to be chosen in the insensitive region and therefore allows an estimate of the molecular weight to be made. Choosing $\beta = 2.15 \times 10^6$ and rearranging Eq. (11-6) yields

$$M = \frac{4{,}700(S_{20,w}^0)^{3/2}[\eta]^{1/2}}{(1 - \bar{v}_2\rho)^{3/2}} \tag{11-7}$$

Caution must be exercised in applying the dimensions deduced from hydrodynamic measurements to real particles. For instance, a value of $\beta \simeq 3 \times 10^6$ does not require that the molecule be a prolate ellipsoid of revolution; molecules of other shapes may yield similar β values. Such a value merely implies that the particle may be represented by the same equivalent hydrodynamic ellipsoid of revolution for purposes of viscosity and sedimentation-velocity measurements. If the particle is not rigid or has an irregular shape, identical equivalent hydrodynamic ellipsoids may not be applicable to shearing stress and sedimen-

FIG. 11-3 The function β versus the logarithm of axial ratio for oblate and prolate ellipsoids of revolution. The vertical line at log $(a/b) = 0$ indicates the range of observed values for occluded coils. (Drawn from tabulation in Ref. 3.)

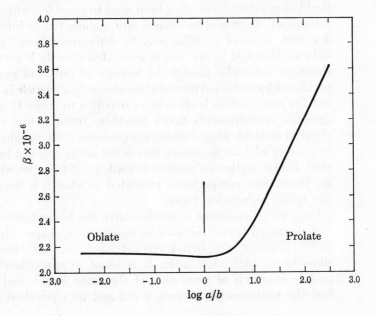

tation. Models other than ellipsoids of revolution have not been considered because of their mathematical complexity. Native globular proteins are probably fairly well represented as rigid, impenetrable, equivalent hydrodynamic ellipsoids of revolution. Results for denatured proteins may be interpreted in the same way, only with reservations. In those cases in which denaturation is nearly an isotropic swelling rather than a complete uncoiling, the ellipsoid of revolution might be used profitably. Upon denaturation, V_e increases, while the partial molar volume $\bar{V}_2$ is unchanged. Despite its shortcomings, representation of molecules on this basis is in most cases preferable to the method of Sec. 9-3.

Macromolecules that behave like non-free-draining flexible coils in solution have $\beta_c = 2.3 \times 10^6$ to 2.7×10^6. This range of β is indicated by the vertical line at $\log{(a/b)} = 0$ in Fig. 11-3. In the absence of other information, an observed value of β in this range can be interpreted as an occluded coil or as an equivalent prolate ellipsoid of axial ratio about 15. One of the most powerful methods for eliciting further information about macromolecules is the determination of the radius of gyration from light-scattering or small-angle x-ray scattering measurements.

11-3 CORRELATION OF HYDRODYNAMIC PROPERTIES WITH RADII OF GYRATION

Radii of gyration have often been used to provide additional information about shape and to remove any ambiguities in interpretation of β values. Radii of gyration may be determined from light-scattering data as described in Sec. 8-3 or evaluated directly if particle size and shape are otherwise known. An increase in radius of gyration is also paralleled by increased frictional resistance to a particle in the medium, but the combination is often more sensitive to shape than two hydrodynamic measurements taken together. Investigators familiar with physical methods make indirect comparisons from one physical method to another with an assurance that is not always shared by the uninitiated. In this section an attempt is made to systematize what, in effect, are these same comparisons, presented in what it is hoped is a direct and useful pedagogical form.

Only for ellipsoids of revolution have the hydrodynamic properties just discussed been evaluated as functions of shape. Most long particles, however, are better characterized as rods than as prolate ellipsoids of high axial ratio. It is usual to approximate rods with prolate ellipsoids of revolution of the same length and volume. To find the relationships between a rod and its equivalent ellipsoid, we equate the expressions for particle volume,

$$\frac{\pi d^2 l}{4} = V = \frac{4\pi ab^2}{3} \tag{11-8}$$

where d is the diameter, and l the length, of the rod. For the ellipsoid of revolution, a is the semiaxis of rotation, and b the equatorial semiaxis. Combination of Eq. (11-8) with the expression $l = 2a$ yields

$$p = \frac{a}{b} = \left(\frac{2}{3}\right)^{\frac{1}{2}} \frac{l}{d} = \left(\frac{2}{3}\right)^{\frac{1}{2}} v \simeq 0.82v \tag{11-9}$$

and

$$8b^2 = 3d^2 \tag{11-10}$$

where $v = l/d$, and the axial ratio of the ellipsoid of revolution $p = a/b$. For prolate ellipsoids of revolution, $p > 1$.

Radii of gyration for several particle shapes have been considered in Sec. 8-3. The radius of gyration for circular cylinders is given by

$$R_Y^2 = \frac{2l^2 + 3d^2}{24} = (2v^2 + 3)\frac{d^2}{24} \tag{11-11}$$

Substitution of Eqs. (11-9) and (11-10) into Eq. (11-11) gives

$$R_Y^2 = (p^2 + 1)\frac{b^2}{3} = \frac{a^2 + b^2}{3} \tag{11-12}$$

Equation (11-12) expresses the radius of gyration of a circular cylinder in terms of an equivalent prolate ellipsoid of revolution of the same length and volume. By slightly altering Eq. (11-12) to

$$R^2 = (5p^2 + 4)\frac{b^2}{15} = \frac{5a^2 + 4b^2}{15} \tag{11-13}$$

we obtain an equation which reduces to the radius-of-gyration-of-spheres equation (8-10) when $p = 1$, while retaining the appropriate limit for rods when $a \gg b$ [Eq. (8-11)]. Equation (11-13) expresses, as a continuous function, the radii of gyration from spheres to rods

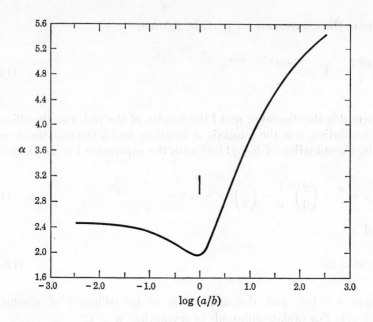

FIG. 11-4 The function α versus the logarithm of axial ratio. The vertical line at $\log (a/b) = 0$ indicates the range of values expected for occluded coils. Tabulated values appear in the appendix.

in terms of the parameters of a corresponding prolate ellipsoid of revolution.†

Substitution of the right-hand equality of Eq. (11-8) into Eq. (11-13) yields

$$R^2 = \left(\frac{3V}{4\pi}\right)^{\frac{2}{3}} \frac{5p^{\frac{4}{3}} + 4p^{-\frac{2}{3}}}{15} \tag{11-14}$$

If we take the volume in Eq. (11-14) as equal to the volume of the equivalent hydrodynamic ellipsoid of Eq. (11-1), we obtain

$$\alpha \equiv \frac{R}{[\eta]^{\frac{1}{3}} M^{\frac{1}{3}}} = \left(\frac{75}{\pi N}\right)^{\frac{1}{3}} \left(\frac{5p^{\frac{4}{3}} + 4p^{-\frac{2}{3}}}{15}\right)^{\frac{1}{2}} \frac{1}{v^{\frac{1}{3}}} \tag{11-15}$$

† The alteration involved in converting Eq. (11-12) to Eq. (11-13) implies that $32b^2 = 15d^2$ and that the volume of the equivalent prolate ellipsoid is 1.25 times that of the rod. Since the radius of gyration is determined mainly by the length in the rod region, and the axial ratio appears as a logarithm in Figs. 11-4 and 11-5, no serious changes are required as a result of the conversion. For short rods, approximation of a rod by an ellipsoid of the same length seems unsatisfactory, as will be discussed later, so that volume and diameter relationships are of little quantitative significance.

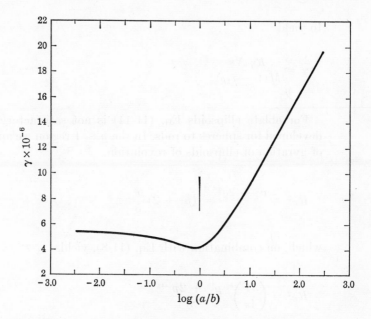

FIG. 11-5 The function γ versus the logarithm of the axial ratio. The range of values observed for occluded coils is indicated by the vertical line at log $(a/b) = 0$. Numerical values are tabulated in the appendix.

The function α is expressed in terms of experimental parameters on the left and the axial ratio p and ν, which is a function only of p, on the right. The first term in parentheses has a value of 3.41 when R is expressed in angstrom units. A plot of α versus log p for $p \geq 1$ according to Eq. (11-15) is shown in Fig. 11-4.

Similar equating of volumes in Eq. (11-3) for the frictional coefficient and Eq. (11-14) yields

$$\gamma \equiv \frac{R\eta_0}{f} = \frac{F}{6\pi} \left(\frac{5p^{4/3} + 4p^{-2/3}}{15} \right)^{1/2} \tag{11-16}$$

A plot of γ versus log p for $p \geq 1$ according to Eq. (11-16) is shown in Fig. 11-5. For $p > 8$, γ may be represented by $10^{-6}\gamma = 7.0 \log p + 2.2$. Experimentally, f is determined from diffusion measurements,

$$f = RT/ND$$

and $\gamma = R\eta_0 ND/RT$, or from sedimentation-velocity experiments,

$$f = M(1 - \bar{v}_2\rho)/Ns$$

to yield

$$\gamma = \frac{R\eta_0 N s}{M(1 - \bar{v}_2 \rho)}$$

For oblate ellipsoids Eq. (11-14) is not satisfactory, since it was developed for spheres to rods. In the $p \leq 1$ region we apply the radius of gyration of ellipsoids of revolution,

$$R_E{}^2 = \frac{a^2 + 2b^2}{5} = (p^2 + 2)\frac{b^2}{5}$$

which, on combination with Eq. (11-8), yields

$$R_E{}^2 = \left(\frac{3V}{4\pi}\right)^{2/3} \frac{p^{4/3} + 2p^{-2/3}}{5} \tag{11-17}$$

Elimination of volume between Eqs. (11-17) and (11-1) gives

$$\alpha = \frac{R_E}{[\eta]^{1/3} M^{1/3}} = \left(\frac{75}{\pi N}\right)^{1/3} \left(\frac{p^{4/3} + 2p^{-2/3}}{5}\right)^{1/2} \frac{1}{\nu^{1/3}} \tag{11-18}$$

A plot of α versus log p according to Eq. (11-18) for $p \leq 1$ is presented in Fig. 11-4. By combination of Eqs. (11-17) and (11-3), we obtain, for oblate ellipsoids,

$$\gamma = \frac{R_E \eta_0}{f} = \frac{F}{6\pi} \left(\frac{p^{4/3} + 2p^{-2/3}}{5}\right)^{1/2} \cdot \tag{11-19}$$

Figure 11-5 shows a plot of γ versus log p in the $p \leq 1$ region. Equations (11-18) and (11-19) for α and γ, respectively, are applied in the $p \leq 1$ region, while Eqs. (11-15) and (11-16) are used when $p \geq 1$.

The functions α and γ are related to the function β of the last section by $\alpha\beta = \gamma$. Comparison of Figs. 11-3 to 11-5 reveals that all three functions are relatively insensitive to p when $p < 1$, but that α and (particularly) γ are more sensitive to p than is β in the $p > 1$ region. While $10^{-6}\gamma = 7.0 \log p + 2.2$ for $p > 8$, in the same region

$$10^{-6}\beta = 0.81 \log p + 1.60$$

a result almost nine times less sensitive to the logarithm of the axial ratio. For $\alpha > 2.5$ and $\gamma > 5.3 \times 10^6$, an oblate ellipsoid is not possible, and the particle is better represented as a prolate ellipsoid, rod, or occluded coil.

In a similar way the rotational frictional coefficient may be combined with the radius of gyration by equating hydrodynamic and light-scattering volumes. The resulting function $R(\eta_0 \theta / T)^{1/3}$ increases smoothly by a factor of only 1.94 on proceeding from spheres to $p = 300$. For oblate ellipsoids the corresponding function exhibits less than 9 % increase on passing from spheres to $1/p = 300$. Due to the relative insensitivity of this function and its infrequent determination, no plots are presented, and no further discussion is given.

For non-free-draining coils the radius of gyration R_c is related to an equivalent sphere of radius r by $r = \xi R_c$, where ξ is a constant less than unity whose exact value depends upon the measurement employed. Combination of the volume of the equivalent sphere, $4\pi \xi^3 R_c^3 / 3$, with Eq. (11-1) when $\nu = 2.50$ for spheres yields

$$\alpha_c = \frac{R_c}{[\eta]^{1/3} M^{1/3}} = \left(\frac{30}{\pi N}\right)^{1/3} \frac{10^8}{\xi_\eta} \tag{11-20}$$

where the 10^8 factor is introduced because we are expressing R in angstrom units, and the viscosity value of ξ_η seems to vary from 0.78 to a theoretical value of 0.875. The corresponding range of α_c for occluded coils, $2.9 < \alpha_c < 3.2$, is represented by the vertical line at $\log a/b = 0$ in Fig. 11-4.

The frictional coefficient, when expressed in terms of an equivalent sphere, is

$$f = 6\pi \eta_0 \xi_f R_c$$

Upon combination of the above equation with γ, we obtain

$$\gamma_c = \frac{R_c \eta_0}{f} = \frac{10^8}{6\pi \xi_f} \tag{11-21}$$

where the 10^8 allows R_c to be expressed in angstrom units, and the theoretical value of $\xi_f = 0.665$ lies within the range of experimental results, $0.55 < \xi_f < 0.75$, calculated from sedimentation-velocity experiments. The corresponding range of γ_c for occluded coils is $7.0 < 10^{-6}\gamma_c < 9.7$ for R in angstrom units. This range is represented by the vertical line in Fig. 11-5.

From Eqs. (11-20) and (11-21) we obtain, for occluded coils,

$$\beta_c = \frac{\gamma_c}{\alpha_c} = 2.11 \times 10^6 \frac{\xi_\eta}{\xi_f}$$

Substitution of theoretical values for ξ_η and ξ_f yields $\beta_c = 2.78 \times 10^6$. For the midpoint value of $\beta_c = 2.5 \times 10^6$ in Fig. 11-3, ξ_η/ξ_f must equal 1.2. Evidently the effective volume of the equivalent hydrodynamic sphere for occluded coils is greater under shearing stress than under sedimentation or diffusion.

As an example of the application of the α, β, and γ functions, we shall consider tobacco mosaic virus, for which $\beta = 2.6 \times 10^6$, $\alpha = 3.81$, and $\gamma = 9.9 \times 10^6$. From the value of β alone, Fig. 11-3 shows, in conjunction with Eq. (11-9), that a rod with $v \simeq 20$ or an occluded coil are permissible representations of the structure. Reference to Fig. 11-4 for α immediately rules out the occluded-coil structure. Other applications of the α, β, and γ functions are given in Question 11-6.

The β function is predicated on the assumption that a macromolecule may be treated as the same rigid, impenetrable, equivalent hydrodynamic ellipsoid of revolution for two different hydrodynamic measurements. With these postulates combination of the translational frictional coefficient with the viscosity properties of the same solution leads in a self-consistent fashion to the β function. Unfortunately the derivation of the α and γ functions does not rest on such firm ground. The assumption that a rod may be represented by a prolate ellipsoid of revolution of the same length is convenient and probably fairly adequate. The same cannot be said for the equivalence of the light-scattering and hydrodynamic volumes, an assumption that is introduced in deriving Eq. (11-15) from Eqs. (11-1) and (11-14), for instance. There is evidence to indicate that for spherical particles impossibly low values of α and γ can be obtained experimentally. Since the axial ratio is known for a particle of this shape, the relation between the larger hydrodynamic volume and the smaller light-scattering volume may be calculated. For bushy stunt virus $\alpha = 1.69$ and $\gamma = 3.65 \times 10^6$. The difference in volumes that these results imply may be ascribed to an external water of hydration of about 0.5 g H_2O per gram of virus if the densities of bound water and solvent water are about the same. Water of hydration will be included in the radius of gyration only if the bound water has a density appreciably different from that of solvent water. An implicit assumption in the derivation of α and γ is that particles have uniform mass distributions. For mixed particles such as viruses, the radius of gyration depends upon the distribution of components of different densities.

Since the water of hydration should increase the diameter of a rod by a greater percentage than the length, it might be predicted that the axial ratio of a hydrodynamic rod would be less than that of the real particle. The variation of the ν and F functions with axial ratio is such, however, that the effect of hydration in decreasing the axial ratio of rods is nearly offset by the increase in hydrodynamic volume, so that α and γ, as well as β, are almost independent of hydration at high axial ratios. A consequence of this cancellation is that α, β, and γ values obtained from hydrodynamic experiments on long rodlike molecules are close to those calculated independently from x-ray diffraction and electron-microscope studies.

An apparent exception to the conclusion of the last paragraph is observed for a relatively short rod, tobacco mosaic virus, TMV, with a length-to-diameter ratio of about 17. In short rods, end effects will be of importance in hydrodynamic measurements, and the approximation of the rod as a prolate ellipsoid of revolution of the same length will not be tenable. It has been suggested that short rods be approximated with prolate ellipsoids of revolution of the same volume and axial ratio, with the result that the major and minor axes of the equivalent hydrodynamic ellipsoid are 14% greater than the rod length and diameter, respectively. In this way the axial ratio calculated from the β function is made to agree with the results obtained from x-ray diffraction and electron microscopy.

Though the axial ratios of TMV calculated from the α and γ functions are slightly low, assumption of an equivalent ellipsoid of the same volume and axial ratio overcompensates and yields too high axial ratios. In addition, axial ratios calculated on an equal volume and axial-ratio basis for long rods are in much poorer agreement with observations than the values obtained from the α and γ functions. For these reasons the α and γ functions were derived by representing a rod as an equivalent ellipsoid of the same length. If equivalent ellipsoids of the same volume and axial ratio had been assumed instead, then the α and γ values for long rods would be 87.4% as great for the same p value.

A third approach to relating rods to ellipsoids of revolution is to equate the radii of gyration of circular cylinders and prolate ellipsoids of revolution: $R_Y = R_E$. In the limit of long rods and ellipsoids, we obtain $2a = 1.29l$, which accounts for the 29% longer lengths calculated from a radius of gyration when an ellipsoidal rather than a rod model is used. Further manipulation reveals that $V_E = 1.076 V_Y$; the volume of a prolate ellipsoid is almost 8% greater than a circular cylinder of the same radius of gyration. If the α and γ functions had been evaluated on this basis, their values would be only 77.5% as great for the same p value in the long-rod region; the difference in the relationships between p and v is not great enough to restore agreement with particles of known dimensions.

Of the three suggestions discussed for relating rods to prolate ellipsoids of revolution, that of equal lengths seems empirically to be of the most general validity. Equating volumes and axial ratios seems to have some merit for evaluating short rods in terms of the β function, but it overcompensates for the α and γ functions and seems to fail completely for long rods. Any choice is an approximation, and hence calculated axial ratios are taken only as indications of dimensions. When used in conjunction with the β function or with each other, the α and γ functions provide a rapid means of ascertaining the general shape of a molecule (whether it is nearly spherical, rodlike, or an occluded coil) and of offering suggestions as to its probable dimensions. Perhaps when more experimental results are available it will be possible to establish, in terms of real particles, a useful and accurate empirical scale of the form suggested by the α and γ functions, but with different numerical values.

Whatever choice is made for relating prolate ellipsoids and rods, the α and γ values always maintain the same ratios of experimental quantities. The appearance of the radius of gyration R in the numerators and the molecular weight M in the denominators of the α and γ functions has the fortunate result of making α and (particularly) γ more accurately known than either R or M separately, since their ratio is deduced from only the slope of a Zimm plot of light-scattering data at zero concentration. Since R and M as obtained from a Zimm plot do not correspond to the same kind of average, homogeneous material has been assumed throughout this section.

SELECTED BIBLIOGRAPHY

1 J. T. Yang, Viscosity of Macromolecules, *Advan. Protein Chem.*, **16**, 323–400 (1961).

2 C. Tanford, "Physical Chemistry of Macromolecules," chap. 6, John Wiley & Sons, Inc., New York, 1961.

3 H. A. Scheraga and L. Mandelkern, Consideration of the Hydrodynamic Properties of Proteins, *J. Am. Chem. Soc.*, **75**, 179–184 (1953).

QUESTIONS

11-1 What are the units of viscosity number?

11-2 What are the units of β?

11-3 Verify Eq. (11-7).

11-4 What are the units of α and γ?

11-5 A sphere and an occluded coil exhibit the same value of the radius of gyration. Which particle has the larger radius?

11-6 From the following experimentally observed data for macromolecular solutions, discuss likely representative structures for each of the particles. Radii of gyration are in angstrom units, intrinsic viscosity in deciliters per gram, S in Svedbergs, and $\bar{v}_2$ in cubic centimeters per gram.

Particle	$M \times 10^{-3}$	R	$[\eta]$	$S^0_{20,w}$	$\bar{v}_2$
(a) Light meromyosin	120	222	0.90	3.0	0.73
(b) Bovine plasma albumin	67	29.8	0.04	4.4	0.73
(c) Collagen	374	865	12.5	3.0	0.73
(d) TMV-RNA	2,150	398	1.18	26	0.578
(e) Bushy stunt virus	9,000	120	0.04	132	0.71

11-7 Predict the viscosity change accompanying the denaturation of collagen described in Sec. 8-3.

11-8 Bushy stunt virus has a radius of gyration of 120 A as determined by small-angle x-ray scattering. Given the values of α and γ of Sec. 11-3, calculate the diameter of the equivalent hydrodynamic sphere, and verify that the difference between implied hydrodynamic and light-scattering volumes may be accounted for by about 0.5 g H_2O per gram of virus.

12 | Electrophoresis

12-1 ELECTROPHORESIS

Often one of the most significant differences between otherwise quite similar protein molecules is charge. Macromolecules were separated on the basis of charge differences in 1937 by A. Tiselius, whose achievement earned him a Nobel prize in 1948. Under the influence of an external electric field, molecules with a net charge migrate toward the terminal or electrode of opposite charge. The ratio of the velocity v of the molecules to the electric field strength E is defined as the mobility $u = v/E$ in cm^2/volt-sec. For many small ions in solution, u is of the order of 4×10^{-4} to 9×10^{-4} cm^2/volt-sec, but for H^+, $u = 36 \times 10^{-4}$, and for OH^-, $u = 20 \times 10^{-4}$ cm^2/volt-sec at 25°. Values for proteins commonly are in the range 0.1×10^{-4} to 1×10^{-4} cm^2/volt-sec. Since mobilities are temperature-dependent, precise temperature control is essential.

Because of charge fluctuations, a protein at a given pH exists in a variety of ionic forms. The mobility is an average value measured over a time that is long compared to the lifetime of any particular protein species. Near the isoelectric point the mobility is directly proportional to the equivalents of H^+ bound. In this region plots of mobility u versus pH are often linear. Slopes of such plots are frequently different for individual proteins. Where the curves for two proteins cross, a separation may not be achieved by electrophoresis. At the isoelectric point, $u = 0$. The pH at which $u = 0$ is dependent upon the buffers bound; simple singly charged buffer components usually alter the isoelectric point of pure protein less than do more complex buffer types.

Electrophoretic mobilities may be determined in solution by moving-boundary electrophoresis. The apparatus is similar to that used in diffusion experiments, with the addition of electrodes to generate an applied field. As in diffusion or ultracentrifuge experiments, Schlieren, Rayleigh, or other optical systems are used to follow movement of the boundary. Complex experimental details and involved interpretation of the boundary movement make further discussion impractical here. Since the mobility varies directly as the charge and inversely as the frictional coefficient, it is in principle possible to infer a great deal of information from mobilities. Even molecular weights can be estimated if a shape is assumed. Unfortunately, the results are compromised by theoretical and experimental difficulties to such an extent that electrophoresis is not a method of choice for molecular-weight determinations and is seldom used for this purpose.

Electrophoresis has proved useful in analyzing complex mixtures such as blood serum into albumin and various globulin fractions. Since nonaqueous solvents are not used and runs are often made at 1°C, electrophoresis subjects proteins to gentle conditions. Electrophoresis provides a sensitive criterion of purity; in favorable situations less than 1% impurity may be detected. Two methods are available for tests of purity. In the first, studies are made over as wide a range of pH, buffers, ionic strength, and protein concentration as is practicable. Usually pH values displaced from the isoelectric point tend to minimize protein interactions. The second method is reversible boundary spreading at the isoelectric pH. An impure protein will spread faster than can be accounted for by diffusion alone. Convection effects, arising from thermal gradients, also cause spreading but are not affected by reversal of polarity of the electric field.

Complete separations are not achieved in the solution electrophoresis just described. In zone electrophoresis the use of rigid media such as paper, starch gel, and cellulose permits isolation of components of an initially complex mixture, because the media can be cut into pieces after separation or the absorbed components eluted by an appropriate solvent. Only microgram quantities of material are required in paper electrophoresis. One powerful technique is to pass a current at high voltage through moistened paper previously spotted with the mixture and then to run, perpendicular to this, an ordinary paper chromatogram with a suitable solvent. The result is a two-dimensional separation of the initial mixture. When applied to the enzymatic digests of proteins, the two-dimensional pattern formed is called a *peptide map* (or "fingerprint") because it is reproducible and characteristic of a particular protein and kind of digestion used. Location of the separated components often is achieved by reaction with suitable reagents which yield a color, such as ninhydrin for amino acids and peptides. If the adsorbed components are eluted, absorbance measurements provide a convenient way to follow the appearance of solute in the eluent. Perhaps the most discriminate technique of all is immunoelectrophoresis, in which identifications are achieved by a combination of two properties: electrophoretic mobility and highly specific immune reactions.

12-2 INTERACTING SYSTEMS

Interactions between molecules of a single protein, between different proteins, and between proteins and small ions occur at varying rates. Diffusion, ultracentrifugation, and electrophoresis experiments all require several hours to obtain the requisite information. In this interval protein interactions may affect the results, depending upon the reaction rates. Consider a general equation for the reversible reaction of a protein molecule P with ν molecules of unspecified species N, which may be another molecule of P, another macromolecule, or a small ion or molecule:

$$P + \nu N \underset{k_2}{\overset{k_1}{\rightleftarrows}} PN_\nu \tag{12-1}$$

Several cases of the relative values of the rate constants k_1 and k_2 should be discussed individually.

1. Values of k_1 small and k_2 large imply little or no complex formation, and the system consists of noninteracting components.

2. Values of k_1 large and k_2 small indicate that complex formation is fully developed and that the system will consist of two components: complex and excess reactant. When there is no excess reactant, a single boundary of complex is all that is observed.

3. Values of k_1 and k_2 similar in magnitude and both small compared to the rate of separation yield a three-component system of both reactants and product. Care must be exercised, because the system may or may not have been at equilibrium initially.

4. Values of k_1 and k_2 both large and of the same order of magnitude present a system in which equilibrium is attained more rapidly than the rate of separation. In an electrophoresis experiment a P|P,N,PN$_\nu$ boundary is observed in one limb of the apparatus, and an N|P,N,PN$_\nu$ boundary in the other. In the ultracentrifuge both the shape and movement of boundaries may be altered. This case is frequently encountered and has been solved exactly for dimerization reactions.

5. A case intermediate between cases 3 and 4, in which all rates, reaction and separation, are comparable, gives patterns dependent upon the rate of separation.

In this section we have only qualitatively outlined an engaging field of current research.

12-3 ABNORMAL HUMAN HEMOGLOBINS

Nowhere is the sensitivity of electrophoresis better illustrated than in application to blood proteins. When fresh blood is subjected to mild centrifugation, leucocytes and erythrocytes sediment, leaving a straw-colored supernatant called plasma, which consists of serum and the rodlike clotting protein fibrinogen. Serum is composed of several electrophoretically distinguishable proteins, including albumin and the globulins. Using electrophoresis, Tiselius showed that the globulin fraction consists of several heterogeneous components, including the antibody-bearing γ-globulins. About 40% of the whole blood is composed of erythrocytes or red cells, which in turn are 35% hemoglobin, a protein of molecular weight 64,500. Red cells are simply a packaging device to prevent diffusion of hemoglobin out of the bloodstream. Normal adult human hemoglobin, designated HbA, consists of four polypeptide chains, two identical α chains, each of 141 amino acid residues, and two longer identical β chains, each with 146 amino acid residues. The N-terminal sequences are as follows: α chains, Val—Leu—Ser—Pro—Ala—Asp—Lys—; β chains, Val—His—Leu—Thr—Pro—Glu—Glu—Lys—. Each chain contains one iron-bearing heme group; hence there are four heme groups per hemoglobin molecule. The iron is in the ferrous $(2+)$ state. One may question the practice of calling the $\alpha_2\beta_2$ structure a molecule rather than a dimer of $\alpha\beta$. Under normal conditions, however, it is the $\alpha_2\beta_2$ structure which is the physiological O_2 carrier, and the features of the oxygen-carrying capacity of hemoglobin described in Sec. 22-5 show that the behavior of $\alpha_2\beta_2$ is entirely unlike that expected of a simple dimer of $\alpha\beta$. Other results including the titration data and dissociation equilibria discussed below also support $\alpha_2\beta_2$ as a convenient fundamental entity. Details of the spatial arrangement of the $\alpha_2\beta_2$ structure of hemoglobin are presented in Sec. 15-2.

In 1949 Pauling, Itano, Singer, and Wells reported that hemoglobin from persons with sickle-cell anemia, HbS, is electrophoretically distinguishable from normal human hemoglobin, HbA. The results of this experiment, which implied a charge difference between the two hemoglobins, initiated a study of molecular diseases of the blood. Geneticists have found sickle-cell anemia to be inherited by simple mendelian rules. HbS is allelic (same genetic locus) with HbA. Homozygous HbS individuals usually die young and often retain significant amounts of fetal hemoblogin. Heterozygous individuals, said to have sickle-cell trait, have about 40% HbS and experience discomfort after exercise or in unpressurized aircraft. In the oxygenated forms, HbA and HbS are indistinguishable except by electrophoresis, but when deoxygenated, HbS is 50 to 100 times less soluble, causing the usually spherical red cells to assume a characteristic sickle shape. The gene frequency of HbS is much higher than the normal mutation rate. HbS is favored in malarial regions of the world, owing to an accompanying marked increase in resistance to malaria. Other abnormal human hemoglobins have been found. They have been alphabetized in approximate order of discovery and are numerous enough to require use of most of the letters of the alphabet.

Boundary electrophoresis of HbA and HbS indicates only one unit of charge difference per half hemoglobin molecule. Possibly this charge difference is caused by the alteration of only one amino acid in either the α or β chain. A complete amino acid sequence analysis of both chains of both hemoglobins would provide the answer. Locating the difference in amino acid content of two varieties of hemoglobin molecules is possible, however, without a complete sequence determination. Trypsin, a proteolytic enzyme, catalyzes the hydrolysis of peptide bonds located on the carboxyl side of lysine or arginine residues. Both lysine and arginine have relatively long unbranched side chains with a positive charge at the end. Each half-molecule of hemoglobin contains about 26 lysine and arginine residues out of 287 amino acid residues. Tryptic digests of a half hemoglobin molecule should therefore contain about 28 peptides (because there are two different chains in each half-molecule) with an average amino acid content of slightly more than 10 residues. In practice a resistant "core" containing about one-quarter of the half-molecule is obtained. Analysis demonstrates that when this core is removed from the other peptides of the tryptic digest by centrifugation, cores from HbA and HbS possess the same amino acids, presumably in the same order. After sedimentation the peptides of the tryptic digest remaining in solution are spotted on moist filter paper and subjected to an electric current at high voltage. The peptides are thus separated linearly, primarily on the basis of charge. The paper is turned 90°, and conventional chromatography is applied to yield a further separation on a different criterion in a second dimension. After drying, the peptides are located with a color-producing reagent such as ninhydrin.

Comparison of the peptide maps so obtained for HbA and HbS indicates only a single change: a slight displacement of one peptide. Further accumulation and purification of this peptide reveals the following amino acid sequences:

HbA: Val—His—Leu—Thr—Pro—Glu⁻—Glu⁻—Lys⁺—

HbS: Val—His—Leu—Thr—Pro—Val—Glu⁻—Lys⁺—

HbC: Val—His—Leu—Thr—Pro—Lys⁺—Glu⁻—Lys⁺—

HbG: Val—His—Leu—Thr—Pro—Glu⁻—Gly—Lys⁺—

Hemoglobins C and G are two other abnormal hemoglobins listed here for comparison. Hemoglobins A and S evidently differ only by the substitution of valine for glutamic acid in one position of one chain, accounting for the single charge difference per half-molecule. It is not clear why this change should produce such a large difference in solubility. Hemoglobin C contains another alteration of charge at the same site, a positively charged lysine residue. An additional peptide is therefore obtained in a tryptic digest of HbC. Hemoglobins A, S, and C are allelic with each other, but geneticists have found HbG to be nonallelic with the other three. Interestingly, HbG contains a single alteration at an amino acid residue neighboring the variants in hemoglobins S and C. The differences in hemoglobins displayed here may only be those revealed by the electrophoretic techniques used. Other abnormal hemoglobins have been demonstrated by the same technique, which primarily reveals charge differences. Only complete amino acid sequence studies will determine whether more subtle changes or exchanges of amino acids also occur in these and other hemoglobins. Changes of amino acids may not be sufficient to produce an abnormality in the function of hemoglobin, and then the alteration is only of genetic and not physiological significance. This situation appears to be the case for HbG.

Now that it has been established that HbS differs from HbA by the substitution of a valine for a glutamic acid residue, the question remains as to the chain, α or β, in which the alteration occurs. To answer this question, radioactive leucine is added to a medium synthesizing hemoglobin A or S to yield HbA* or HbS*. In acid solutions at pH 4, hemoglobin dissociates into approximate half-molecules. This process is reversible on return to neutral pH. When radioactive HbA* is mixed with unlabeled HbS under acid conditions, the reconstituted HbS* has radioactive α*-terminal Val—Leu*—, whereas the β-chain terminus Val—His—Leu is unlabeled. The α* chain of the resulting HbS* must have come from reactant HbA*. Therefore, the abnormality in sickle-cell hemoglobin must occur in the β chain. Similarly, when HbS* is mixed with HbA under dissociating conditions, the resulting HbA* is radioactive only in the α chain, again indicating that the two hemoglobins have different β chains. This result is confirmed by amino acid sequence studies already listed in the previous discussion. By chance the peptide containing the abnormalities is the N-terminal peptide of the β chain, as may be verified by comparing the sequence for the critical peptide in HbA with that given previously for the N terminus. At earlier stages in the investigations, the sixth amino acid from the N terminus of the β chain was unknown, and hence the fact that the critical peptide is also N-terminal was not yet verified.

Though these abnormalities have been located in the β chain, there remains the question as to whether the reversible dissociation of hemoglobin in acid solutions is symmetric,

$$\alpha_2\beta_2 \rightleftarrows 2\alpha\beta$$

rather than asymmetric,

$$\alpha_2\beta_2 \rightleftarrows \alpha_2 + \beta_2$$

or whether the transformations just described can proceed by an exchange of single chains. If we consider the charges relative to carbomonoxyhemoglobin A as zero (carbon monoxide derivatives are used to reduce oxygen susceptibility), we may write $(\alpha_2^A\beta_2^A)^0$ for HbA and $(\alpha_2^A\beta_2^S)^{2+}$ for HbS. Superscripts A and S indicate respectively whether the β chain contains glutamic acid or valine as the sixth amino acid from the N terminus. Since the α chain is the same in HbA and HbS, the latter is also considered to contain α^A.

The abnormality of HbS that occurs only in each β chain yields a molecule with a net charge of $2+$ units compared with HbA as zero. Upon mixing at acid pH and restoration of neutral pH, we predict that in addition to molecules with the same charges as the reactants, symmetric dissociation will also give $(\alpha_2^A\beta^A\beta^S)^+$, while asymmetric dissociation will yield only whole molecules with the same charges as the reactants. The new electrophoretic component of relative charge $1+$ that is expected from a mixture of HbA and HbS by symmetric dissociation is not observed experimentally. Exchange of single chains would also yield some of this component. Since the $+1$-charged component is not observed, the reversible acid dissociation of hemoglobin must be asymmetric.

We may now formulate the conclusions drawn from the two preceding paragraphs for a mixture of HbA and HbS as follows:

HbA*: $\qquad \alpha_2^{A*}\beta_2^{A*} \rightleftarrows \alpha_2^{A*} + \beta_2^{A*}$ $\Big\}$ Reactants plus $\alpha_2^{A*}\beta_2^S$ and
HbS: $\qquad \alpha_2^A\beta_2^S \rightleftarrows \alpha_2^A + \beta_2^S$ $\Big\}$ $\alpha_2^A\beta_2^{A*}$

The reader may satisfy himself that this scheme is consistent with the labeling experiments just described.

We shall consider one more electrophoretic experiment which verifies the same points. Normally the iron in hemoglobin is in the ferrous $(2+)$ state. Oxidation of HbA to the ferric $(3+)$ condition yields a molecule with a relative charge of $4+$ compared to HbA, because there are four heme groups per hemoglobin molecule. Let us mix carbomonoxyhemoglobin S $(\alpha_2^A\beta_2^S)^{2+}$ with ferrihemoglobin C $(\alpha_2^{A+}\beta_2^{C+})^{8+}$. The $8+$ charge relative to HbA on the latter molecule is accounted for by $4+$ for four ferrihemes and $2+$ for the substitution of positively charged lysine for negatively charged glutamic acid in each β chain. If symmetric dissociation occurs, a new component $(\alpha^A\beta^S\alpha^{A+}\beta^{C+})^{5+}$ of relative charge $5+$ is expected. For asymmetric dissociation, on the other hand, we would predict the formation of two new components:

$(\alpha_2{}^A\beta_2{}^{C+})^{6+}$ and $(\alpha_2{}^{A+}\beta_2{}^S)^{4+}$. If exchange of single chains occurs, all these new components, plus new components of relative charges $3+$ and $7+$, are expected. Figure 12-1 shows the electrophoretic pattern obtained when this experiment was performed. The pattern on the left is the control for reactants only at neutral pH. The pattern on the right was also obtained at neutral pH, but after the solution was acidified to pH 4 and subsequently neutralized. The four peaks representing molecules of relative charges $2+$, $4+$, $6+$, and $8+$ clearly demonstrate asymmetric dissociation as the sole mechanism for the reversible acid dissociation of human hemoglobin. Under acid conditions, human hemoglobin exchanges chains with canine hemoglobin in a fashion consistent with asymmetric dissociation in both species. Several aspects of hemoglobin dissociation remain puzzling, however, and the detailed mechanism of exchange of chains is not understood.

When human fetal hemoglobin HbF is mixed with labeled HbA* at pH 4 and the solution returned to neutrality, a fetal hemoglobin with a labeled α^* chain results. Evidently the α chain is interchangeable and identical in HbA and HbF. The second pair of chains of HbF has an N terminus of Gly—His—Phe—, and HbF is denoted as $\alpha_2{}^A\gamma_2{}^F$. A homozygous individual with HbS should have normal HbF. On the other hand, individuals carrying hemoglobins with abnormal α chains might be expected to have had an abnormal fetal hemoglobin. Sequences in the γ and β chains are more similar to each other than either is to the α chain, and it has been suggested that β chains have evolved from γ, which in turn evolved from α chains. An HbH composed of $\beta_4{}^A$ has also been found; it is presumably due to an excess of β chains in the

FIG. 12-1 Electrophoretic patterns of refractive-index gradient versus distance in a boundary electrophoresis cell obtained with a mixture of carbomonoxyhemoglobin S and ferrihemoglobin C. Both patterns are observed at neutral pH, but the mixture of the pattern on the right has been subjected to acid pH. [Redrawn from S. J. Singer and H. A. Itano, *Proc. Natl. Acad. Sci. U.S.*, **45**, 174 (1959).]

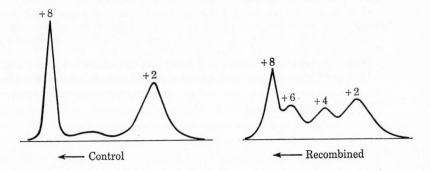

red cells. The mode of occurrence of abnormal human hemoglobins is neatly explained by a one-gene–one-polypeptide-chain hypothesis, as yet unproved. We shall again mention this subject of interest to protein chemists and geneticists in Chap. 20.

SELECTED BIBLIOGRAPHY

1 M. Bier (ed.), "Electrophoresis," Academic Press Inc., New York, 1959.
2 H. A. Itano and E. Robinson, Specific Recombination of the Subunits of Hemoglobin, *Ann. N.Y. Acad. Sci.*, **88**, 642–654 (1960).

QUESTIONS

12-1 How do the values of the quantities Π, B, K_θ, R, D, f, θ, S, $[\eta]$, ν, α, β, γ, and u for a solution of macromolecules of nearly spherical shape compare with those for a solution of rodlike molecules? Assume the same concentration and identical-molecular-weight solutes for both solutions.

12-2 Summarize the applications, advantages, and disadvantages of all methods for the determination of molecular weight, size, and shape.

12-3 A system which can be represented by Eq. (12-1) is at equilibrium. Describe the change in products and reactants when a sample is diluted twofold for a second experiment.

12-4 Hemerythrin, the oxygen-carrying pigment of certain worms, is a protein of molecular weight 107,000. Treatment of the protein with urea, sulfhydryl blocking, and some other reagents yields 8 subunits. Amino acid analysis indicates that for an average subunit weight of 13,500 the protein contains about 11 lysyl and 3 arginyl residues. Tryptic digestion produces about 30 spots on a peptide map. On this evidence what can be inferred about the identity of the subunits of hemerythrin?

12-5 One molecule of hemoglobin contains 38 histidine residues. If the bicarbonate ion content of the blood is 0.027 equiv/liter, estimate the principal buffer of the blood at the physiological pH 7 from the pK_a values in this book. How is the result affected if 22 of the histidine residues are masked (unavailable for titration)?

12-6 How many peptides would have been obtained from a tryptic digest of hemoglobin if hemoglobin consisted of four unlike chains? Of four like chains?

12-7 What are the products observed when a mixture of HbA and HbS* is subjected for a time to acid conditions?

12-8 Formulate the exchange reaction that occurs when labeled HbA* is mixed with HbF at low pH.

12-9 Enumerate all the possible hemoglobin molecules (and their relative charges) that can result from exchange of single chains when carbomonoxyhemoglobin S and ferrihemoglobin C are mixed. Indicate which of these molecules are also produced by symmetric or asymmetric disssociation.

12-10 Carbomonoxyhemoglobin A and ferrihemoglobin C are mixed and subjected to acid pH; the solution is then restored to neutral pH. Predict the molecular species and relative charges expected on the basis of symmetric and asymmetric dissociation and exchange of single chains.

13 | X-ray Diffraction

The potential of x-ray diffraction as the only method for the elucidation of the detailed structure of macromolecules is just beginning to be realized. Other methods discussed up to this point indicate only the molecular weight and gross shape of macromolecules. Under favorable conditions, x-ray diffraction can yield weight, shape, conformation in space, and, in the case of proteins, the amino acid sequence. In this chapter we review certain fundamentals of x-ray diffraction; in the two succeeding chapters we discuss x-ray-diffraction results for fibrous and globular proteins. X-ray-diffraction results obtained for nucleic acids, analogous to those described in the next chapter for fibrous proteins, are reserved until Chaps. 18 to 20.

X-rays are produced when a metal target is subjected to bombardment by fast electrons. The incident electrons expel inner-shell electrons from target atoms. When electrons from outer levels fall into now unfilled inner shells, radiation of x-ray wavelengths may be emitted. For example, in the bombardment of a copper target with electrons of sufficient energy, if a vacancy produced in the K shell is filled by the dropping of an L-shell electron into the K shell, radiation of 1.542 A wavelength is emitted. These x-rays are about 2,500 times shorter than the lower wavelength limit of detection by the human eye. X-radiation can be rendered monochromatic by the use of nickel filters to separate it from other wavelength radiation produced by the several possible electronic transitions in the target atoms. The resulting monochromatic x-radiation is usually collimated by lead disks and directed at a mounted crystal under study.

A 1-mm or smaller crystal subject to x-rays is rotated or oscillated about one of its crystallographic axes. Special x-ray-sensitive film is wrapped about the crystal in a cylindrical shape, with the cylinder axis perpendicular to the x-ray beam, so that the photographed layer lines are horizontal rather than hyperbolic, as would be the case if a flat plate were used.

13-1 BRAGG EQUATION

Since the spacing of atoms in the crystal is of the same order of magnitude as the x-ray wavelength, a diffraction pattern results from the reinforcement of diffracted x-rays at certain critical angles of a rotating crystal. These critical angles may be related to the x-ray wavelength λ by the useful device of considering the crystal to be composed of a series of parallel reflecting planes separated by a distance d as in Fig. 13-1. The condition for reinforcement requires that the rays reflected at angle θ from two different planes be in phase. As explained in the caption of Fig. 13-1, the additional distance l traversed by ray M is $2d \sin \theta$. Reinforcement occurs only when this additional distance is equal to an integral number of wavelengths $n\lambda$, where n is an integer. Thus the equation $n\lambda = 2d \sin \theta$, first enunciated by W. L. Bragg, relates the incident and reflected angle θ to the x-ray wavelength λ on a crystal with spacing d and order of reflection n. Reflections of higher order than $n = 1$ occur for larger critical values of θ.

FIG. 13-1 Construction for deriving the Bragg equation. A, B, and C are parallel planes in the crystal, separated by a distance d, which reflect incident parallel x-rays L and M to yield reflected ray R at an angle θ (which is also the angle of incidence). The additional distance traversed by ray M may be computed by simple geometrical considerations from the construction shown in dashed lines. The difference in path length l between rays L and M is $NO - OP$, but $NO = OQ$, so that $PQ = l$. Since the interior angle is also θ, $l = 2d \sin \theta$.

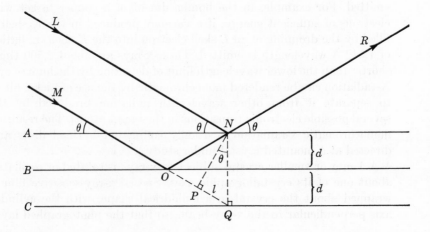

A single crystal rotated about one of its crystallographic axes and subjected to monochromatic x-radiation produces sharp spots arranged in parallel layer lines on a film placed perpendicular to the incident beam. As different crystal planes arrive at the Bragg-relation position, constructive interference occurs, and a negative is darkened at discrete points. Unavoidable thermal vibration of atoms causes some blurring. If, instead of a single crystal, a set of identical, imperfectly aligned crystals is rotated, the resulting points of the layer lines widen into arcs of circles. Crystals completely random in orientation, such as in a powder, contain only a few crystals which are accidentally aligned so as to yield diffraction maxima. Because these crystals may occur in any position, the diffraction pattern consists of a layer-line pattern which has been rotated about the x-ray beam and thus appears as concentric circles. All three kinds of patterns have been observed with macromolecules. Crystalline globular proteins exhibit sharp spots, aligned fibrous proteins and nucleic acids yield arcs, and unaligned fibers display concentric rings.

13-2 FOURIER SYNTHESIS

Reflecting the orderly arrangement of atoms in crystals, x-ray diffraction patterns are both regular and symmetrical. High electron densities occur near the centers of atoms, and low electron densities between atoms. A crystal is a three-dimensional, periodic, repeating distribution of electron density. Since only the electrons diffract x-rays, a diffraction pattern is determined by the regular repetition of regions of high electron densities in a crystal. Heavy atoms with higher electron densities scatter more strongly than light atoms.

The *unit cell* is the smallest repeating unit of a structure from which the crystal can be built by translation. In general, the unit cell is a parallelepiped.

The atomic-scattering factor f is the ratio of the amplitude of a wave scattered by an atom to the amplitude of a wave scattered by a single electron. For small scattering angles, f is proportional to the number of electrons in the atom but is less for larger angles (recall the situation in light scattering). Superposition of waves of differing amplitudes and phases is accomplished by vectorial addition: $F = \sum_{n} f_n e^{i\alpha}$, where F, the structure factor, is the resultant amplitude for waves scattered from a particular crystal plane summed over the n atoms of amplitude f and phase α in the unit cell. The phase difference is the amount by which a ray scattered from an atom in a unit cell is out of step with a ray scattered from an atom at the origin. The structural amplitude F is the ratio of the amplitude produced by all the electrons in a unit cell to the amplitude that would be produced if a single electron occupied the unit cell. Since the intensity of radiation is measured by the square of the amplitude, F^2 is determined from the intensity of darkening of spots on the photographic film.

The electron density distribution of a crystal may be mathematically analyzed to yield the observed x-ray diffraction pattern. A Fourier analysis, consisting of a converging infinite sine and cosine series, can be made of the electron density distribution of a crystal. This analysis is similar to that in music, where a fundamental tone and its overtones may be described as a one-dimensional superposition of sine waves. Conversely, the sine waves may be synthesized to represent the original harmonic. The problem facing x-ray-diffraction investigators is to perform an appropriate two- or three-dimensional Fourier synthesis of the x-ray diffraction pattern to yield the electron density distribution of the crystal.

The Fourier coefficients of the series of terms representing the electron density distribution of a crystal may be shown to be equal to the structure factor F divided by the volume V of the unit cell. Thus the three-dimensional electron density distribution ρ of a crystal may be expressed as a triple Fourier series, with the coefficient of each series term given by the value of the structure factor divided by the unit cell volume; $\rho = g(F/V)$, where g represents a function of the term in parentheses. If all the F were known, ρ could be evaluated, and the crystal structure solved. However, the darkness of a spot on the photographic film indicates the intensity or F^2. Taking the square root of the intensity yields the absolute value of the amplitude $|F|$, but since the sign is not known, the phase is undetermined. In general, F^2 is the product of an imaginary number and its complex conjugate, and a phase angle must be determined. We have considered here, for purposes of illustration, one of the special cases in which the phase angle is zero and F is real, so that only the sign is unknown.

13-3 PHASE PROBLEM

Diffracted x-rays are characterized by three quantities: direction, magnitude, and phase. In interpreting the photographic negative, direction is determined from the position of spots, and intensity from the square root of degree of blackening of spots. The phase, a component of the structure factor, is lost when the square root of the intensity is taken and hence is not directly determinable from the x-ray diffraction pattern.

The fundamental dilemma of x-ray-diffraction investigations is the determination of the phase, the extent to which a train of waves is out of step with its neighbors. This is not obtainable from the x-ray diffraction pattern, and hence only part of the required information for determining the structure is available. To extend our musical analogy, a certain harmonic is representable by means of two sine waves of known amplitude (height) and phase (the amount by which the second sine wave lags the first). We cannot recreate the original harmonic unless both the amplitude and phase are known.

Several special techniques have been devised to cope with the phase problem. For simple molecules, a trial structure can be used to calculate an x-ray pattern which is then compared with that obtained experimentally. By successive refinements, the correct structure may be determined. This computation is too complicated to be useful for large molecules. Some methods for determining phases are discussed in Chap. 15.

One attempt to circumvent, but not solve, the phase problem is the construction of the Patterson function, $P = h(F^2/V)$, where h is a function of the terms in parentheses. This function depends upon the intensity F^2, rather than the amplitude F, and hence avoids the phase problem. Physically, the Patterson function, ignoring the absolute coordinates of the atom pairs, transfers all the interatomic vectors of a structure to a common origin. The distances between successive maxima in a Fourier treatment correspond to the distances between the origin and various peaks in the Patterson synthesis. A structure of n atoms has $n(n-1)/2$ unique vectors, but only simple structures can be deciphered because of overlapping vectors. For large molecules the number of vectors is enormous, and resolution depends upon the occurrence of a regular pattern. The primary application of the Patterson synthesis in the elucidation of the structure of macromolecules is in the isomorphous-replacement method for the study of proteins (Chap. 15).

13-4 RECIPROCAL SPACE

Each spot on the photographic plate corresponds to a separate Fourier component of the periodically repeating electron density distribution of the crystal. An inverse relationship exists between the position of the spots and spacings in the crystal, as may be seen by inspection of the Bragg equation, where $\sin \theta$ is inversely proportional to d. Spots near the center of the plate correspond to long spacings in the crystal and hence yield the broad, low-resolution features of the crystal. Conversely, spots near outer edges of the x-ray pattern correspond to short spacings in the crystal and give the fine, high-resolution details of the crystal. The higher the resolution desired, the greater the number of spots that must be considered as the circumference becomes greater. The position of a spot relative to the center of the pattern also determines the direction of the spacings in the crystal. A spot corresponding to 1.5 A vertically above the center (meridional) indicates the existence of parallel, horizontal regions of high electron density 1.5 A apart.

Observed x-ray diffraction patterns are only two-dimensional, whereas crystals are always three-dimensional. The picture therefore contains only part of the whole diffraction pattern of the crystal. It is but a plane, passing through the origin, of the three-dimensional reciprocal lattice of the whole crystal. The word reciprocal is used because the position of the spots is an inverse measure of the spacings in the real crystal.

The dimensions of the smallest repeating unit of the real crystal, the unit cell, may be obtained from the dimensions of the reciprocal lattice, which in turn are deduced from the plane through the origin that is the x-ray pattern. Due to the reciprocal relationship, the smaller the unit cell, the farther apart the spots in the x-ray picture.

If the positions of all the atoms and hence the centers of electron density in a unit cell are known, the diffraction pattern of a crystal can be calculated. The reverse procedure, the determination of the position of the atoms in the unit cell from the diffraction pattern, entails the problem of determining the phases. As stated previously, only part of the necessary information is available, since only the amplitude, but not the phase, of each Fourier term is obtainable from the darkness of the spot on the photographic plate.

13-5 SYMMETRY

Most biopolymers contain only one variety of optically active components such as the L-amino acids of proteins. Reflection of the protein in a mirror plane is not a symmetry operation, because the result is a protein consisting of D-amino acids. Two symmetry operations exist for proteins.

1. An *n*-fold *rotation axis* exists if rotation of a structure through $360°/n$ yields a structure identical with that before rotation. The only possible values of n are 2, 3, 4, and 6. A regular fivefold axis is not possible in crystalline solids, because it cannot be repeated periodically and indefinitely throughout the structure. Fivefold symmetry may be important in liquids in which some degree of regularity is broken by regions of disorder.

2. A *screw axis* exists if a two-, three-, four-, or sixfold rotation as in (1), plus a translation parallel to the rotation axis, yields a structure identical with that of the original.

The symmetries of the real crystal and the reciprocal lattice are closely related, though the latter has the higher symmetry (always a center of symmetry, which many crystals, such as proteins, do not have). An n-fold axis of symmetry in the reciprocal lattice implies an n-fold rotation and/or screw axis in a protein crystal. Since the screw axis causes certain x-ray spots to be zero systematically, while the rotation axis does not, the two can usually be separated. Therefore, both the size of the unit cell and the symmetry elements are generally amenable to unambiguous determination.

The *asymmetric unit* is the smallest part of a structure which, when operated upon by the symmetry elements, will reproduce the complete structure. Asymmetric units are equal to or smaller than unit cells, which contain integral multiples of one, two, or three asymmetric units. Asymmetric units are related by symmetry elements, and unit cells by translation. The asymmetric unit may be smaller than, the same size as, or larger than a chemist's molecule, whereas the unit cell always contains an integral number of molecules. Hemoglobin, a molecule of 67,000 molecular weight, consists of two identical (within 2 to 3 A resolution) 34,000 subunits. Each subunit is a single asymmetric unit related by a twofold axis of rotational symmetry. There are two asymmetric units, and hence one hemoglobin molecule, per unit cell. Horse hemoglobin also crystallizes in an orthorhombic form in which the asymmetric unit is the whole molecule. Insulin, of molecular weight 6,000, has an asymmetric unit of 12,000 which crystallizes in two forms with three and four asymmetric units per unit cell. Volumes of asymmetric units may be found quickly.

13-6 USES OF X-RAYS

1. Bond lengths and angles are less accurately obtainable with x-rays than by other methods because it is difficult to determine accurately the intensity of spots on the photographic plate. Nevertheless, many bond lengths and angles have been measured by x-ray-diffraction techniques; we shall use some of these results in Chap. 14.

2. Determination of absolute configuration by anomalous diffraction has been successfully applied to tartaric acid to demonstrate that the convention established by Emil Fischer is correct.

3. A molecular weight M may be accurately determined in favorable cases from the equation $M = dVN/n$, where d is the crystal density, V the volume of the unit cell, N Avogadro's number, and n the number of molecules in the unit cell. Considerable care is required to obtain an accurate value for the crystal density. Allowance must be made for shrinkage, salt (if present), and the exact amount of water, considerable quantities of which are found in most protein crystals. The volume of the unit cell may be calculated from the lengths determined

from the meridional layer-line spacing when each of the three crystallographic axes is alternately made the axis of oscillation.

4. Structure determinations have been made by x-ray-diffraction techniques for many years. The structure of vitamin B_{12}, $C_{63}H_{88}O_{14}$-$N_{14}PCo$, was worked out by x-ray methods when only 45 of the 181 atoms had been assigned to chemically known constituents. In addition, the structure was found to contain a ring system not previously identified in biological systems. This determination indicates the power of x-ray techniques in dealing with complex, asymmetric molecules. In addition to the mode of bonding of the constituent atoms, also derived by organic chemists, x-ray crystallographers determine the conformation of atoms in space. The method of x-ray crystallography is, however, no simpler than the techniques of organic chemistry.

5. Polypeptide chain conformation is discussed in Chap. 14.

6. Structure and folding of globular proteins are considered in Chap. 15.

7. Polynucleotide structure will be presented in Chaps. 18 and 19.

It is usually impossible to locate hydrogen atoms accurately by x-ray diffraction, because their low electron density does not produce a significant diffraction of x-rays. However, the position of the hydrogen atoms has been approximated in some favorable cases. A difference Fourier between the observed electron density distribution of adenine hydrochloride and that calculated on the basis of scattering due to carbon, nitrogen, oxygen, and chlorine gave peaks at the positions of the hydrogen atoms.

SELECTED BIBLIOGRAPHY

1 F. H. C. Crick and J. C. Kendrew, X-ray Analysis and Protein Structure, *Advan. Protein Chem.*, **12**, 133–214 (1957).

2 J. M. Robertson, "Organic Crystals and Molecules," Cornell University Press, Ithaca, N.Y., 1953.

3 S. C. Nyburg, "X-ray Analysis of Organic Structures," Academic Press Inc., New York, 1961.

4 D. C. Hodgkin, J. G. White, et al., The Structure of Vitamin B_{12}, *Proc. Roy. Soc. London*, **242A**, 228–263 (1957); **251A**, 306–352 (1959); **266A**, 440–517 (1962).

QUESTIONS

13-1 What is the minimum crystal spacing that can be determined with copper K_α radiation? How could smaller spacings be observed?

13-2 If the location of the atoms in a unit cell is known, the x-ray diffraction pattern may be calculated. Explain the difficulties involved in reversing the procedure.

13-3 What effects might impurities in a crystal have on an x-ray diffraction pattern?

13-4 What is the relation between amplitude and intensity? With which does the Patterson synthesis deal? What are the advantages and disadvantages of a Patterson synthesis?

13-5 Explain why the x-ray crystallographer does not take every fifth spot on an x-ray diffraction pattern in order to obtain a rough indication of structure.

13-6 Convince yourself that you could not pave a floor with identical regular pentagonal tiles without leaving empty spaces or overlapping some tiles.

13-7 The fungal antibiotic gliotoxin has a crystal density of 1.54 g/cc and a volume of 1,451 A³ per unit cell. Chemical evidence indicates an approximate molecular weight of 330. Calculate the number of molecules per unit cell and an accurate molecular weight.

13-8 Why are hydrogen-bond distances stated so as to bypass the hydrogen atom? For example, in the N—H---O=C hydrogen-bond system, it is the N to O distance that is given.

14 | Fibrous Proteins

The fibers of fibrous proteins comprise regions of crystallinity embedded in a less ordered structure. Long protein chains may pass through several regions of relative order and disorder. In a well-oriented fiber, the chains lie mainly lengthwise along the fiber axis. Fiber diagrams are obtained by diffraction of x-rays from a fiber oscillated or rotated about the fiber axis. The x-ray diffraction patterns are often diffuse, owing to nonparallel orientation of some crystalline regions or crystallites. Considerable technical skill is required to obtain informative patterns.

The more periodic the atoms, and hence the electron density in space, the sharper the spots in an x-ray picture. From relatively uniform unit cells, the average diffraction produces sharp spots; if the unit cells lack uniformity, indistinct spots are obtained. Fibrous proteins give patterns of unclear spots and, often, hints of concentric ring patterns characteristic of randomly oriented diffracting units. X-ray diffraction patterns only provide information about the ordered regions of a structure. The percentage of a structure that is ordered usually is not obtainable from x-ray data.

Extensive study of wide-angle x-ray patterns by W. T. Astbury in the 1930s and 1940s indicated that fibrous proteins could be divided into two groups. The first, referred to as the *keratin* group, includes keratin of hair and horns, myosin of muscle, epidermin of skin, fibrinogen from blood, silk fibroin, bacterial flagella, and porcupine quill. More recently, several synthetic polypeptides, among which are poly-L-alanine and poly-γ-methyl-L-glutamate, have been shown to be in the keratin group. A discussion of the second or *collagen* group is deferred until later in this chapter.

14-1 KERATIN GROUP

Although this is a diverse group of proteins and polypeptides, it is possible to make some generalizations about the group as a whole, provided these generalizations are not applied too literally to any one member. Members of the group exhibit extensibility and, usually, the ability to undergo reversible stretching on treatment with heat or alkali. In the contracted or α form, the molecule may be half the length of the extended or β form. The forms may also be prepared by crystallization from appropriate solvents: *m*-cresol or dichloroacetic acid yields the α form, and formic acid the β form.

Fiber diagrams of both the α and β forms have equatorial reflections which correspond to crystal spacings at 4.7 A and 10 A; the exact value of the latter is dependent upon the side chains. Both equatorial reflections are perpendicular to the fiber axis, and lateral compression of the β fiber indicates that they are also perpendicular to each other. Stretching the α form to produce the β form does not alter the equatorial reflections, but the meridional (vertical) reflections at 5.1 A and 1.5 A of the α form are replaced by 3.3-A and 1.1-A reflections in the β form. The crystallographic repeat distance along the fiber axis can be obtained from the meridional layer-line spacing. Evaluation of unit-cell dimensions and symmetry is more difficult.

Model Compounds. A 15-year program at the California Institute of Technology involving the detailed x-ray analysis of about 10 crystalline amino acids and simple peptides resulted in enunciation of the following canonical principles for polypeptide chains:

1. All amino acid residues are equivalent. Variations in the side chains do not produce effects large enough to influence the x-ray analysis, because side chains do not repeat regularly, and most have similar electron densities. For this reason, x-ray diffraction is not a good method for determining whether two similar proteins are identical.

2. The
$$\begin{matrix} O & & C_\alpha \\ \backslash\!\!\backslash & & / \\ & C\!\!-\!\!N & \\ / & & \backslash \\ C_\alpha & & H \end{matrix}$$
system is always planar, owing to steric

hindrance and the resonance contribution of
$$\begin{matrix} ^-O & & C_\alpha \\ \backslash & & / \\ & C\!\!=\!\!^+N & \\ / & & \backslash \\ C_\alpha & & H \end{matrix}$$
. The

peptide bond is a hybrid, not easily diagrammed, of the two structures just depicted. In this hybrid structure the carbon-nitrogen bond is shorter than a C—N single bond because of a 40% contribution of the resonance structure with a C=N double bond. Rotation about the carbon-nitrogen bond is restricted by an energy barrier of about 21 kcal/mole, yielding a planar conformation. Rotation about both single bonds to C_α can occur, however.

3. Studies indicate that the trans conformation of the C_α carbon

atoms about the planar structure is favored over the cis by more than 2 kcal/mole.

4. The dimensions of an extended polypeptide chain are as given in Fig. 14-1.

FIG. 14-1 Dimensions of an extended polypeptide chain. [After R. B. Corey and L. Pauling, *Proc. Roy. Soc. London*, **B141**, 10 (1953).]

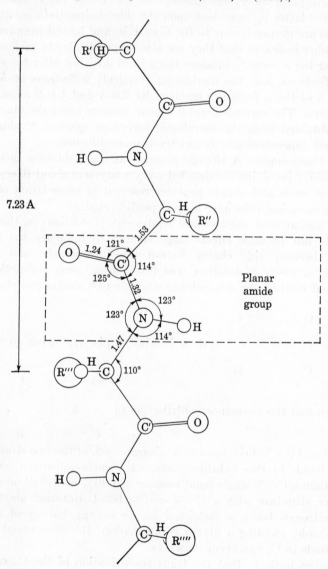

5. All possible $\diagdown N-H\cdots O=C\diagup$ hydrogen bonds are formed with an N to O distance of 2.8 $\pm$ 0.1 A.

6. Due to the resonance of point 2, the N—H---O hydrogen-bond angle is within 30° of 180°. The greatest stability occurs when all four atoms of point 5 are collinear.

7. Relatively sharp x-ray patterns indicate some symmetry and periodicity in the electron density distribution.

In combination with the usual van der Waals radii of atoms, the seven points place severe restrictions on the stereochemistry of polypeptide chain conformation. X-ray-diffraction data and exhaustive model building usually eliminate all but a few structures from further consideration.

Pleated Sheets. Let us compare the dimensions in Fig. 14-1, given by Pauling, with those observed for the β form of the keratin group, assuming a rectangular three-dimensional array of fully extended polypeptide chains along the fiber axis. The equatorial reflection observed at 4.7 A is the approximate distance expected for the interval between the axes of adjacent parallel chains in a plane with hydrogen bonds of 2.8 A length. The 10-A distance corresponds to the expected distance between planes and is dependent upon the extent of the side-chain projection, the greater values being for the larger side chains.

However, the 3.3-A meridional reflection is considerably less than the 3.6 A (one-half of 7.23) of one amino acid residue in the fully extended polypeptide chain. Partly for this reason and partly because of stereochemical interference of neighboring R groups in the fully extended chain, Pauling suggested a crumpling of the chain into pleated sheets, predicting a 6.7-A repeat distance in good agreement with that observed (2 $\times$ 3.3 A). Two pleated sheets were proposed: If the chains are parallel, their separation is 6.5 A; if antiparallel, 7.0 A. Figures 14-2 and 14-3 represent the pleated sheets.

The antiparallel-chain pleated sheet has been suggested as the structure of the β form of poly-L-alanine and tussah silk, which contains about 27% glycyl residues. *Bombyx mori* silk, which consists of 44% glycyl residues, may have glycine as every other residue, an alternation which allows a back-to-back fit of chains to give a double sheet. Details of the sheet structure may be in error, but postulation of some kind of sheet is probably necessary to account for the x-ray patterns of the β form of the keratin group. Naturally occurring molecules may be neither purely parallel nor antiparallel sheets, but rather random mixtures of chains running in both directions.

α Helix. Many attempts had been made to find a structure which could account for the characteristic x-ray pattern of the α form of the keratin group of fibrous proteins. Various helical forms were proposed, all with integral screw axis (Sec. 13-5). By strict application of his previously enumerated principles to a helical conformation, Pauling formulated the α helix. (There is not necessarily a connection between the α form of the keratin group and the α helix.) The α helix is favored over other helices on both stereochemical and energetic arguments because it has the least bond strain, possesses the smallest hole down the middle, and forms the smallest rings containing hydrogen bonds.

Figure 14-4 is a diagrammatic representation of the α helix. This structure has 3.6 residues per 360° turn, and the corresponding translational distance along the rotation axis (pitch) is 5.4 A. Consequently, the rise per residue is $5.4/3.6 = 1.5$ A, and the rotation per residue is $360/3.6 = 100°$. A distance of 5.1 A separates tipped planes of the helix. The C_α carbon atoms are at a radius of 2.3 A from the axis. The hydrogen bonds, 2.8 A in length, nearly linear, and parallel to the axis, hold the structure together. As five complete turns yield an integral $(5 \times 3.6 = 18)$ number of residues, an identical repeat occurs after every 18 residues or every $5 \times 5.4 = 27$ A along the axis, since residues are then directly above each other. This last feature is unimportant, since a slight extra twist would alter the dimensions.

Only short-range spacings of chain segments show up on fiber

FIG. 14-2   Parallel-chain pleated sheet. (From L. Pauling, "The Nature of the Chemical Bond," 3d ed., Cornell University Press, Ithaca, N.Y., 1960.)

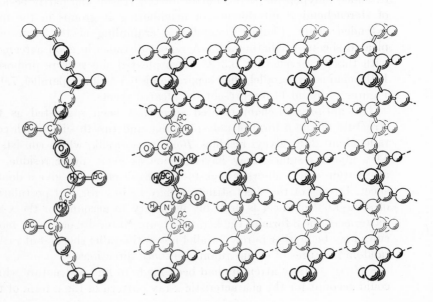

diffraction patterns, since long-range spacings do not repeat systematically enough to yield a diffraction maximum. The pitch of a helix can be obtained from the meridional layer-line spacings, but not the long-range identical repeat. The long-range repeat, if slightly altered, would not change a diffraction pattern, and the consequent adjustment in pitch would be too small to be detected in layer-line spacings. X-ray diffraction patterns of helices are immediately recognizable as such because certain meridional-layer lines are missing or weak.

Pauling's main departure from previous attempts to formulate a helix for polypeptide-chain folding was to abandon the requirement of an integral number (two, three, four, or six) of residues per turn. There is no reason why an isolated helix may not have 3.6 residues per turn, since the environment of each residue is the same, and the previously described considerations favor this conformation. If the helices are to pack together, however, only a two-, three-, four-, or sixfold screw axis will allow an indefinite repeat in three dimensions. Therefore, the presence of a nonintegral screw axis means that the intramolecular interactions of the molecule are much stronger than interactions with its neighbors.

At the time of the announcement of the α helix, its correspondence with the observed x-ray patterns of the α form of keratin-group pro-

FIG. 14-3 Antiparallel-chain pleated sheet. (From L. Pauling, "The Nature of the Chemical Bond," 3d ed., Cornell University Press, Ithaca, N.Y., 1960.)

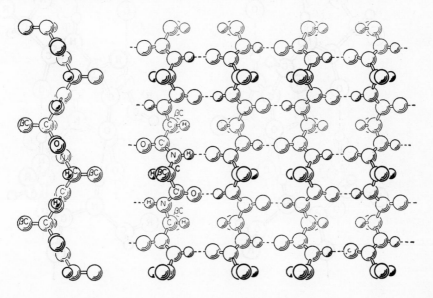

teins and polypeptides was deficient on two counts. The α helix predicted an undiscovered meridional reflection at 1.5 A and could not account for the observed but unsplit meridional reflection at 5.1 A. Subsequently, however, the 1.5-A meridional reflection was found in diagrams of several tilted natural and synthetic fibers of the α form;

FIG. 14-4 Left- and right-handed α helices composed of L-amino acids. The right-handed version on the right is theoretically more stable and has been found to occur naturally. (From L. Pauling, "The Nature of the Chemical Bond," 3d ed., Cornell University Press, Ithaca, N.Y., 1960.)

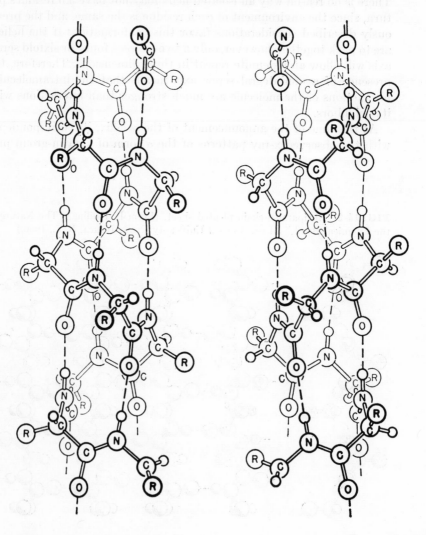

it has been verified many times as a strong reflection in this type of structure and in hemoglobin. Of all helices, only the α helix predicts the 1.5-A reflection.

The strong unsplit meridional reflection at 5.1 A was later accounted for in principle on the basis of several coiled coil structures. Two-, three-, or seven-stranded ropes, with each strand an α helix, are intertwined, and the rope as a whole forms a new helix with a much larger pitch than the α helix. An indefinite repeat can be obtained from α helices coiled around one another, so that groups such as —S—S— bridges may be opposite each other. Details of the coiled coils have not yet been elucidated and are likely to be different for the various members of the group.

The α helix may be coiled in a clockwise or counterclockwise manner analogous to a right- or left-handed screw thread. Since proteins usually contain only L-amino acids, the two coils are not mirror images. The mirror image of a right-handed α helix composed of L-amino acids is a left-handed helix of D-amino acids. Purely structural arguments favor the right-handed helix for L-amino acids. X-ray studies have confirmed that the right-handed α helix occurs in poly-L-alanine and myoglobin.

The structures of polypeptides and proteins have still to be refined by comparison of calculated and observed x-ray patterns. The gross features of the α helix and the pleated sheets (or something very similar) are probably correct, but the details have yet to be clarified. We have here presented only a surface picture of an intricate field.

The development of satisfactory structures for fibrous proteins illustrates the general procedures of scientific investigation: patient collection of data by many workers, formulation and rejection of unsuitable proposals, innovation and break with tradition, advancement of a more promising hypothesis, its prediction of previously unobserved phenomena, their subsequent verification, and general acceptance of a new theory. The student may trace this pattern in the above account of the development of the α-helix structure. This structure has been much criticized, doubted, and worked over, but only a theory presented with such precision is capable of so much serious consideration. For his efforts in this field and other no less significant contributions to molecular structure, Linus Pauling was awarded a Nobel prize in 1954.

14-2 COLLAGEN GROUP

In contrast to the keratin group, the collagen group of fibrous proteins are only about 10% extensible. In addition, the two groups yield different x-ray patterns. Although collagen does not occur in plants, it composes about one-third of all the protein in the body and is a constituent of cartilage, tendons, bone, and skin. Amino acid analyses show that just about one-third of the amino acid residues are glycine; cysteine and tryptophan do not occur, other sulfur-containing and aromatic amino acids are rare, and about 20% of the amino acids are proline and hydroxyproline. The last-named amino acid and hydroxylysine are found only in collagens and similar proteins. There is evidence to suggest that the hydroxy groups are added after the protein is assembled.

The denaturation temperature of collagen upon heating to yield gelatin varies with the source; lower temperatures in general correspond to animals living in colder environments. At one time the denaturation temperature was correlated with the hydroxyproline content of the collagen sample, implying that the —OH groups stabilize the structure in some way, perhaps by hydrogen bonding. More recent evidence suggests that just as good or better correlation exists between denaturation temperature and the total pyrrolidine (proline plus hydroxyproline) content of a collagen sample. This fact can be accounted for by considering the thermodynamics of transitions of equilibrium processes, such as melting, which occur at a single temperature. For such a process, the free-energy change is

$$\Delta G_t = 0 = \Delta H_t - T_t \Delta S_t$$

hence $T_t = \Delta H_t / \Delta S_t$. The correlation between transition temperature and hydroxyproline content accommodates a change in T_t by a change in ΔH_t through hydrogen bonding or some other means. To the extent that either imino acid residue, proline or hydroxyproline, occurs in a chain, the number of conformations allowed in the random form is reduced because bond rotations are restricted. This reduction, resulting in a decreased entropy of transition, must increase the transition temperature for a constant enthalpy of transition.

Because there are large amounts of glycyl and prolyl residues in collagen, we shall discuss the structures of the synthetic polypeptides polyglycine and poly-L-proline before further elaborating the structure of collagen.

Polyglycine. Depending on the solvent, polyglycine can be precipitated in two different forms. Polyglycine I yields a typical β x-ray pattern and may be a parallel pleated sheet to which side chains can be added. Polyglycine II gives a distinctive x-ray picture which has been interpreted in terms of an integral threefold screw axis with a true repeat of 9.3 A and a residue repeat of 3.1 A, which gives 120° rotation per residue. Figure 14-5 illustrates the proposed hexagonal array with each chain joined, by hydrogen bonds approximately perpendicular to the chain axis, to six other chains in an indefinite three-

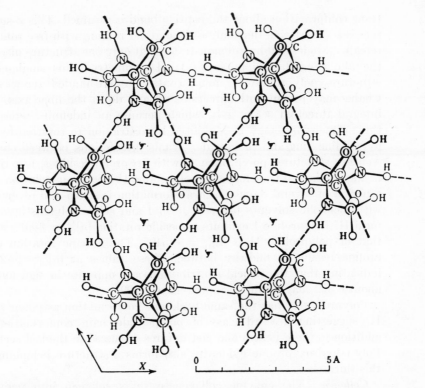

FIG. 14-5 Projection down the screw axis of polyglycine II. [From F. H. C. Crick and A. Rich, *Nature*, **176**, 780 (1955).]

dimensional network. Intermolecular hydrogen bonding leading to an indefinitely repeating pattern requires an integral screw axis. Because only half the hydrogen bonds originate on any one chain, the screw axis is threefold and not sixfold. Since one chain may be removed, inverted, and replaced, yet still yield a satisfactory hydrogen-bonded structure, the chains may run in both directions, but all the chains must be either right- or left-handed. Side chains cannot be added to this structure.

Poly-L-proline. Since proline is an imino acid, poly-L-proline possesses no hydrogen atoms that may be donated for hydrogen-bond formation. As a result, an α helix, among other hydrogen-bonded structures, cannot be formed by this polymer. Its x-ray pattern indicates a threefold screw axis with a residue repeat every 3.1 A. The puckered ring in proline greatly restricts free rotation in the molecule. To arrive at a satisfactory structure, the usual planar and trans conformation about the peptide bond is assumed. This assumption is so restrictive that only one bond per residue with free rotation remains. Model building demonstrates that only one structure meeting the above conditions possesses triad symmetry. This single-chain structure, polyproline II, must contain a left-handed screw axis. Chains may run in both directions up and down the fiber axis. The integral threefold screw axis, which permits an indefinite repeat in three dimensions, may be stabilized by restriction to rotation by the pyrrolidine ring and to van der Waals interactions between chains. Another structure, polyproline I, with *cis*-prolyl residues, is a right-handed helix and transforms to polyproline II in aqueous solution over a period of several days. The transformation is sharp and reversible, with alcoholic solvents favoring form I and acidic solvents favoring form II. Polyproline I exhibits a specific rotation $[\alpha]_D^{25} = +40°$, while that of polyproline II is $[\alpha]_D^{25} = -540°$. The specific rotation of a proline residue is midway between these values at $[\alpha]_D^{25} = -250°$, indicating that the helical contributions are opposite in sign and of about equal magnitude at approximately 290°.

Polyproline II has the same backbone conformation as polyglycine II, suggesting a third class of polypeptide-chain conformation in addition to the α-helical and β structures discussed in the last section. Poly-L-hydroxyproline evidently also forms a structure belonging to this third class.

Collagen. The enzyme collagenase splits collagen into peptides in which glycine is the N-terminal residue. Glycine appears in all the peptides produced. Gly—Pro—Hypro is the most common sequence, followed by Gly—Pro—Ala. Since over one-third of the amino acids are glycine, these sequence results provide strong suggestive evidence that every third residue is glycine.

Collagen gives an x-ray pattern accounted for by a nonintegral screw axis of 108° rotation and 2.86 A translation with three amino acid residues per asymmetric unit. Due to the large number of proline and hydroxyproline residues, collagen cannot form an α helix. However, the x-ray diffraction pattern exhibits blank spaces about the meridian characteristic of some kind of helix.

Many attempts have been made to interpret the pattern of collagen. A current description called collagen II (Fig. 14-6) is probably correct, at least in outline. Three polypeptide chains intertwine in a slowly winding triple helix consistent with the mild extensibility. The major triple helix so formed is right-handed, with a 28.6-A repeat after 10 residues. Each of the three chains forms a left-handed (due to proline) minor helix with a pitch of 3 × 28.6 A. When one minor helix places an amino acid residue other than glycine near the fiber axis, only a glycyl residue from one of the two remaining helices can fit.

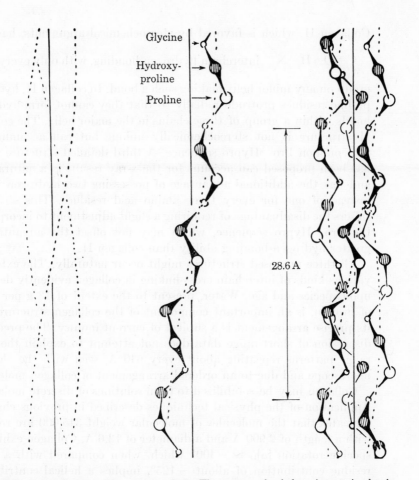

Glycine

Hydroxy-
proline

Proline

28.6 A

FIG. 14-6 Collagen II structure. Left: The screw axis of three intertwined poly-peptide chains (dotted lines) about the fiber axis (solid line). Center: One chain as it coils around its screw axis. Only C_α carbon atoms are drawn. Right: All three chains of collagen. Note how the chains successively place a glycine residue near the fiber axis. [From F. H. C. Crick and J. C. Kendrew, *Advan. Protein Chem.*, **12**, 169 (1957).]

Thus a glycine as every third residue is an essential part of the structure. The triple-helix assumption is supported by the light-scattering results discussed in Sec. 8-3.

Collagen structures possess the same backbone conformation as polyproline II. Collagen I has systematic hydrogen bonding between

C=O of one chain and −OH of hydroxyprolines of the next chain.

Collagen II, which is favored by stereochemical arguments, has only

$$\begin{array}{c} \diagdown \\ C=O\cdots H-N \\ \diagup \end{array} \begin{array}{c} \diagup \\ \diagdown \end{array}$$
interchain hydrogen bonding, with only every third

group on any minor helix making such a bond. In collagen II, hydroxyproline residues protrude radially so that they cannot form hydrogen bonds within a group of three chains in the major helix. The collagen II structure is not stereochemically unique but can accommodate the common Pro—Hypro sequence. A third detailed structure which has been proposed can account for the x-ray results in a natural way and has the additional advantage of possessing two hydrogen bonds instead of one for every three amino acid residues. This structure suffers the disadvantage of requiring a slight adjustment to incorporate the Pro—Hypro sequence, which may not offset the advantage of greater hydrogen-bonding ability than collagen II.

All three proposed structures might occur naturally. The extent of various kinds of interchain cross-linking in collagen evidently depends upon species and age. Water, present to the extent of 13 g per 100 g of protein, is an important component of the collagen structure, and its precise arrangement is a subject of current inquiry. The preceding discussion of short-range data does not attempt to explain the long-range patterns repeating about every 640 A, seen with the electron microscope and due to an ordered arrangement of collagen molecules.

Collagen may be solubilized to form solutions of discrete molecules. Application of the physical techniques described in previous chapters indicates that the molecules of molecular weight 345,000 are rodlike, with a length of 2,900 A and a diameter of 13.6 A. Collagen exhibits a specific rotation $[\alpha]_D \simeq -400°$ which, when compared with a mean residue contribution of about $-125°$, implies a helical contribution of about $-275°$, only slightly less than that inferred above for polyproline II. When heated in solution, collagen is denatured to three smaller and more flexible components, a mixture called *gelatin* (Sec. 8-3).

14-3 INFRARED DICHROISM

Matter absorbs light of a specific frequency in the infrared region when excitation of a normal mode of vibration of the molecule gives rise to a change of dipole moment. Characteristic frequencies of infrared absorption are often associated with certain bonds in the molecule. Oriented fibers display dichroism, a variation in absorbed intensity depending upon whether the incident radiation is polarized parallel or perpendicular to the fiber axis. Parallel dichroism (∥) occurs if a fiber absorbs more light of a given frequency when the electric vector of the polarized incident light is parallel rather than perpendicular to the fiber axis. Perpendicular dichroism ($\perp$) exists when greater absorption occurs when the incident light is polarized with the electric vector perpendicular to the fiber axis.

Because the ╲N—H⋯O═C╱ system is nearly parallel to the fiber axis, stretching frequencies associated with backbone hydrogen bonding in the α helix show parallel dichroism. Bending or deformation frequencies of the same group of the helix exhibit perpendicular dichroism because the bending motion is normal to the fiber axis. In pleated-sheet structures, the hydrogen-bonding system is approximately perpendicular to the fiber axis, so that the dichroism is opposite to that observed in the α helix. The results are summarized in Table 14-1, where a range of about 5 cm^{-1} to either side of each quoted value is observed. In both α and β conformations the N—H stretching frequency, at about 3,300 cm^{-1}, is markedly less than a value of about 3,450 cm^{-1} observed in non-hydrogen-bonded structures. This shift to lower energies, due to slight loosening of the N—H bond, is evidence supporting the hydrogen-bonded nature of the α and β structures.

TABLE 14-1 *Infrared Frequencies and Dichroism in α and β Forms of Fibrous Proteins and Polypeptides*

Frequency	α, cm^{-1}	β, cm^{-1}
N—H bend	1,545 $\perp$	1,525 $\parallel$
C═O stretch	1,650 $\parallel$	1,630 $\perp$

Infrared dichroism indicates that oriented films of poly-L-glutamic acid exist in the α form, whereas the sodium salt has a β conformation. Apparently, electrostatic repulsion between negatively charged carboxyl groups renders the helix unstable. However, the helix may be stabilized in some way by hydrogen bonds involving carboxyl hydrogens. This additional stabilizing factor would be lost upon complete ionization of carboxylic acid groups.

Further investigations of infrared frequencies and dichroism reveal that nonhelical conformations are favored by synthetic polypeptides composed of L-amino acids substituted on the β carbon by oxygen, sulfur, or two groups other than hydrogen. The amino acids are arranged in Table 1-1 according to their tendency to form an α helix or nonhelical structures when present in polypeptide chains. Thus poly-L-leucine forms an α helix, and poly-L-valine a pleated sheet. That polypeptides of these two apparently similar amino acids should yield such different structures indicates the profound effect that amino acid residues have on secondary structure. Whether or not a section of protein forms an α helix may depend on the number and sequence of amino acids that are predisposed toward a helical conformation.

Usually, dichroism is not complete, because of imperfect alignment of molecules in the fiber. In addition, the amide frequencies are not exclusively due to the vibration of a single bond but are composite vibrations due to interactions with neighboring atoms. These vibrational interactions, in addition to the hydrogen bonding, induce frequency splittings and make the analysis more complex than has been outlined here.

SELECTED BIBLIOGRAPHY

1 F. H. C. Crick and J. C. Kendrew, X-ray Analysis and Protein Structure, *Advan. Protein Chem.*, **12**, 133–214 (1957).

2 L. Pauling and R. B. Corey, The Configuration of Polypeptide Chains in Proteins, *Fortschr. Chem. Org. Naturstoffe*, **11**, 180–239 (1954). A review in English of the contributions of these authors.

3 L. Pauling and R. B. Corey, Configurations of Polypeptide Chains with Favored Orientations around Single Bonds: Two New Pleated Sheets, *Proc. Natl. Acad. Sci. U.S.*, **37**, 729–740 (1951).

4 L. Pauling, R. B. Corey, and H. R. Branson, Two Hydrogen Bonded Helical Configurations of the Polypeptide Chain, *Proc. Natl. Acad. Sci. U.S.*, **37**, 205–211, (1951).

5 C. H. Bamford, A. Elliott, and W. E. Hanby, "Synthetic Polypeptides," Academic Press Inc., New York, 1956.

6 W. F. Harrington and P. H. von Hippel, The Structure of Collagen and Gelatin, *Advan. Protein Chem.*, **16**, 1–138 (1961).

7 A. Rich and F. H. C. Crick, The Molecular Structure of Collagen, *J. Mol. Biol.*, **3**, 483–506 (1961).

8 T. Miyazawa and E. R. Blout, The Infra-red Spectra of Polypeptides in Various Conformations, *J. Am. Chem. Soc.*, **83**, 712–719 (1961).

QUESTIONS

14-1 Summarize the canonical principles of polypeptide-chain conformation.

14-2 What are the characteristics of the α helix?

14-3 How many hydrogen bonds hold the following amino acid residues to an α helix: end residue, second from end, third from end, and fourth from end?

14-4 How many amino acid residues are held in an α-helical conformation by one hydrogen bond?

14-5 How many hydrogen bonds must be broken to release from the helical conformation one amino acid residue embedded in an α-helical section?

14-6 What is the minimum number of amino acid residues required so that at least one amide bond is both a hydrogen-bond donor and acceptor in an α helix?

14-7 Under what conditions is an integral screw axis necessary? What are the implications of a nonintegral screw axis?

14-8 Utilizing the Bragg equation, explain why it is necessary to tilt from the vertical well-oriented α-helical fibers in order to observe the 1.5-A reflection with copper K_α radiation.

14-9   Which of the following proteins and polypeptides could take up an α-helical conformation: *Bombyx mori* silk, collagen, feather keratin, myoglobin, polyglycine, poly-L-glutamic acid sodium salt, and polyproline? What reasons can you give for the failure of those that do not form α helices?

14-10   A poly-L-alanine chain is removed from an ordered portion of the α fiber. The chain is reflected in a mirror plane, inverted, rotated 180° on its axis, and reflected again in a mirror plane. How does the resultant chain compare with the original? Will the resultant chain fit back into the fiber?

14-11   What prevents other proteins from having a collagen structure?

14-12   Suggest reasons why *Bombyx mori* silk does not form a collagen structure. Why doesn't collagen form a *Bombyx mori* silk structure?

14-13   What effect would substitution of a β-amino acid for an α-amino acid have on the structures of this chapter?

14-14   What effect would substitution of a D-amino acid for an L-amino acid have on the structures of this chapter?

14-15   At approximately what angle relative to the fiber axis is the

$$\text{N—H---O=C}$$

system placed in the α and β forms?

14-16   The infrared spectrum of polyglycine I has bands at $1{,}632 \perp$ and $1{,}530\|$ cm^{-1}, while polyglycine II absorbs at 1,648 and 1,558 cm^{-1}. What inferences about the structures of polyglycine may be made from these data?

15 | Globular Proteins

Unlike fibrous proteins, which form rigid structures, globular proteins are found in biological fluids, where they perform transport, storage, enzymatic, and other functions. Globular proteins can be crystallized from solution; they then give sharp and detailed x-ray patterns from which details of the molecule as a whole may be obtained in addition to the character of the repeating structural unit. To glean the information potentially available for such large molecules, it is necessary to solve the phase problem posed in Chap. 13. From the square root of the intensity of blackening of a spot on the photographic film, the amplitude, but not the phase, of a Fourier component can be determined. Recent technical advances, foremost of which is the application of the method of isomorphous replacement to protein crystals, permit a solution of the phase problem. In this chapter we describe methods for solving the phase problem and discuss the results obtained for two proteins, myoglobin and hemoglobin.

15-1 SOLUTIONS OF THE PHASE PROBLEM

Heavy-atom Method. The only crystal required for the heavy-atom method is that of the molecule under study, with a heavy atom introduced in the same position in all molecules of the crystal. A point scatterer, the heavy atom scatters in phase, while the scattered intensity from the remainder of the molecule is reduced by interference. If the heavy atom succeeds in dominating the scattering from the crystal, its position in the unit cell is revealed by a Patterson synthesis. This information is used to calculate the diffraction pattern, including both amplitudes and phases, that would be observed if the heavy atom were the only atom in the unit cell. This calculated pattern will resemble the observed pattern because the heavy atom is the sole scatterer in the former and the dominant scatterer in the latter.

As discussed in Sec. 13-3, the amplitudes can be evaluated from the observed pattern, but not the phases. The next step is therefore to combine the observed amplitudes with the phases calculated from the heavy atom alone to construct a Fourier synthesis of the electron density distribution. The resulting pattern is somewhere between that of the heavy atom alone and that of the crystal with a heavy-atom substituent. Successive refinements are applied until the structure obtained yields a calculated pattern in close agreement with the observed pattern.

The heavy-atom method was used in initial stages of the work on vitamin B_{12}. In order to control the phases of a protein with 20,000 molecular weight, three or four mercury atoms have to be attached simultaneously.

Isomorphous Replacement. More powerful than the heavy-atom method, the method of isomorphous replacement was successfully applied to the protein hemoglobin by Perutz in 1954. Four years later, contours of the polypeptide chain in the globular protein myoglobin were outlined, and within six years many more details, including large segments of the amino acid sequence, were described. These results are discussed further at the end of this chapter.

The method of isomorphous replacement requires two crystals, one of the protein and the other of the protein with a heavy atom substituted at a unique site with no alteration in the crystal structure. One mercury atom in 35,000 molecular weight would be sufficient for perfect isomorphism. In practice, several isomorphous replacements at different positions in the unit cell are required to sharpen the analysis and serve as checks.

Changes in the diffraction pattern caused by the heavy atom are used to calculate its position in the unit cell by means of a difference Patterson $(\Delta F)^2$ synthesis. The contribution of the heavy atom to the amplitude and phase of any observed reflection can then be calculated. Let us assume for reference below that such a calculated contribution is -2.7.

For two-dimensional Fourier projections, crystal symmetry requires that some vectors are either parallel or antiparallel, and only two values of the phase, 0 and π, are possible. Such reflections, called *real* because the imaginary component of the phase vector is zero, are usually indicated by a $+$ or $-$. For this simplest of cases, the following example illustrates the principles of determination of the phase.

Suppose that on some arbitrary scale a certain real reflection has an intensity of 100 for the protein and 49 for the protein with a heavy atom substituted in an isomorphous replacement. Taking the square roots of the intensities will yield the amplitudes, but, since we do not know the signs, the phases are not determined. To determine the phases we note that the contribution of the heavy atom to the reflection may be ± 17 or ± 3 as follows:

$$
\begin{array}{rcl}
\text{Protein and heavy atom} & - \text{ Protein } = & \text{Heavy atom} \\
+7 & - \ (-10) = & +17 \\
-7 & - \ (+10) = & -17 \\
-7 & - \ (-10) = & +3 \\
+7 & - \ (+10) = & -3
\end{array}
$$

Usually the contribution of the heavy atom to a reflection is less than that of the protein alone, so that ± 17 are eliminated. To decide whether $+3$ or -3 is the contribution of the heavy atom, we compare them with the result stated two paragraphs above, where the calculated contribution of the heavy atom is -2.7. Since this figure is nearer -3 than $+3$, reference to the chart indicates that the bottom row of figures actually applies, so that the contribution of the protein is $+10$. Thus we have determined the phase and the amplitude of a particular reflection in the protein.

Two-dimensional Fourier projections calculated by solving many reflections as illustrated above are usually about 20 or more atoms thick and not decipherable in projection. To make a three-dimensional analysis, imaginary reflections and phase angles, as well as signs, must be calculated. At least two isomorphous replacements are required. As a result, the computations are more time-consuming and less accurate than the simple illustrative example.

No assumptions are made concerning the structure in the isomorphous-replacement method.

15-2 STRUCTURE DETERMINATIONS

Globular proteins crystallized from salt solutions or organic solvents often contain considerable amounts of mother liquor in the unit cell as well as between crystallites. Salts in the mother liquor contribute to the low-resolution features of the x-ray pattern. Drying results in shrinkage and poor x-ray pictures. A protein binds about 30% of its own weight of solvent in the crystal; the remainder is unbound and unorganized. Heavy-atom reagents are added, either by crystallizing the protein in a medium containing the heavy atom or by allowing the reagent to diffuse into crystals over a period of time. In either case the crystals are obtained from aqueous solutions. X-ray pictures are taken of wet crystals mounted in thin-walled capillaries, with humidity controlled by the addition of a few drops of mother liquor. X-ray analyses, therefore, are performed on crystals in an environment similar to their natural habitat.

In addition, the bonding responsible for protein conformation is principally intramolecular and hence, to a first approximation, independent of whether the environment is a hydrated crystal or some other highly organized arrangement such as occurs in living systems. Even though protein conformations are sensitive to environment, as discussed in Chap. 16, the conformations of globular proteins in their crystalline forms are probably fairly specific, because the forces producing these forms are cooperative. Crystallization itself implies repeating regular structures of considerable definition. X-ray crystallographers determine in great detail molecular conformations that are identical (or nearly so) with those occurring in biological systems. Though other methods might be used to analyze molecules in more native conditions, none of them provides anywhere near the amount of specific information available from a detailed x-ray study.

A brief review of the various bond lengths may be helpful. For most atoms found in proteins, covalent bond lengths vary from 1.0 to 2.0 A. Contact distances of nonbonded atoms may be calculated from van der Waals radii, which are about 0.8 A greater than single-bond covalent radii. Interposition of a hydrogen atom between electronegative atoms in a hydrogen bond reduces the normal van der Waals distances by a few tenths of an angstrom unit. As discussed in Sec. 14-1, protein chains lie 5 to 10 A from each other, whether they are α helical or not.

Myoglobin. The oxygen-carrying protein of mammalian muscle, responsible in part for the red color of meat, is particularly prevalent in diving mammals. Sperm-whale myoglobin, with a molecular weight of 17,500, consists of a single polypeptide chain of 153 amino acid residues and an iron-containing heme group. Though it contains no cysteine residues and hence no disulfide bonds or free sulfhydryl groups, several isomorphous replacements with heavy-atom-containing reagents have been achieved. Earlier work on hemoglobin and myoglobin, in which a row of molecules was projected onto a plane, was undecipherable, indicating the necessity of a three-dimensional analysis if substantial information was to be gained. In 1958 the three-dimensional x-ray analysis of myoglobin to 6 A resolution was achieved by deducing the phases of 400 reflections with spacings greater than 6 A in the protein and in four different isomorphous-replacement derivatives. The protein chain was represented as a rod of high electron density intertwined in a remarkably complicated yet compact three-dimensional intestine-like structure. Due to the high density of the iron atom, the heme group was easily identified. Outlines of the protein folding were revealed, but greater detail became apparent only when a Fourier synthesis was performed to a higher degree of resolution.

In order to increase the resolution by a factor of 3 in 3 dimensions, about 3^3 more reflections must be considered. In 1960 x-ray analysis of sperm-whale myoglobin was reported accomplished to 2 A resolution by determining the phases of 9,600 reflections. High-speed computers were used to analyze the enormous amount of data. The electron density contribution was determined along 48 parallel sections $\frac{2}{3}$ A apart in the unit cell. The protein rod of high electron density in the 6-A study became, in the 2-A Fourier synthesis, a hollow cylindrical tube in the straight portions of the chain. These tubes are helical, with an axial repeat of about 5.4 A, identical with that expected of an α helix. Further analysis reveals that all the straight sections are right-handed α helices. There are eight such straight sections, of 24, 20, 19, 16, 9, 7, and 7 amino acid residues. The total of 118 amino acid residues in helical sections comprises 77% of the molecule. Thus the right-handed α helix is an important component of protein structure in some globular as well as fibrous proteins.

FIG. 15-1 Model of the protein myoglobin as deduced from x-ray diffraction studies at 2 A resolution. A white cord follows the course of the single chain. The gray sphere represents the iron atom in the heme group, which is observed nearly edgewise in this picture. The neighboring white sphere represents the oxygen atom of a water molecule coordinated to the iron. [From J. C. Kendrew et al., *Nature*, **190**, 666 (1961).]

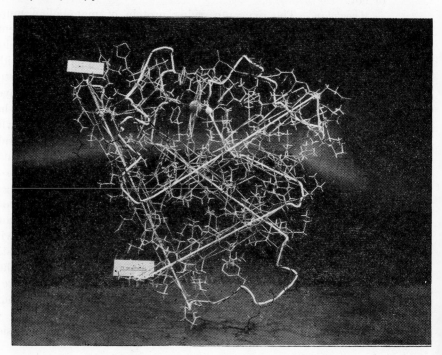

Though covalent bond lengths are of the order of 1.5 A, the 2-A-resolution Fourier synthesis of myoglobin has permitted identification of many side-chain residues, shown in Fig. 15-1. To identify a side chain, nearby main-chain atoms must be located precisely. Sufficient precision is most difficult to attain in nonhelical portions of the molecule, where corners are turned, and near sites of heavy-atom substitutions, where perfect isomorphism is not achieved. In several cases, such as in side chains protruding into ambient solution, thermal effects permit several energetically similar conformations to occur, with a consequent smearing of the x-ray pattern. Nonetheless, 78 out of 153 side chains have been identified from x-ray data alone, and 19 more with help from the composition of peptides produced by enzymatic action of trypsin; for most of the remainder the choice is narrowed to two or three possibilities. Thus not only a large part of the amino acid sequence, but also the positions in space of the constituent atoms, have been determined.

Of eight nonhelical regions in the molecule, one is at the carboxyl terminus, while the others are corners between straight helical chain sections. The corners contain from zero to eight residues, each different from all others. All four proline residues are located at corners; an α helix cannot accommodate a proline residue except at its amino terminus. One of the corners consists only of a proline residue on the terminus of one helical section joined to a new helical portion. Features of corner turning are important, because it is in them that protein conformation is at least partly determined. In one case only an alanine occurs between two helical portions, indicating that groups other than those at the corner can be important in corner turning.

The surface of the molecule is composed mainly of amino acid residues with polar groups, while the interior is dominated by nonpolar residues at van der Waals contact distances from their neighbors. Although all polar groups on the surface bind water molecules, little or no water appears within the myoglobin molecule. Some of the specific extrahelical hydrogen-bonded groups that have been delineated are serine, threonine, and tyrosine bonded to peptide carbonyl groups, imidazole $=$NH of iron-bound histidine to peptide carbonyl group, and an arginine residue to a propionic acid group of the porphyrin. It appears that some carbonyl groups partake in forked hydrogen bonds of which one may be in a helical section and the other may involve a side-chain group like serine.

The iron atom, almost in the planar heme group, is attached to an imidazole nitrogen of a histidine residue, while the sixth coordination position in the crystals investigated contains water. The angle of the heme group agrees with that determined from electron spin-resonance studies. Polar propionic acid groups of the porphyrin lie near the exterior of the molecule, while nonpolar vinyl groups are buried in the interior. The inner part of the heme group is surrounded by nonpolar side chains, and a number of aromatic side chains lie in the surrounding volume. Apart from the iron-histidine link, all bonds holding the heme group in position are of the weak variety, such as hydrophobic and hydrogen bonds. In contrast, the heme group of cytochrome c is covalently bonded to two cysteine residues.

With the results of the 2-A-resolution study, the use of heavy atoms in the isomorphous-replacement method has served its purpose. Now that many details are known, successive refinements are possible by direct Fourier calculations on crystalline myoglobin containing no heavy atoms. This analysis has been performed at 1.4 A resolution; it involved plotting the electron density at one-half million points in the molecule. At such high resolutions other problems appear, such as radiation damage to crystals due to the long exposure required to obtain data near the periphery of the x-ray diffraction pattern. Sensitive detecting instruments have replaced photographic film, and the data are fed directly into appropriately programmed high-speed computers. Of the many years required for this study, the majority involved development of techniques. Now that these are established, work on other globular proteins may proceed more quickly. The analysis of myoglobin was a fortunate choice, however, due to its high helical content, which permitted simplifications in calculations because large parts of the backbone positions were known. As will be seen in Sec. 16-4, myoglobin is unusual in possessing an abnormally large helical content for a globular protein.

Hemoglobin. The oxygen-carrying protein of vertebrate blood is about four times the size of myoglobin and contains four iron-containing heme groups. Earlier work had established the characteristically α-helical 1.5-A spacing in hemoglobin. Fourier synthesis is more difficult for hemoglobin than for myoglobin; for 5.5 A resolution, 1,200 reflections were used in the protein and each of six isomorphous replacements. The two pairs of identical symmetrically placed subunits of horse oxyhemoglobin lie in a tetrahedral array. Fortunately, each subunit of hemoglobin goes through remarkably similar contortions, which mimic those of myoglobin, so that much can be learned of hemoglobin structure from the myoglobin results. Figure 15-2 shows a model of the horse oxyhemoglobin molecule, with each pair of identical subunits a different color. The two pairs of chains form a complementary structure of about $64 \times 55 \times 50$ A. The four heme groups are separated from each other by 25 and 35 A, and their angles are accurately known from electron spin-resonance studies. Of the sulfhydryl groups in horse hemoglobin, the two on the β chain combine more readily with mercury atoms. These two groups, 13 and 21 A from

FIG. 15-2 Model of oxyhemoglobin as determined by x-ray diffraction studies at 5.5 A resolution. Both α chains are shown in white, and the β chains in black. The large grey disks are heme groups with the positions of oxygen molecules indicated. [From M. F. Perutz et al., *Nature*, **185**, 416 (1960).]

the iron atoms, may be important in heme-heme interactions and lie next to the heme-linked histidine residues. Some kind of heme-heme interaction is implied by the increased ability of hemoglobin to pick up oxygen as more oxygen is added to the molecule. Of the four oxygen molecules that combine reversibly with hemoglobin, the fourth is added most easily. Detailed analysis reveals that this enhancement is primarily an entropy effect in a direction which may be attributed to a greater disorganization of the protein. Heme-heme interactions do not occur in myoglobin, which possesses only a single heme group; they are discussed further in Sec. 22-5.

The spatial structures of both pairs of chains of horse hemoglobin are similar to those of sperm-whale myoglobin. Seal myoglobin and bovine hemoglobin also possess chains with folding similar to those pictured. How, then, do the amino acid sequences compare for all these chains of similar folding? At first sight the amino acid sequences of the polypeptide chains seem different; indeed, even the amino acid contents display marked dissimilarities. Closer examination reveals, however, that large numbers of identical and homologous sequences occur when α and β chains of hemoglobins are compared with each other and with myoglobins. By leaving gaps in one or the other chain, two chains may often be brought into register with each other. Identities between chains include prolines for turning corners, glycines for close approaches of helical segments, tyrosines for hydrogen bonding between segments, and histidines for combination with iron. Differences at corners tend to be small, while most disparities occur in helical regions. Some amino acid residues are more important for conformation than others. Evidently, amino acid residue sequences do correspond, or else the differences are unimportant in those regions of the chain which are decisive for determination of the folding in space.

Enormously significant advances in the understanding of proteins have resulted from the studies of hemoglobin and myoglobin by Max Perutz and John Kendrew and their collaborators. Results inferred from other physical and chemical studies are either confirmed or dropped from further consideration, according to whether they agree or disagree with the definitive results of x-ray analyses. Years of labor in developing x-ray techniques have yielded a method which can confirm or disprove the results of other studies achieved over a similar interval. By further refining resolution, crystallographers will gain more information on the mode of folding of proteins and the intricacies of oxygen pickup in hemoglobin. Finally, Perutz and Kendrew, honored by a Nobel award in 1962, in these companion pioneer studies have developed techniques which are being applied to the determination of the three-dimensional conformations of other proteins. To appreciate these studies fully, the reader is strongly advised to consult Refs. 2 and 3 of this chapter. X-ray crystallographers are unusually adept at interpreting their work for the general reader, and in this field there are no better expositions than those of the experts themselves.

SELECTED BIBLIOGRAPHY

1 F. H. C. Crick and J. C. Kendrew, X-ray Analysis and Protein Structure, *Advan. Protein Chem.*, **12**, 133–214 (1957).

2 J. C. Kendrew et al., Structure of Myoglobin, *Nature*, **185**, 422–427 (1960), **190**, 666–670 (1961); *Science*, **139**, 1259–1266 (1963).

3 M. F. Perutz et al., Structure of Hemoglobin, *Proc. Roy. Soc. London*, **A265**, 161–187 (1962); *Nature*, **185**, 416–422 (1960), **194**, 914–917 (1962), **199**, 633–639 (1963); *Science*, **140**, 863–869 (1963).

QUESTIONS

15-1 Approximately how many reflections must be analyzed to obtain a Fourier synthesis of myoglobin to 1.4 A resolution?

15-2 Compare the N-terminal sequences of the α and β chains for hemoglobin given in Sec. 12-3. Observe the deletions and substitutions required to match the two chain segments.

16 | Protein Conformation

So many studies have been made on the wide varieties of proteins that a single chapter in a book of this kind cannot begin to exhaust the subject. Several examples of particular protein properties, such as masking of groups when in a compact protein structure, have already been cited (Sec. 5-2). In this chapter an attempt will be made to enumerate and discuss certain principles of protein chemistry which should be generally, though not universally, applicable. Proteins are large, unstable molecules that interact with almost all other substances, including cations, anions, small organic molecules, lipids, carbohydrates, and each other. Through the perseverance of protein chemists, reproducible protein preparations have been obtained from the mass of impure chemicals that constitute living systems. Some of the criteria for purity have been discussed in the chapters on physical methods; others are mentioned here. The word *conformation* in the chapter title applies to the secondary and tertiary structures of proteins defined below. *Configuration* is reserved for use in optical isomerism, e.g., the two configurations of α-alanine, L and D. Study and discussion of protein conformation is important because the biological activity of the protein is often determined thereby.

16-1 LEVELS OF ORGANIZATION AND BONDING

When considering proteins (or nucleic acids), it is convenient to divide the structure into four levels of organization. The first three levels were originally formulated by K. U. Linderstrøm-Lang, and the fourth by J. D. Bernal. Since the divisions are to some extent arbitrary, the original definitions have been modified slightly, in the light of more recent experimental results, and generalized in order to make them applicable to nucleic acid structure, where the same terms are frequently encountered.

As a minimum, the *primary structure* of a protein refers to the number, configuration, and sequence of amino acid residues that are linked in a chain by repeating peptide bonds. This chain sequence may be referred to as the one-dimensional primary structure. Primary structures may be extended to include the number and nature of covalent cross-linkages that may bind two or more chains together or hold one chain to a more limited conformation. Covalently bound groups such as coenzymes, metal ions in metal enzymes, heme, phosphate, carbohydrate, and acetyl groups, as well as other functions such as the thiazoline ring in bacitracin A, may also be considered as part of the primary structure. The primary structure is comparable to that which an organic chemist would write in a structural formula of covalent bonds with bond energies greater than 35 kcal/mole. By bond energy is meant the approximate energy required to break the bond in question. Covalent bond energies of less than 35 kcal/mole do occur, but none have so far been found to be significant in biological systems. Insulin, the first protein to have its complete amino acid sequence delineated (for which achievement Fred Sanger was awarded a Nobel prize in 1958), consists of two polypeptide chains of unequal length joined by two disulfide (—S—S—) cross-links. Figure 16-1 is a representation of the insulin structure. Ribonuclease, the second protein for which the amino acid sequence was determined, consists of a single polypeptide chain of 124 amino acid residues held in a restrained conformation by four disulfide cross-links between eight cysteine residues. Owing to cross-linking, no free —SH groups appear in insulin or ribonuclease, though both contain cysteine residues.

Secondary structure refers to any regular and periodic folding that occurs in the backbone of a polymer molecule. Usually this folding

FIG. 16-1 Insulin molecule. The *a* and *b* chains are joined by two interchain disulfide links. One intrachain disulfide link occurs in the *a* chain. The numbers refer to the position of the amino acid residues in each chain beginning with the N-terminal residues on the left.

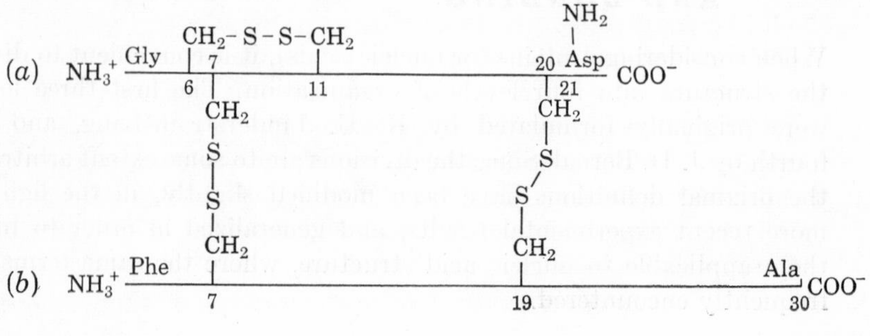

results from formation of hydrogen bonds in a regular and systematic fashion. Often the hydrogen bonding is between elements of the backbone of the chain, as in the pleated-sheet structures of Sec. 14-1 and the α helix. Other structures included in the definition are nucleic acids and collagen I; in the latter, systematic hydrogen bonds occur between regularly recurring hydroxyproline residues. A random-coil molecule would be described as having no secondary structure. Helix formation is an example of secondary structure. Although secondary structure is often due to hydrogen bonds, they are not essential for the appearance of secondary structure, as may be seen by recalling the helical polyproline II structure (Sec. 14-2).

In addition to or apart from the folding in the secondary structure just described, proteins often undergo folding due to forces which are neither regular nor systematic. Folding due to these irregular causes yields the *tertiary structure*. Many globular proteins, such as myoglobin, possess long polypeptide chains yet are nearly spherical in shape and must fold back upon themselves. This folding usually involves interactions between side chains in proteins but may involve backbone interactions. Globular proteins may, like myoglobin, exhibit tertiary folding superimposed on an α-helical secondary structure or have substantial tertiary structure with little secondary structure, as is apparently the case for β-lactoglobulin.

Quarternary structure refers to the organization resulting from interactions of subunits, as in hemoglobin and insulin. In the latter, the monomer unit of molecular weight 6,000 is realized only in concentrated solutions of guanidinium salt or urea. At this level the definition of molecule lacks precision, but usually a reasonable choice may be made.

The division of protein and other structures into four levels of organization is solely a matter of convenience as an aid to thinking and communication. No further knowledge is gained about protein structure by this division. For this reason lengthy and detailed discussions about how to define the properties and limits of each division are fruitless. The divisions should be retained only so long as they are useful; they may be modified in the light of further results, and they should be discarded when they become a burden.

Having described a set of divisions into which it may be convenient to classify levels of organization in protein structure, we now proceed to enumerate the types and principles of bonding that are involved. First we shall define bond energy as the approximate amount of energy required to break a bond. Again the classifications are made for convenience; they must not be considered ironclad nor become a bar to imaginative thinking.

1. Covalent bonds of bond energies greater than 35 kcal/mole occur

in the main-chain sequence of peptide bonds in the primary structure and in disulfide bonds between cysteine residues. Rotation is hindered about a disulfide bond which, in the absence of other restraints, forms a dihedral angle of about 90°, similar to that in hydrogen peroxide. This bond may be visualized by holding this book open at 90° and imagining a sulfur atom at each end of the binding joined by a bond along the binding. The substituent groups attached to each sulfur are disposed diagonally at two opposite corners of the book: at the upper right-hand and lower left-hand corners, for instance. Disulfide bonds restrict the formation of regular repeats in the secondary structure of proteins but abet tertiary structures by providing strong cross-links between chain sections.

It may not always be convenient to classify disulfide bonds as part of the primary structure. In insulin, in which disulfide bonds hold two separately inactive peptide chains together, this classification seems reasonable. Only one set of four pairings of disulfide bonds in ribonuclease seems to yield an enzymatically active molecule. If function is any criterion, the correct pairing of the disulfide bonds may be considered part of the primary structure in ribonuclease. On the other hand, the bond energy of about 60 kcal/mole for a specific disulfide bond will not be apparent if sulfhydryl-disulfide interchange reactions occur,

$$R\text{—}S^- + R'\text{—}S\text{—}S\text{—}R'' \rightleftarrows R\text{—}S\text{—}S\text{—}R'' + R'\text{—}S^-$$

because the free-energy change in such an interchange reaction is nearly zero. Sulfhydryl-disulfide interchange reactions are known to be important in the analysis of proteins; they caused confusion in determining the disulfide pairings in both insulin and ribonuclease. Such interchange reactions may also be biologically significant. Depending upon the particular case, disulfide bonds may be considered as part of the primary structure or the tertiary structure or as a separate component of protein structure.

2. Hydrogen bonds with bond energies of the order of 5 kcal/mole are due to primarily electrostatic interactions in a system consisting of two electronegative atoms, such as F, O, N, or S, separated by a hydrogen atom, usually at unequal distances from the two electronegative atoms so that it is considered covalently bonded to one and hydrogen-bonded to the other. Covalent bond formation involving hydrogen localizes an electron-pair bond between the two atoms, permitting a largely unshielded hydrogen nucleus to interact with a neighboring electronegative atom. Hydrogen bonds make up for their weakness by their number; when they repeat systematically as in an α helix, their total contribution to stabilization of conformation can be very great. Hydrogen bonds are important in aqueous systems, in

which they largely account for the high dielectric constant and high boiling point of water. Numerous groups may act as hydrogen donors and acceptors in proteins. In the list that follows, any donor may hydrogen-bond to any acceptor, and vice versa; all combinations are possible, provided only that bond angles are appropriate for hydrogen-bond formation.

Donors	*Acceptors*
Amide hydrogen	Amide carbonyl oxygen
Carboxylic acid	Carboxylic acid and carboxylate
—OH as in serine and threonine	—OH
Ammonium	Amino
Phenol	Phenolate and phenol
Guanidinium	Guanidate
Imidazolium	Imidazole
Sulfhydryl	Sulfide

Hydrogen bonding in carboxylic acid dimer formation is discussed in Sec. 3-1. Hydrogen bonds may also involve more than two groups. Both unshared pairs of electrons in an oxygen molecule in water are hydrogen-bond acceptors. Other water molecules, or two phenol molecules, may act as hydrogen-bond donors to a single water molecule.

Hydrogen bonds are primarily responsible for the specificity of secondary structure in proteins. Tertiary-structure hydrogen bonds have been found in myoglobin by x-ray diffraction. Intramolecular hydrogen bonds may be disrupted by the addition. of competitive hydrogen-bond formers such as urea and guanidinium salts or even water itself. Urea also interacts favorably with polar side chains in proteins. The ensuing breakdown of the secondary and tertiary structures is often what is meant by denaturation. Dissolution of intra-molecularly hydrogen-bonded proteins in water often results in a competition with water for hydrogen bonds. Such hydrogen-bond interchange reactions entail practically no free-energy change; almost no thermodynamic energy barrier exists for their occurrence.

3. Salt linkages such as

$$-C{\overset{\displaystyle O}{\underset{\displaystyle O}{\Bigg\langle}}}{}^- \qquad \overset{\displaystyle H}{\underset{\displaystyle H}{HN^+}}-$$

have a free energy of formation of about 10 kcal/mole, owing to a favorable entropy term of about 30 cal/deg mole. Salt linkages are more likely to occur in low-dielectric media such as organic solvents and the hydrophobic interiors of globular proteins than in aqueous environments. Because it raises the already high dielectric constants of aqueous solutions, urea should weaken salt linkages. No sharp distinction exists between certain salt linkages and some types of hydrogen bonding, such as in the above example. The binding of alkali-metal ions and some large anions are examples of external salt linkages to proteins. Since proteins are not easily denatured by the addition of salts which reduce electrostatic interactions, salt linkages are probably not by themselves determinant in secondary and tertiary structure. That they can contribute to stability is indicated by the partial breakdown of the quarternary structure of hemoglobin at high salt concentrations.

4. Van der Waals bonding is a short-range polarization interaction of about 5 kcal/mole with an energy dependent on the r^{-6} power of the distance between affected groups. These forces are probably of secondary importance in protein chemistry, except possibly in some unusual cases such as for polyproline II.

5. Hydrophobic bonds result when the apolar side chains found in the amino acids alanine, leucine, isoleucine, valine, phenylalanine, proline, tyrosine, and methionine come together and exclude water to yield a hydrophobic region, as in micelle formation. The energy of hydrophobic-bond formation is only minimally derived from van der Waals interactions. The formation of hydrophobic domains from several smaller regions is characterized by unfavorable positive enthalpy and predominating favorable positive entropy terms, yielding a negative free-energy change according to the equation $\Delta G = \Delta H - T \Delta S$. These results have been interpreted as indicating a greater organization of water with more hydrogen bonds about apolar groups than in bulk water. Two separated hydrophobic regions possess a greater total area than the region resulting from their merger. Consequently, a smaller number of water molecules surrounds the merged hydrophobic region, and an energy gain on merger results from reorganization of water to a more disordered state. The strength of hydrophobic bonds lies in this reorganization of water, rather than in the apolar additive. Hydrophobic bonds require water for their formation. Since hydrophobic-bond formation is slightly endothermic, hydrophobic bonds should become more stable as temperature increases. Though van der Waals interactions furnish only a fraction of hydrophobic-bond energies, distances between atoms engaged in hydrophobic bonds are close to van der Waals contact distances, which are greater than hydrogen- and covalent-bond distances.

In general, a protein might be expected to assume a conformation which maximizes the number of hydrophobic side chains in the interior and spreads hydrophilic groups over the surface in contact with water. Amino acid side chains in a pleated sheet are better positioned to form hydrophobic bonds than those in an α helix. For each mole of methylene groups transferred from an aqueous to a hydrophobic environment, the free-energy change is about -0.75 kcal. Organic solvents weaken hydrophobic bonds by diluting water and provide an environment not incompatible with apolar groups. Urea seems to be a mild hydrophobic-bond breaker. Since proteins are usually less stable the higher the temperature, factors other than hydrophobic bonds must contribute to their stability. The small positive heat terms that arise on hydrophobic bond formation are easily masked by the larger negative heat terms involved in other kinds of bonding. Nonetheless, hydrophobic bond formation is an important contributor to protein stability. Just how important it is is an area of current research which has stimulated a renewed interest in the fundamental physical-chemistry problem of nonpolar molecules in aqueous solutions, a problem which has lain nearly dormant for almost 15 years. The formation of relatively nonspecific hydrophobic bonds may provide a great deal of the driving force for tertiary folding in proteins, while specificity is a result of hydrogen bonds and salt linkages.

6. When proteins are near the isoionic point, low electrostatic energy produces a general stability which may result in aggregation and precipitation. The accumulation of positive or negative charge on addition of acid or base is usually destabilizing. Neutral proteins at low ionic strengths tend to associate, owing to charge fluctuations producing regions of opposite charge on neighboring molecules.

7. Metal ions might stabilize tertiary structure by forming cross-links between the sections of a chain. In mercury-mercaptalbumin dimer one mercuric ion links two mercaptalbumin molecules through sulfhydryl groups, an example of a metal ion promoting quarternary structure.

8. Where possible, hydrogen atoms and other groups tend to form staggered, rather than eclipsed, conformations. This principle is illustrated by a barrier to internal rotation of 2.8 kcal/mole in ethane, in which the three positions of minimum potential energy about the carbon-carbon bond occur when the hydrogen atoms of opposite methyl groups are staggered relative to each other. The interconversion of conformers is achieved rapidly, however. Application of this principle to proteins limits the conformation of side chains so that, instead of flopping about, they are restricted to a few relatively stable positions.

In the preceding discussion of the bonds involved in protein structure, we noted that urea (NH_2CONH_2) acts primarily as a hydrogen-bond breaker in producing the unfolding of secondary and tertiary structures to more random conformations. Urea is frequently used in concentrations up to 10 M to denature proteins. The consequences of such high concentrations of a foreign substance in protein systems are noteworthy. Even if 99.9% pure, a 10 M urea solution containing an impurity of the same molecular weight would be 10^{-2} M in impurity, a concentration that is at least an order of magnitude greater than that of most protein concentrations. An 8 M urea solution contains a slowly attained equilibrium concentration of 0.02 M cyanate ion (recall the synthesis of urea from ammonium cyanate by Wohler). Cyanate ion is reactive toward amino and sulfhydryl groups and may be responsible for instances of irreversible denaturation when urea is added to protein solutions.

16-2 FORMATION OF TERTIARY STRUCTURE IN RIBONUCLEASE

As explained in Chap. 20, the sequence of amino acid residues in a protein chain is under genetic and enzymatic control. If the one-dimensional primary structure is externally determined, are the features of protein conformation, disulfide links, and secondary and tertiary structures also so determined? Or is the sequence of amino acids in the one-dimensional primary structure sufficient to promote the precise folding necessary for the functions of protein molecules? These questions have been answered elegantly for ribonuclease, an enzymatic protein which cleaves ribonucleic acid, and whose sequence of 124 amino acid residues is known. If the one-dimensional sequence of amino acid residues is numbered from the N-terminal end, the eight cysteine residues occur at positions 26, 40, 58, 65, 72, 84, 95, and 110. In the native protein the cysteine residues are all cross-linked to form four disulfide bonds in the following pairings: 26–84, 40–95, 58–110, and 65–72. These pairings reduce the permissible amount of α helix, but hydrodynamic measurements indicate that ribonuclease is nearly spherical and hence must be extensively folded back upon itself in a tertiary structure stabilized by side-chain interactions.

The four specific intact disulfide linkages of native ribonuclease may be reduced to free sulfhydryl groups with mercaptoethanol in the presence of urea, yielding a single polypeptide chain, containing eight cysteine residues, which is enzymatically inactive and possesses no secondary or tertiary structure. The presence of urea is essential, since the disulfide links are not reduced unless the secondary and tertiary structures are disturbed. Upon oxidation (with oxygen) of a urea-free solution of reduced ribonuclease to form disulfide links, any of a whole gamut of possibilities between two extremes may occur. If disulfide links are formed at random, the first sulfhydryl group has a choice of seven cysteine residues with which to form a disulfide link, leaving six free cysteine residues, one of which has a choice of five cysteine residues, etc., so that there are $7 \times 5 \times 3 \times 1 = 105$ possibilities. The probability of forming the unique set of pairings in the native enzyme is less than 1%. This calculation is oversimplified, since the cysteine residues are not equally spaced along the chain, and no weighting has been introduced to allow for greater probability of pairing with neighboring sulfhydryl groups. Some of the 105 possibilities are more probable than others, but introduction of these factors does not significantly alter the result. Therefore, if only the native form of the protein is enzymatically active, we would expect about 1% of the initial activity on reduction and reoxidation if random pairing occurs. For specific pairing, results near 100% activity for regenerated enzyme might be achieved, and results between the limits of 1% and 100% are conceivable. Upon reduction and reoxidation of native ribonuclease at a concentration of less than 0.1%, the experimental result is that about 70% of reoxidized material is soluble, and this soluble product possesses from 80 to 100% of the activity of the native enzyme. Presumably the precipitate contains intermolecularly cross-linked material. No active product is obtained if urea is present during oxidation. Evidently, the one-dimensional amino acid sequence is sufficient to determine the folding of the protein so that only the single (or one of the few) enzymatically active product of disulfide pairing (out of 105 possibilities) is formed.

These significant results imply that the one-dimensional amino acid residue sequence is sufficient to determine the conformation of enzymatically active protein and that no special enzymes are necessary for appropriate geometric pairing of cysteine residues. The specific disulfide links spontaneously formed apparently stabilize an enzymatically active conformation but are not necessary for producing this conformation. Reduced and reoxidized ribonuclease has the same enzymatic activity, ultraviolet spectra, intrinsic viscosity, optical rotatory dispersion, and immunological properties as does the native enzyme, and both yield identical peptide maps on enzymatic digestion. If both did not have the same disulfide pairings, the disulfide-containing peptides from an enzymatic digest would not appear at the same positions on a peptide map.

Experiments have compared the rate of disappearance of sulfhydryl groups and optical-rotation changes on reoxidation of reduced ribonuclease with the rate of reappearance of enzymatic activity. A concentration-dependent induction period is observed for reappearance of enzyme activity, which lags the rate of disappearance of sulfhydryl groups and the decrease in levorotation. Analysis reveals that some intermolecular disulfide pairings are formed initially, but these are later corrected by sulfhydryl-disulfide interchange reactions to yield the thermodynamically favored native structure. This view is supported by the observation that enzymatically inactive, fully cross-linked, oxidized ribonuclease molecules produced under special conditions may be activated by the addition of sulfhydryl compounds, including reduced ribonuclease, under conditions known to favor sulfhydryl-disulfide interchange reactions.

Under appropriate conditions, the enzyme subtilisin splits the peptide bond between residues 20 (alanine) and 21 (serine) of ribonuclease, yielding a short peptide (called S-peptide) of 20 residues and a longer peptide (called S-protein) of 104 residues. This cleavage occurs before the first cysteine residue 26, so that appearance of the 20-residue S-peptide means that just a "tail" of the enzyme is removed. When tail and S-protein are separated, neither exhibits enzymatic activity, but an equimolar mixture of the two is active. Apparently the appropriate tertiary structure is formed by side-chain interactions without an amide bond between residues 20 and 21. Reduction of S-protein in the absence of S-peptide as described above for the whole enzyme, followed by oxidation, yields regenerated S-protein with the same disulfide pairing as the original. Upon addition of S-peptide to reduced-reoxidized S-protein, high yields of enzymatic activity result. Evidently S-peptide is not essential for appropriate disulfide pairing in S-protein. S-peptide does seem to be helpful in increasing efficiency, however, in that it reduces the amount of precipitate, which presumably consists of intermolecularly cross-linked material. When the same reduction-reoxidation experiment is performed on a mixture containing both components, higher yields of soluble, active material are obtained.

Experiments indicate that results similar to those from ribonuclease are obtained for some other proteins. Even in human serum albumin with 17 disulfide cross-links, 50% of the specific combining capacity is restored upon oxidation of reduced protein. The reversible denaturation of enzymes and other proteins has long been investigated. In tobacco mosaic virus, protein cylinders consisting of many individual protein molecules are formed from denatured protein that contains no disulfide linkages in the absence of nucleic acid (Sec. 20-2). A growing body of evidence indicates that the one-dimensional primary structure frequently dictates the formation of a fairly specific (depending upon how precisely one cares to define atomic positions) three-dimensional protein conformation with a specific biological activity. Disulfide bonds would be expected to inhibit the process of helix formation. The ribonuclease results indicate that, in nascent proteins, secondary and tertiary structures, formed prior to disulfide cross-links, serve to lock the correct conformation into position. Some current examples of irreversible denaturation may also reveal reversible characteristics if appropriate conditions are found. In biological systems, where proteins folded into unsatisfactory conformations would be more susceptible to proteolysis, this debris of biologically inactive protein would be hydrolyzed to yield the building blocks for subsequent combination into a biologically significant protein. By isolation procedures, protein chemists promote the retention and purification of active material, particularly in the case of enzymes where inactive protein is discarded. It is interesting to speculate as to whether such discarded protein is an example of a biologically inactive would-be enzyme as well as material inactivated by isolation procedures. The isolation of any active protein by some rather severe procedures may be a manifestation of a primary structure redetermining active conformations upon a return to milder conditions.

16-3 HELIX - COIL TRANSITIONS

In the absence of restraining forces, a linear polymer chain in dilute solution can assume a large number of random conformations of approximately the same energy. A detailed analysis of each of the many possibilities is impractical; instead a statistical averaging is applied to the so-called random coil. Let h be the distance between the ends of a linear chain containing n linkages, each of length l. If no restrictions are made on bond angles, the root mean square value of h is given by

$$(\overline{h^2})^{1/2} = n^{1/2}l \tag{16-1}$$

The root mean square average end-to-end distance increases with the square root of the number of linkages in the chain and hence increases as $M^{1/2}$, where M is the molecular weight of the polymer. In Eq. (8-12), we have already related the average distance between the ends of a coil to the radius of gyration. The number of permissible conformations for only a moderately long random-coil molecule exceeds the number of molecules in solution. For real polymers, restrictions on bond angles exist, and suitable modifications should be introduced into Eq. (16-1). With these corrections,

$$(\overline{h^2})^{1/2} \simeq 5.3n^{1/2} \tag{16-2}$$

where length is expressed in angstrom units, and n is the number of repeating trans peptide units (Sec. 14-1) with free rotation elsewhere in the polypeptide backbone. As described in Sec. 14-2, polyproline has an additional rotational restriction, but the numerical factor in Eq. (16-2) is increased only to 5.7. For this reason, substitution of a few prolines in a polypeptide chain such as a protein does not significantly alter Eq. (16-2) for random polypeptide coils. Experimental values of $(\overline{h^2}/n)^{1/2} \simeq 6.5$, observed for denatured collagen, give satisfactory agreement with theory.

Many synthetic polymers in solution take up the random-coil conformation referred to in the previous paragraph, yet few biological macromolecules do so in their normal or biological states. Several helical forms assumed by polypeptide biopolymers have been described in Chap. 14. Helix stabilization is provided by intramolecular secondary binding, usually due to hydrogen bonds among closely spaced units. In this section we propose to describe the reversible transition from random coil to the commonly occurring α helix for synthetic polypeptides with a common substituent, in the absence of side-chain interactions. Results obtained are relevant to polypeptides with a variety of side-chain groups, such as proteins.

When a solution containing sufficiently long polymer molecules in helical form is heated, a marked increase in optical rotation (a convenient measure of helical content) occurs in a narrow temperature range as molecules take up a random-coil conformation. Such sharp, reversible transformations are similar to phase transitions, while the helix-coil conversion is analogous to melting. In the random-coil state, a molecule meets resistance in forming the first turn of the helix, owing to the concomitant large decrease in rotational entropy, but, once formed, this first turn serves as a nucleus for further turns. This process, similar to promoting crystallization from solutions with a seed crystal, is consistent with an abrupt transition.

Let n be the number of hydrogen-bonded segments or amino acid residues in a polypeptide chain, and K the equilibrium constant for incorporation into an already formed helical section of the first neighboring residue of a long nonhelical section. This equilibrium constant is dependent upon temperature and solvent. Because a hydrogen bond that initiates a new helical section forms only with difficulty, the equilibrium constant for this initial nucleation process is σK, where the temperature-independent σ is less than 10^{-2}. The smaller the value of σ, the sharper the transition. Zimm and Bragg have performed a statistical analysis of an α-helix–coil transition assuming hydrogen-bond donation only between a given amide group and the third preceding group. Some of their results relating K and n are presented in Table 16-1. They found that the value $K = 1$ is critical, that a lesser value implies no helix regardless of chain length, and that a greater value yields at least some helix formation if a certain value of n is exceeded. If half the residues are to be contained in helical sections when $\sigma = 10^{-4}$, then for K values of 1.1, 2, 3, and 7, the corresponding required values of n are about 60, 15, 11, and 8, respectively. If initiation of a new helical section is simpler, say $\sigma = 10^{-2}$, then for $K = 2$, n need only be 9 for half the residues to be in helical sections. In a study of the temperature dependence of the transition in chains of poly-γ-benzyl-L-glutamate of different lengths, a value of $\sigma = 2 \times 10^{-4}$ is found to give the best fit to the data. A value of $\sigma = 1 \times 10^{-4}$ was used in constructing Table 16-1.

TABLE 16-1 *Dependence of Polypeptide-chain Conformation on Number of Amino Acid Residues n and Equilibrium Constant K for Hydrogen-bond Formation between Helical and Random Sections*

n \ K	<1	1	2	4
<7	Random chains			
10^1			Random chains and helical chains	
10^2		Chains with alternating random and helical sections	Helical chains with occasional disordered ends	Unbroken helical chains
10^3				
10^4				
10^5			Helical chains with scattered, short random sections and disordered ends	

If we select a polypeptide with a given n in the random condition and decrease the temperature of its solution, we may follow the progress of the transition to a helix by reading across Table 16-1. The composition of the solute at the transition temperature at which half the residues are in helical sections and half in random sections is strongly dependent on chain length. Short chains at the transition temperature are either wholly random or wholly helical and exhibit an all-or-none character. Each long chain, however, consists of half helix and half coil at the transition temperature. The short, scattered random sections in long helical chains contain at least three residues. In general, non-hydrogen-bonded segments tend to coalesce rather than occur at random, singly, or in pairs. On heating, a short helix transforms to a coil by unzipping from the ends, while a long helix lengthens the sections that are already random at the expense of neighboring residues in helical sections. Because a long chain contains many random sections, unzipping from the ends is unimportant in the transition to a coil.

Since independent short chains in the transition region exhibit helix-coil heterogeneity between chains rather than between sections of a single chain, transitions are broader for short chains than for long chains. Globular proteins contain only short helical regions because the molecule so often doubles back on itself to form a compact structure, yet they display sharp transitions. Therefore, the short helical regions are not independent, and globular proteins yield sharp transitions because the transformation is cooperative among various parts of the molecule. Since proteins also contain a heterogeneity in side-chain groups that is missing in the synthetic polypeptides (which the theory assumes), transitions of proteins should be broader than those of polypeptides of the same length.

We can express the results in thermodynamic terms by recalling the relationships among equilibrium constants, free energy, enthalpy, and entropy:

$$-RT \ln K = \Delta G^o = \Delta H^o - T \Delta S^o \tag{16-3}$$

In inert solvents, the helix is unstable at high temperatures. The free-energy change associated with helix formation will be negative at low temperatures and positive at high temperatures if ΔH^o and ΔS^o are both negative. When ΔH^o is a small negative number, it can dominate the entropy term only at low temperatures at which ΔG^o is negative and $K > 1$. When the negative entropy of folding becomes predominant at high temperatures, ΔG^o becomes positive, and $K < 1$.

In previous discussion, the solvent in which the helix-coil transitions take place has been considered inert. This assumption is seldom valid because the solvent preferentially associates with either helix or coil. Water associates more with a random coil, so that the equilibrium being studied is a hydrogen-bond interchange reaction between a hydrated helix and a more hydrated coil. Hydrogen-bond formation to yield a helix must compete with hydrogen-bond formation of the same groups with the solvent. Strong hydrogen-bonding agents such as urea, guanidine, formic acid, dichloroacetic acid, and trichloroacetic acid favor the random-coil form, while poor hydrogen-bonding solvents such as ethylene dichloride, chloroform, and 2-chloroethanol promote intrachain or interchain hydrogen-bond formation. Reversible helix-coil transitions occur abruptly over a small range of mixed solvent composition.

Preferential association in mixed-solvent systems can lead to an inversion of the usual stabilities; in mixtures of ethylene dichloride and dichloroacetic acid (DCA), the high-temperature form of poly-γ-benzyl-L-glutamate is helical. This inversion can be described by Eq. (16-3) where both ΔH^o and ΔS^o are positive. Then, by arguments similar to those just given for inert solvents, $K < 1$ at low temperatures, and $K > 1$ at high temperatures. One way to interpret this result is by considering the reaction

$$\text{coil (DCA)}_a \rightleftarrows \text{helix (DCA)}_b + (a - b)(\text{DCA})$$

where $a - b$ is positive. The reaction is endothermic because energy is required to break hydrogen bonds between coil and DCA, and the entropy of mixing of released DCA more than offsets the greater entropy of coil over helix, producing a positive net entropy change. Such inversions are possible only in mixed-solvent systems.

Helix stability depends on both temperature and solvent environment. As an approximation, a helix-coil transition occurs when the free-energy change accompanying bond rotation in a solvated coil becomes equal to the free-energy difference between intrahelical and solvent-coil hydrogen bonds. Side-chain groups of proteins provide additional interacting centers that may tip the balance to either helix or coil. These interactions can be electrostatic; poly-L-glutamic acid is helical in acid solution but random in neutral solutions in which charge repulsion among ionized carboxylate groups disrupts the helix.

16-4 ESTIMATION OF PROTEIN CONFORMATION IN SOLUTION

Optical Rotatory Dispersion. In their native states many proteins are levorotatory, with specific rotations in the range

$$-80° < [\alpha]_\text{D} < -30°$$

(Definitions of specific rotations and other terms are given in Sec. 1-2.) When these native proteins are subjected to denaturing conditions (exposure to urea, guanidinium salts, acid, alkali, or heat), the levorotatory properties frequently increase to give a range of

$$-120° < [\alpha]_\text{D} < -80°$$

Though the exact value of the increase in levorotation on denaturation is dependent upon both the protein and the solvent, the uniform increase for so many proteins implies a common underlying transformation.

The levorotatory properties of denatured proteins may be ascribed to their common structural unit of L-amino acids. For their relative abundance in proteins, the mean specific rotation of the L-amino acids is about $-100°$, the same magnitude as the value for denatured proteins. Evidently some structural element or elements in native proteins result in less negative levorotations. We shall now examine how macromolecules, composed of residues of a single configuration and folded into a helical conformation, display optical rotatory power, a sum of the contributions due to asymmetric monomeric units and dissymmetric helical folding of one hand over the other.

When optical rotation measurements are performed on denatured proteins over a range of wavelengths, the rotatory-dispersion curves are plain and may be fitted by the one-term Drude equation (1-2) with $\lambda_c \simeq 210$ mμ. This value is close to the absorption region of the peptide chromophore but should not be taken to imply that the optical rotation is necessarily due to a single absorption band. Native proteins usually exhibit plain curves to about 300 mμ, but λ_c calculated from a simple Drude expression may be well over 250 mμ. Such values of λ_c have lost their original significance, because the absorption band of the peptide chromophore does not exhibit a similar increase in wavelength. In addition, the λ_c values for native proteins are dependent upon solvent and temperature even if the protein conformation is not altered. The quantitative standardization of rotatory dispersion changes for molecules as diverse as proteins is so difficult that pioneering work was directed to a study of synthetic polypeptides of uniform composition.

From a variety of hydrodynamic and absorption measurements, poly-L-glutamic acid is known to exist in a random-coil form at neutral pH, and as an α helix under acid conditions in which no charge repulsion among negative carboxylate groups occurs. Figure 16-2 shows a plot of $\lambda^2[\alpha]$ versus $[\alpha]$ for poly-L-glutamic acid at several pH values yielding a variety of helical contents from 100% coil to 100% helix. According to the simple Drude equation (1-2), the slope of the straight line obtained from such a plot is the dispersion constant λ_c. Figure 16-2 indicates that as the helical content increases, $[\alpha]_D$ (indicated by the dashed line) becomes less levorotatory, and λ_c increases. Similar changes in proteins were mentioned above. At high helical contents, however, the dispersion data are no longer adequately described by the simple Drude equation, as shown by the curvature in the upper curves of Fig. 16-2. The two-term Drude equation (1-3) fits the data at high helical contents, but an alternative equation which also accounts for the rotatory-dispersion data is preferred:

$$[m'] = \frac{a_0\lambda_0^2}{\lambda^2 - \lambda_0^2} + \frac{b_0\lambda_0^4}{(\lambda^2 - \lambda_0^2)^2} \tag{16-4}$$

where $[m']$ is the vacuum value of the mean residue rotation $[m]$, corrected for the refractive index n of the solvent. If MRW is the mean residue weight, then

$$[m'] = \frac{3[m]}{n^2 + 2} = \frac{3[\alpha](\text{MRW})}{(n^2 + 2)100}$$

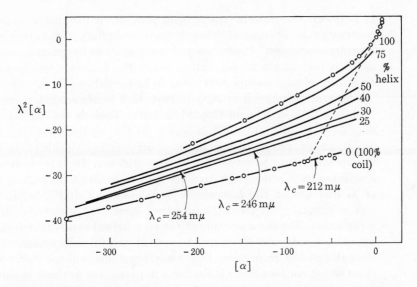

FIG. 16-2 Plot of $\lambda^2[\alpha]$ versus $[\alpha]$ for poly-L-glutamic acid with solvents of various helix-promoting abilities. The dashed line passes through points of $\lambda_0 = 5,893$ A corresponding to the sodium D lines. [From J. T. Yang and P. Doty, *J. Am. Chem. Soc.*, **79**, 761 (1957).]

Equation (16-4) enjoys a semitheoretical coupled-oscillator basis and contains three adjustable parameters instead of four as in the two-term Drude equation. Unlike a_0, which is dependent upon the environment, b_0 and λ_0 have been found to be largely independent of solvent. Since the second term on the right of Eq. (16-4) accounts for the complex dispersion at high helical contents, b_0 is taken as a measure of secondary structure in a macromolecule. Most data are precise enough to permit the accurate evaluation of only three parameters. Equation (16-4) is applied by plotting $[m'](\lambda^2 - \lambda_0^2)$ versus $1/(\lambda^2 - \lambda_0^2)$ and calculating b_0 from the slope. The appropriate value of λ_0 is found by trial and error until a straight line is obtained. Fortunately, $\lambda_0 \simeq 212$ for both the disordered and α-helix forms of many polypeptides and proteins, permitting b_0 to represent simply the α-helix contributions. For uniformity, Eq. (16-4) is applied even though the simple Drude equation may be adequate. For several kinds of molecules, $b_0 \simeq 0$ for disordered molecules and about -630 for completely α-helical molecules. Polyproline and polypeptides substituted in the β-carbon by atoms other than hydrogen or saturated carbon exhibit different dispersion parameters. These amino acids usually make up less than 20% of a protein. If the correspondence between α-helical content and

b_0 is linear, the determination of b_0 provides a measure of α-helical content in the absence of other forms of secondary structure. Optical rotatory-dispersion studies on polymers of γ-methyl-L-glutamate in dimethylformamide reveal that between the 7- and 9-unit polymers an abrupt change occurs in favor of helix formation.

The x-ray studies described in Sec. 15-2 indicate that myoglobin contains 77% of a right-handed α helix. Though optical rotatory-dispersion studies are difficult owing to the highly absorbing heme group, an analysis performed on the short-wavelength side of the heme absorption yields $b_0 = -390$ and $\lambda_0 = 216$ mμ. In this short-wavelength region it is necessary to allow for the greater than 212 mμ value of λ_0 and adjust the b_0 scale to $b_0 = -535$ for 100% helix. Then $100 \times {}^{390}\!/_{535} = 73\%$ helix, in excellent agreement with the definitive x-ray value. The good agreement between helical contents determined by solid x-ray and by solution optical rotatory-dispersion studies strengthens the conviction that x-ray crystallographers study molecules whose conformation is similar if not identical to those in solution and that their results are significant in interpreting biological functions. For poly-L-alanine, for which only a right-handed α helix fits x-ray data, $b_0 \simeq -500$. These two results suggest that a negative b_0 corresponds to a right-handed α helix.

The synthetic polypeptide poly-β-benzyl-L-aspartate yields

$$b_0 = +611$$

in chloroform, indicating a left-handed α helix. Consistent with the left-handedness of the α helix is its weakness; addition of less than 10% dichloroacetic acid to the chloroform solution yields the random-coil conformation. In contrast, it is necessary to have a nearly 70:30 mixture of dichloroacetic acid and chloroform to effect the right-handed α-helical–to–random-coil transition in poly-γ-benzyl-L-glutamate. A molecule with equal amounts of helix of opposite senses would have $b_0 \simeq 0$. In the absence of other forms of secondary structure, the parameter b_0 of Eq. (16-4) provides a measure of excess helical content of one sense over the other. Most proteins seem to contain only right-handed α helices, so that determination of b_0 directly yields the apparent helical content.

Scales of helical content based on λ_c or $[\alpha]_D$ have also been established, but they are more dependent than b_0 on extraneous factors such as temperature and choice of solvent. In addition, the λ_c scale suffices only up to about 40% helical content, because the dispersion becomes complex for higher helical contents, and the dispersion constant is not defined for situations in which the simple Drude equation (1-2) is not applicable. Qualitatively, though, the decreased levorotation of native proteins compared to their denatured counterparts, measured by $[\alpha]_D$ and described at the beginning of this section, may be ascribed to a positive contribution of the rotation due to formation of a right-handed α helix superimposed upon the mean residue rotation of L-amino acids.

Some caution must be exercised, because the preceding quantitative interpretation is predicated on the existence of only two conformations, α-helical and disordered. To the extent that secondary structures which are not α-helical, such as β structures, are important in proteins, the discussion will require modification. Pleated-sheet or β structures are characterized by positive b_0 values, opposite in sign to those of right-handed α helices. Helical arrays other than the α helix also yield different results. In denaturation, the levorotation of collagen decreases rather than increases, and both native and denatured forms exhibit simple dispersion.

Table 16-2 provides an estimate of the apparent excess right-handed α-helical content of several proteins from b_0 measurements. In applying the analysis to proteins, the assumption is made that side-chain contributions are unimportant or cancel. When proteins are placed in 2-chloroethanol or other non-hydrogen-bonding organic solvents, b_0 values frequently become more negative, increasing the apparent percentage helix to about 60% for the proteins of low helical content studied by rotatory dispersion and listed in Table 16-2. An exception is insulin, which is unchanged. Addition of 2-chloroethanol should weaken hydrophobic bonds by dilution of water and promote intramolecular hydrogen bonds through reduced competition from solvent.

T A B L E 1 6 - 2 *Apparent Percentage of α-Helical Contents of Proteins in Aqueous Solution*

	Rotatory dispersion	Deuterium exchange	Ultraviolet absorption
Paramyosin	95		93
Hemoglobin	80	60	
Myoglobin	75	50	67
Bovine albumin	46	40	
Insulin	38	60	44
Ovalbumin	31	50	
Lysozyme	29	45	
Ribonuclease	16	35	35
Chymotrypsin	23	43	
Chymotrypsinogen	12	20	
β-Lactoglobulin	11	25	25

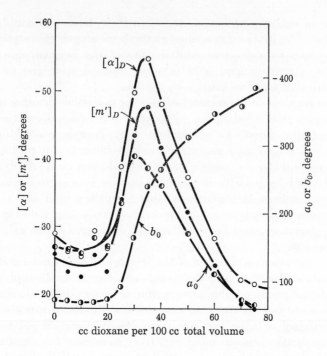

FIG. 16-3   Effect of addition of dioxane to an aqueous solution of β-lactoglobulin at pH 3 and ionic strength 0.02. The plot shows the specific rotation $[\alpha]_D$, the mean residue rotation $[m']_D$, and a_0 and b_0, two parameters of Eq. (16-4), with $\lambda_0 = 212\ m\mu$. [From C. Tanford, P. K. De, and V. G. Taggart, *J. Am. Chem. Soc.*, **82**, 6028 (1960).]

Figure 16-3 shows the effect on both $[\alpha]_D$ and b_0 of the addition of dioxane to an aqueous solution of β-lactoglobulin. The transformation takes place in two steps, as indicated by an increase in levorotation followed by a decrease. The latter occurs simultaneously with increasing negative values of b_0. The increase (but neither the decrease in levorotation nor the change in b_0) may be brought about by addition of hydrogen-bonding reagents such as urea or formamide. This suggests that an initial unfolding of the largely hydrophobic-bond-stabilized native structure of low helical content is succeeded by a refolding to a helical structure only in the absence of a competitive hydrogen-bonding solvent. Between the initial native structure and the final highly helical conformation, a more random intermediate conformation occurs. The final decrease in levorotation shown by $[\alpha]_D$ at high concentrations of organic solvent is consistent with the appearance of α-helical contributions. The initial increase in levorotation of $[\alpha]_D$ has been ascribed to a change from a hydrophobic to an aqueous environment or to contributions from β structures. Little experimental evidence exists to support either explanation. However, the percentage of α helix invoked (55%) to account quantitatively for the results by the latter explanation is much greater than the helical contents inferred from two independent methods in Table 16-2. On the other hand, the protein carries a predominant positive charge at pH 3, and, at the relatively low ionic strength of 0.02, electrostatic effects due to the addition of low-dielectric-constant solvents and to counter-ion binding may not have been fully evaluated.

In the α-helical form, synthetic polypeptides such as poly-L-glutamic acid display a negative Cotton effect with a trough at 233 mμ and a point of inflection at 225 mμ, as well as a stronger positive Cotton effect with a peak at 198 mμ and an inflection point at about 190 mμ. The random-coil form of the same polypeptide exhibits only a weak negative Cotton effect with a trough at 204 mμ, an inflection point at 197 mμ, and a peak at about 190 mμ. In conjunction with results for wholly helical polypeptides, the strength of the Cotton effects in muscle proteins, bovine albumin, and other proteins yields estimates of helical contents in good agreement with those obtained by other methods.

In another type of study, optically inactive cationic dyes, when attached to the helical form of poly-L-glutamic acid, yield a large induced Cotton effect which crosses the line of zero rotation near an absorption band of the dye (Fig. 1-1). This Cotton effect is of opposite sign for poly-D-glutamic acid and disappears when the macromolecules take up a random conformation, even though the dye remains bound. Evidently, the dye assumes optical activity because of interaction with a dissymmetric helix. Proteins containing iron-bearing heme groups carry their own "dyes" and exhibit Cotton effects in the visible region of the spectrum where the heme groups absorb. In heme-bearing myoglobin, hemoglobin, catalase, and peroxidase, the Cotton effects, but not the visible absorptions, disappear upon denaturation. Addition of non-optically-active, reduced nicotinamide adenine dinucleotide to liver alcohol dehydrogenase (a zinc enzyme) induces a Cotton effect in the region of the spectrum in which the nucleotide absorbs. In this case, however, it is believed that the Cotton effect is induced, not through dissymmetry of the helix, but by asymmetry at the binding site. As an example of the latter, optically active, transparent amino acids induce Cotton effects in the visible absorption ranges of their copper complexes.

Hydrogen-isotope Exchange. Hydrogen atoms bound to atoms with a free pair of electrons ordinarily exchange rapidly with one another, within about a minute, in contrast to a very much slower exchange, of the order of weeks or more, when hydrogen atoms are bound to atoms with no free electron pairs. In the case of proteins in aqueous solutions, hydrogen atoms bound to nitrogen, oxygen, or sulfur would normally be expected to exchange rapidly with solvent hydrogens or each other, while carbon-bound hydrogens would exchange slowly if at all. The hydrogen atoms of proteins, normally rapidly exchangeable, may exhibit a retardation of exchange in aqueous solution because they are involved in hydrogen bonds or are located in hydrophobic regions inaccessible to solvent. Hydrogen-isotope exchange rates are followed by placing a deuterated protein in H_2O and relating the density of cryosublimed solvent obtained at several time intervals to the relative deuterium content, by utilizing the radioactivity of tritium in a similar experiment, or most conveniently by measuring the decrease in intensity of the amide $1,550\text{-cm}^{-1}$ infrared band when a protein is placed in D_2O. It is also possible to follow isotopic exchange rates with other infrared bands, nuclear magnetic-resonance techniques, and Raman spectra in the case of smaller polypeptides. For all these experiments it is important that isotopic substitution does not change the conformation of the protein under the experimental conditions. At pH 4.3, normal ribonuclease exhibits a transition temperature in H_2O at 62°, while the deuterated protein transforms at 66° in D_2O. Since deuteration favors the helical form, the interpretation of exchange experiments conducted near 65° will be complicated by differing relative ratios of several conformers of the protein. For this reason, exchange experiments should be conducted under conditions in which transitions do not occur.

A kinetic analysis of exchange rates determined by the density method on insulin and ribonuclease indicates that it is convenient to divide potentially exchangeable hydrogens into at least three groups: rapidly, moderately fast, and slowly exchangeable hydrogens. Of the 91 potentially exchangeable hydrogens in insulin, of which 48 are in the peptide backbone, 61 exchange within 1 min, 7 exchange relatively rapidly, and 23 exchange slowly. Ribonuclease contains 245 exchangeable hydrogens, 119 of which are in the backbone. Though there are variations dependent upon the history of the sample, in ribonuclease about 175 hydrogens exchange rapidly, 50 more slowly, and about 20 quite sluggishly. In insulin and ribonuclease, 33% and about 25%, respectively, of exchangeable hydrogens do not exchange rapidly. If all the slowly exchanging hydrogens are considered to be in the peptide backbone, 63% and about 55%, respectively, of backbone hydrogens exchange slowly. It is probable that the 20 sluggish hydrogens in ribonuclease at low pH are due to guanidinium protons on four side-chain arginine residues, so that on this basis only about 40% of the backbone hydrogens exchange slowly. Presumably, rapidly exchanging hydrogens are in direct contact with solvent, while very slowly exchanging hydrogens are in hydrogen bonds or in hydrophobic regions of the protein. Those hydrogens exchanging at an intermediate rate are somewhat inaccessible to solvent or else exchange hydrogens only indirectly with solvent via previously exchanged neighboring hydrogens in the protein matrix. Myoglobin, with 77% helix determined by x-ray diffraction, gave only 51% helix by the density method, even when all slowly exchanging hydrogens were considered as backbone hydrogens.

The percentages of slowly exchanging hydrogens listed for several proteins in Table 16-2 were determined from the disappearance of the amide 1,550-cm^{-1} infrared band of the proteins in D_2O. In most of the proteins a core of about 15% of the hydrogens had not exchanged after 24 hours. Since an amide band was measured, the percentages of Table 16-2 correspond to backbone hydrogens, which exchange slowly because they are involved in hydrogen bonds or lie inaccessible to solvent in hydrophobic regions. For insulin and ribonuclease the percentages of Table 16-2 are greater than the percentages of total hydrogens slowly exchanged, as determined by the density method, and less than the percentages given above when all slowly exchanging hydrogens are considered backbone hydrogens. Although the experiments were performed at different temperatures, the comparison suggests that, for insulin and ribonuclease, the slow hydrogen exchange determined by the density method is mainly backbone exchange supplemented by some slowly exchanging side-chain hydrogens. More of the slowly exchanged hydrogens, as determined by the density method, are backbone hydrogens in the case of insulin, consistent with its greater helical content. X-ray studies indicate that ribonuclease is considerably less than half helix. Deuterium-exchange methods measure the direct or indirect availability of exchangeable hydrogens to solvent; the amide-band infrared technique limits the hydrogens considered to those on the backbone.

An estimate of α-helical content may also be made by examining the ultraviolet spectra of proteins at less than 200 mμ where amide-band absorption occurs. In this short-wavelength region, a conformation-dependent absorption appears, about half as great for the helical form of polypeptides as for the random and β forms, which have similar absorption spectra. Ultraviolet dichroism due to the directional properties of the helix is also observed. The last column of Table 16-2 lists the percentage α-helical contents determined from a linear scale correlating helical content with absorption in the 190- to 200-mμ region. In a study at such low wavelengths, light scattering and differential absorption of side-chain groups in the two conformations must be taken into account.

Table 16-2 presents apparent helical contents of a number of proteins estimated by three different methods. Where differences appear, more information may be gained by considering just what it is that each method is actually measuring. As described above, not even the density and infrared techniques for determination of slowly exchanging deuterium atoms have the same significance. In most cases the apparent percentage helical content obtained from rotatory-dispersion measurements is less than that inferred from the other two methods of Table 16-2. Several explanations for this disparity are plausible, apart from experimental variation and the assumptions and difficulties associated with the construction of a suitable scale relating a physical property to helical content. Rotatory-dispersion results measure only the excess of right- over left-handed helix segments, underestimating total helical content. On the other hand, not all slowly exchanging amide hydrogens followed by infrared absorption are necessarily hydrogen-bound in a helix; they may be hydrogen-bonded elsewhere or relatively inaccessible to solvent. The high value for insulin observed by deuterium-exchange techniques may be due to associated insulin monomers. Deuterium exchange in myoglobin and hemoglobin yields low apparent helical contents when the percentage of helix is relatively high. These compact molecules may exchange hydrogens rapidly at the ends of the several short helical sections, or exchange may be catalyzed by the relatively large number of imidazole groups present. In spite of the differences just discussed, the general qualitative agreement between three diverse methods for estimating apparent helical content is satisfactory.

Ultraviolet Difference Spectra. Absorption of light by proteins in the 250- to 300-mμ region of the spectrum is due primarily to the presence of three aromatic amino acids. Tryptophan and unionized tyrosine absorb maximally near 280 mμ, and phenylalanine more weakly near 260 mμ. A protein that absorbs more at 270 mμ than at 280 mμ usually has phenylalanine as a large fraction of its aromatic residues.

When proteins are denatured, small shifts (of the order of 1 mμ) to shorter wavelengths occur in the 250- to 300-mμ spectral region. Because the spectral shifts are small, a denatured or otherwise altered protein is usually compared with the same concentration of native protein, instead of only solvent, to produce a difference spectrum. If the perturbation involves only a shift in a simple spectrum with an absorption maximum, the difference spectrum is a derivative of the original spectrum with a minimum and a maximum near the midpoints of the ascent and descent of the absorption spectrum. When an intensity change or broadening also takes place, the alteration is not so simply formulated. Difference spectra may be induced by change of temperature, enzymatic hydrolysis, or various solvent changes such as addition of acid, base, urea, salt, or nonaqueous solvent. Most of these reagents shift the absorption spectra to shorter wavelengths.

Since absorption in the 250- to 300-mμ region of proteins is due to tryptophan, tyrosine, and phenylalanine residues, evidently some alteration in their condition perturbs the chromophore. With model compounds, indole, phenol, and benzene for the above residues, transfer of solute to a medium of greater refractive index yields a red shift. (The pronounced red shift to about 295 mμ produced by ionization of phenolic hydrogens is not included here.) Although this shift may be formulated quantitatively for nonpolar solvents, in aqueous solutions the general trend holds but is not capable of simple quantitative expression. It is necessary to consider the relative solvent stabilizations of the ground and excited states of the chromophoric groups. The blue shift obtained on disruption of protein structure can be accounted for qualitatively by considering the chromophoric groups to have been transferred from a hydrophobic environment of high refractive index in the protein matrix to an aqueous environment of lower refractive index. A study of difference spectra provides a sensitive measure of the disruption of tertiary structure that is often paralleled by concomitant changes in optical rotation, viscosity, etc. In other instances, large heat and entropy changes occur with little change in secondary structure, as indicated by optical rotation measurements. In such cases, ultraviolet difference spectra may provide an additional probe into changes of tertiary structure. Changes of charge near the chromophore also produce spectral perturbations, but study of model compounds indicates that the charge must be located quite near the chromophore to perturb the spectra. The breaking of hydrogen bonds from tyrosyl hydroxyl groups to hydrogen-bonding receptors such as carboxylate will also yield a blue shift. Spectral shifts due to the disruption of a hydrophobic environment and hydrogen bonds are in the same direction, and there has been some success in achieving their separation. The general environmental change usually accounts for the shift in proteins, and the burden of proof for invocation of the more specific hydrogen bonds is on the proposer.

SELECTED BIBLIOGRAPHY

1 M. A. Stahmann (ed.), "Polyamino Acids, Polypeptides and Proteins," University of Wisconsin Press, Madison, Wis., 1962.

2 W. Kauzmann, Some Factors in the Interpretation of Protein Denaturation, *Advan. Protein Chem.*, **14**, 1–63 (1959). Especially valuable for the discussion of hydrophobic bonds on pages 37 to 47.

3 F. H. White, Jr., Regeneration of Native Secondary and Tertiary Structures by Air Oxidation of Reduced Ribonuclease, *J. Biol. Chem.*, **236**, 1353–1360 (1961).

4 B. H. Zimm and J. K. Bragg, Theory of Phase Transitions between Helix

and Random Coil in Polypeptide Chains, *J. Chem. Phys.*, **31**, 526–53 (1959). See also S. Lifson and A. Roig, *J. Chem. Phys.*, **34**, 1963 (1961), and M. E. Bauer and L. H. Nosanow, *J. Chem. Phys.*, **38**, 578 (1963).

   5 P. Urnes and P. Doty, Optical Rotation and the Conformation of Polypeptides and Proteins, *Advan. Protein Chem.*, **16**, 401–544 (1961).

   6 W. Kauzmann, "Quantum Chemistry," Academic Press Inc., New York, 1957. The author presents more material on the interaction of light with matter than is usual in an elementary text. Extended discussions of light absorption, light scattering, and optical rotatory power are given.

   7 D. B. Wetlaufer, Ultraviolet Spectra of Proteins and Amino Acids. *Advan. Protein Chem.*, **17**, 303–390 (1962).

   8 S. Yanari and F. A. Bovey, Interpretation of the Ultraviolet Spectral Changes of Proteins, *J. Biol. Chem.*, **235**, 2818–2826 (1960).

QUESTIONS

   16-1 Why cannot single hydrogen bonds occur between side-chain groups and the peptide backbone of α-helical regions of a protein?

   16-2 What forces are responsible for maintaining the compact shapes of globular proteins?

   16-3 What agents may cause protein denaturation? What type of bond does each agent primarily affect?

   16-4 By comparing their effects on hydrogen bonds, salt linkages, and hydrophobic bonds, explain why urea stabilizes a random-coil form of a globular protein while organic solvents often favor an ordered form other than the native one.

   16-5 In how many ways can 11 cysteine residues in a polypeptide chain combine to give the maximum number of disulfide bonds?

   16-6 To what variables are helix-coil transitions sensitive?

   16-7 What quantities of Eq. (16-4) would you plot so that a_0 is equal to the intercept and b_0 is equal to the slope?

   16-8 Estimate $[\alpha]_D$ for an aqueous solution of a protein of mean residue weight 110 from Eq. (16-4) for both disordered and right-handed α-helical forms.

   16-9 Optical-rotation parameters change smoothly upon addition of acid to an aqueous solution of poly-L-lysine in the uncharged, high-pH, helical form to yield a nonhelical, positively charged molecule at low pH. Sedimentation analysis of the same transition reveals one component at all pH values and a maximum sedimentation rate at the midpoint (about pH 10) of the optical-rotation changes. At the same point, the viscosity is a minimum compared to values at higher or lower pH. Do these results indicate that all the molecules at pH 10 are half-helical or that half the molecules are completely helical? Explain.

   16-10 How many exchangeable hydrogens are there in glycylglycine and glutathione at neutral pH?

   16-11 Assuming a molecular weight of about 24,000 for both chymotrypsinogen and chymotrypsin, estimate from the data of Table 16-2 the additional number of turns of helix formed when the enzyme precursor is converted to active enzyme.

   16-12 The addition of urea to water increases the refractive index of the medium. Account for the fact that addition of a small amount of urea to an aqueous solution of ribonuclease yields a small red shift in the difference spectrum at 285 mμ, and that at a urea concentration of 5 M a sudden blue shift occurs.

17 | Nucleic Acids

Two linear, long-chain nucleic acids occur naturally: deoxyribosenucleic acid (DNA) and ribosenucleic acid (RNA). DNA, found mainly in chromosomes, is the genetic material. DNA preparations are heterogeneous because usually a single cell contains many kinds of DNA, differing in their base sequences; single molecules of DNA are found in bacteriophage. RNA is an intermediate carrier of genetic information from DNA for protein synthesis. There are several kinds of RNA; most occur in the cytoplasm, with the greatest concentration in the ribosomes. The role of the nucleic acids is considered in succeeding chapters; we are concerned in this chapter with their primary structure.

17-1   PRIMARY STRUCTURE

For both nucleic acids, the fundamental repeating unit is a nucleotide, a combination of an organic base, the sugar β-D-ribofuranose in RNA or β-D-deoxyribofuranose in DNA, and phosphate. When a base is attached at the 1' position (primes refer to the sugar rather than the base ring) of the puckered sugar ring without phosphate, the resulting compound is called a *nucleoside*. Nucleotides result from the esterification of the 2', 3', or 5' position of the ribose or the 3' and 5' positions of the deoxyribose rings with phosphate. Depending upon whether ribose or deoxyribose is the sugar used, nucleotides are often referred to as *ribotides* or *deoxyribotides*. Adenosine-5'-triphosphate, the ribotide discussed in Sec. 2-5, is the energy source of biological reactions. Results of chemical and enzymatic studies indicate that residues of RNA and DNA are linked as shown in Fig. 17-1. Note that the alternate 3' and 5' phosphate linkages give the chain a directional sense.

An important feature of the structure of long-chain nucleic acids, as indicated by the chain fragment in Fig. 17-1, is the presence of one

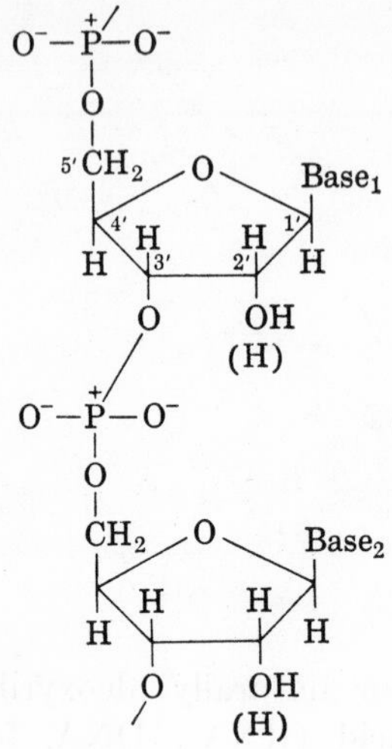

FIG. 17-1 Two nucleotide residues of the nucleic acid chain. RNA has an OH group at the 2' position of the furanose ring, whereas DNA has the hydrogen atom in parentheses. The alternate 3'- and 5'-phosphate residues give the chain a directional sense. If base₁ were adenine, and base₂ cytosine, the shorthand convention for the chain fragment would be · · · pApC · · · , where p represents the phosphate residue, and A and C the adenosine and cytidine residues, respectively.

negatively charged phosphate group for every nucleotide residue. The pK_a of the phosphate group in nucleic acids is about 1. Instead of nucleic acids, we almost always deal with such salts of the acids as sodium deoxyribonucleate. It should be understood that DNA and RNA refer to the salts, usually sodium or potassium salts. The repeating negative charge is important in any discussion of the properties of nucleic acids. Unless dilute neutral solutions of DNA are greater than 10^{-3} M in NaCl, the DNA becomes denatured.

17-2 NUCLEIC ACID BASES

Structures of nucleic acid bases are shown in Fig. 17-2. They are not very soluble in water and are hydrophobic in character. Cytosine, uracil, and thymine (5-methyluracil) are derivatives of pyrimidine. Adenine and guanine are derivatives of the organic base purine. Cytosine, adenine, and guanine are found naturally combined with ribose to yield the corresponding ribonucleosides cytidine, adenosine, and guanosine, or with deoxyribose to give the deoxyribonucleosides deoxycytidine, deoxyadenosine, and deoxyguanosine. In nature, uridine is the nucleoside derived from uracil and ribose, while thymidine is derived from thymine and deoxyribose. RNA contains four bases: cytosine, uracil, adenine, and guanine; the same bases occur in DNA, except that thymine is substituted for uracil. Four bases predominate in each case; other bases occur in lesser amounts, or occasion-

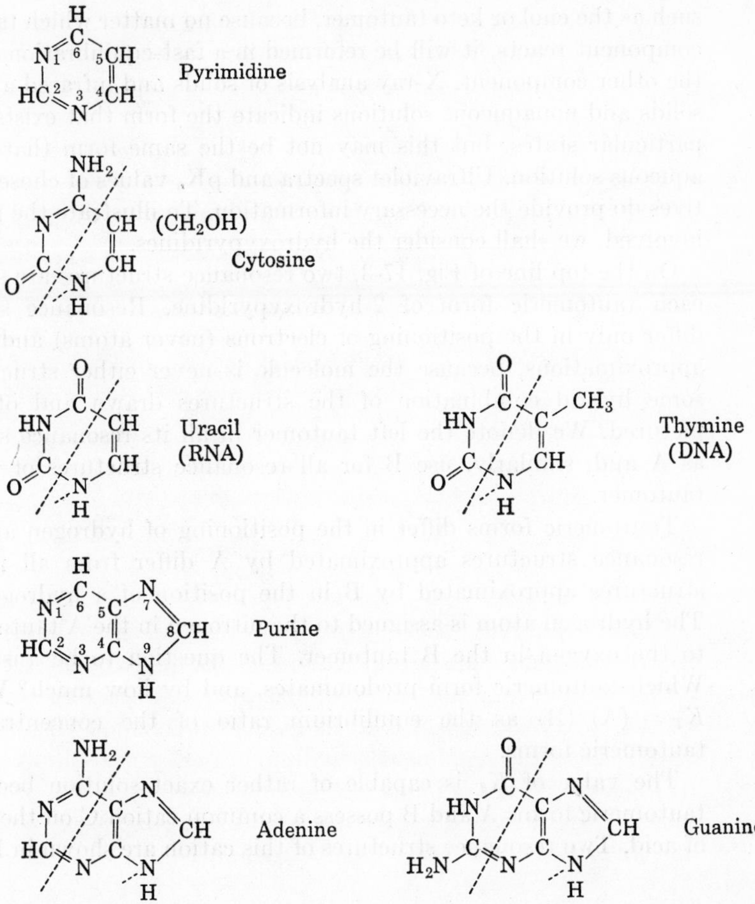

FIG. 17-2 Nucleic acid bases with the parent bases pyrimidine and purine. Dashed lines on the lower nitrogen atoms indicate positions where hydrogen atoms are replaced by sugars in the corresponding nucleosides. Atoms to the upper left of the dashed line are on the hydrogen-bonding side in nucleic acids, as described in Chap. 18.

ally an almost complete substitution takes place, such as the substitution of 5-hydroxymethylcytosine for cytosine in phage DNA.

17-3 TAUTOMERIC FORMS OF BASES

Nucleic acid bases may exist in a variety of tautomeric forms. It is important to determine the predominant forms of bases under normal conditions. Reactions are not helpful in determining a particular form such as the enol or keto tautomer, because no matter which tautomeric component reacts, it will be reformed in a fast-equilibration step with the other component. X-ray analysis of solids and infrared analysis of solids and nonaqueous solutions indicate the form that exists in those particular states, but this may not be the same form that exists in aqueous solution. Ultraviolet spectra and pK_a values of chosen derivatives do provide the necessary information. To illustrate the principles involved, we shall consider the hydroxypyridines.

On the top line of Fig. 17-3, two resonance structures are shown for each tautomeric form of 2-hydroxypyridine. Resonance structures differ only in the positioning of electrons (never atoms) and are only approximations, because the molecule is never either structure, but some hybrid combination of the structures drawn and others not pictured. We denote the left tautomer in all its resonance structures as A and, similarly, use B for all resonance structures of the right tautomer.

Tautomeric forms differ in the positioning of hydrogen atoms. All resonance structures approximated by A differ from all resonance structures approximated by B in the position of a hydrogen atom. The hydrogen atom is assigned to the nitrogen in the A tautomer, and to the oxygen in the B tautomer. The question to be answered is: Which tautomeric form predominates, and by how much? We define $K_T = (A)/(B)$ as the equilibrium ratio of the concentrations of tautomeric forms.

The value of K_T is capable of rather exact solution because the tautomeric forms A and B possess a common cation C on the addition of acid. Two resonance structures of this cation are shown in Fig. 17-3.

FIG. 17-3 Two resonance structures are shown for each tautomeric form (A and B) of 2-hydroxypyridine and its cation C.

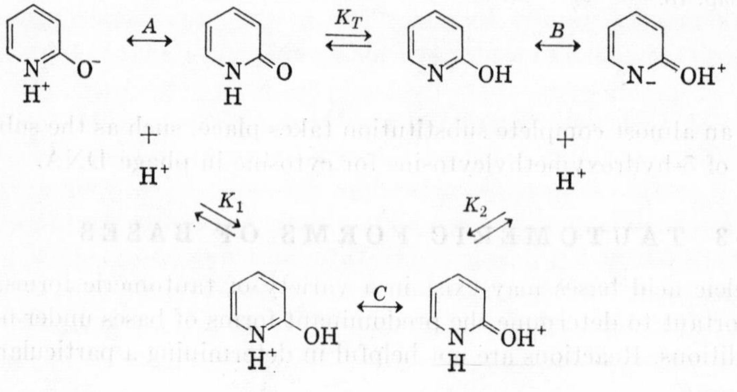

Once again, the resonance structures are approximate examples of a hybrid structure and have no independent existence. The acid ionization constants in terms of concentrations are

$$K_1 = \frac{(A)(H^+)}{(C)} \quad \text{and} \quad K_2 = \frac{(B)(H^+)}{(C)}$$

Hence,

$$K_T = \frac{K_1}{K_2} \tag{17-1}$$

Experimentally, the ionization constant determined by titration is

$$K_a = \frac{(H^+)[(A) + (B)]}{(C)} = K_1 + K_2 \tag{17-2}$$

Since K_a is known, the determination of either K_1 or K_2 would allow the calculation of the other, as well as K_T. Combination of Eqs. (17-1) and (17-2) yields

$$K_T = \frac{K_a}{K_2} - 1 \tag{17-3}$$

and

$$K_T^{-1} = \frac{K_a}{K_1} - 1 \tag{17-4}$$

The ionization constant K_2 may be approximated by titrating 2-methoxypyridine, since this compound cannot exist in the A tautomeric form. Similarly, 2-hydroxypyridine-N-methyl chloride cannot take up the B tautomeric form, and titration should yield an approximate value of K_1. Synthesis and titration of both derivatives provide more than sufficient data for a check to be made to assure that model compounds accurately represent one of the tautomeric forms. This analysis is similar to that given for glycine and its ethyl ester in Sec. 4-4.

Table 17-1 lists negative logarithms of experimental values of ionization constants for three isomeric hydroxypyridines and their N and O methyl derivatives as well as the value of K_T computed from Eq. (17-1). These values are probably more realistic than the values calculated from Eq. (17-3) or (17-4) because any effects of the methyl groups tend to cancel when the model compounds are compared with each other. Use of Eqs. (17-3) and (17-4) would, however, yield consistent values of K_T.

TABLE 17-1 *Acid Ionization and Tautomeric Equilibrium Constants for Hydroxypyridines at 20°C and Zero Ionic Strength (from Ref. 3)*

Isomer	pK_a	pK_1 (N-methyl)	pK_2 (O-methyl)	$K_T = K_1/K_2$
2-Hydroxypyridine	0.75	0.32	3.28	910
4-Hydroxypyridine	3.27	3.33	6.62	1,950
3-Hydroxypyridine	4.86	4.96	4.88	1.2

The high values of K_T for the 2 and 4 isomers demonstrate that the A tautomeric form of Fig. 17-3 is strongly favored. The ratio of nearly unity for the 3 or meta isomer indicates that the A and B tautomeric forms are present in about equal amounts. It is not possible to write the right-hand (amide) resonance structure of tautomer A for the meta isomer. Therefore, considerable resonance stabilization of the A relative to the B tautomeric form is lost in the case of the meta isomer, leading to nearly equal amounts of the A and B tautomeric forms.

The 2 and 4 isomers exist preponderantly as amides. The 4 isomer is a vinylogous amide since one ethylene group separates the constituents of the amide function. These isomers are misnamed hydroxypyridines. It is also incorrect to refer to the isomers as keto tautomers, because the functional group is amide and not ketone. The chemical properties of the compounds are those expected of amides.

Studies of ultraviolet absorption spectra support the conclusions derived from titrations. The spectrum of 2-hydroxypyridine is similar to that of its N-methyl derivative but quite different from that of its O-methyl derivative. Identical statements can be made for the 4 isomer. Significant perturbation of the spectrum by the methyl group does not allow a calculation of accurate K_T values. On the other hand, the spectrum of 3-hydroxypyridine is midway between the spectra of its N- and O-methyl derivatives, which are quite different. Lowering the dielectric constant of the solution by the addition of alcohol shifts the spectrum in favor of that of the O-methyl derivative, because the less polar B tautometer is favored since the 3 isomer has only a polar resonance structure for the A tautomer.

Application of the preceding analysis to uracil or thymine is complicated because two basic sites are available and a cation or anion common to the tautomeric forms does not exist. Consideration of the previous results and qualitative reasoning indicate, however, that uracil and thymine are predominantly amides. Nuclear magnetic-resonance spectroscopy studies support this contention.

The corresponding thio derivatives, in which sulfur is substituted for oxygen, also exist mainly as amides, in this case thioamides.

Thioamides are even more favored than their oxygen analogues. In aliphatic compounds, sulfur exhibits much less tendency to form double bonds than does oxygen. The preference for a thioamide over a sulfhydryl function in nucleic acid bases may be due to resonance interactions with the rings.

Analyses of aminopyridines by titration and spectrophotometric methods as described for hydroxypyridines indicate that the amino (—NH$_2$) form is favored over the imino (=NH) by several powers of 10. By analogy, an amino substitution such as occurs in cytosine favors the amino rather than the imino form. Observations of carbon-nitrogen double-bond infrared absorption in D$_2$O solutions confirm that cytosine is predominantly in the amino form.

Consideration of the above results leads to the formulas shown in Fig. 17-2 as the predominant tautomeric forms of bases occurring in nucleic acids. Minor tautomeric forms may be significant in the production of spontaneous mutations because inappropriate base pairing (Chap. 18) can produce mistakes of incorporation and replication. It can be shown that if the rate of base incorporation into a nucleic acid chain is less than the rate of reversion of the minor tautomer to the predominant form, the spontaneous mutation rate due to a particular base is approximately equal to the equilibrium constant for the formation of the minor tautomer. Unfortunately, equilibrium constants for the formation of minor tautomeric forms are not known, but some of them are probably of the same order of magnitude as the spontaneous mutation rates. Since minor tautomers involving the oxo group probably have greater equilibrium-formation constants than those involving the amino group, minor tautomeric forms of thymine (or uracil) and guanine should give rise to a greater spontaneous-mutation frequency than cystosine or adenine if base-incorporation rates are not too dissimilar. This analysis need not be confined to the normal bases; it is also applicable to analogue bases that are incorporated into nucleic acid chains. Though predominantly in the amide form, on the basis of suggestive chemical evidence, mutagenic 5-bromo-uracil is more likely to be in a minor tautomeric form than thymine.

The preceding discussion has emphasized the complexity of dealing quantitatively with the tautomeric forms of the bases. Upon addition of acid or base, new sets of tautomeric variations become possible. In some instances the major site of ionization is uncertain. Table 17-2 lists the negative logarithms of the ionization constants of bases and nucleosides. The corresponding nucleotides exhibit pK_a values a few tenths of a log unit higher (are more basic), owing to the greater negative charge on the molecule. Too, the nucleotides possess additional acidic groups of pK_a about 1 and 6. The reader interested in the main sites of ionization is referred to discussions in the references.

TABLE 17-2 *Apparent* pK_a *Values of Bases and Nucleosides* (*Averages of values in the literature*)

	Base	Nucleoside[†]
Pyrimidine	1.2	
Uracil	9.5	9.2
Thymine	9.9	
Cytosine	4.6, 12.2	4.2, 12.2
Purine	2.4, 8.9	
Adenine	4.1, 9.7	3.6
Guanine	3.3, 9.3, 12.3	1.6‡, 9.2

[†] In addition, a sugar hydroxyl group has $pK_a \simeq 12.3$.

‡ In this case the deoxynucleoside has a much different value of $pK_a = 2.5$.

SELECTED BIBLIOGRAPHY

1 D. O. Jordan, "The Chemistry of Nucleic Acids," Butterworth & Co. (Publishers), Ltd., London, 1960.

2 J. N. Davidson, "The Biochemistry of the Nucleic Acids," 4th ed., Methuen & Co., Ltd., London, 1960.

3 A. Albert, "Heterocyclic Chemistry," Essential Books, Fair Lawn, N.J., 1959.

4 E. Chargaff and J. N. Davidson (eds.), "The Nucleic Acids," vols. 1 to 3, Academic Press Inc., New York, 1960.

QUESTIONS

17-1 Verify Eqs. (17-3) and (17-4).

17-2 Compute K_T, using Eqs. (17-3) and (17-4), from the data given in Table 17-1. Can you offer any explanation for the variation in the values of K_T?

18 | Deoxyribonucleic Acid

18-1 TRANSFORMING PRINCIPLE

Deoxyribonucleic acid (DNA) is generally regarded as the genetic material. One of the most convincing bits of evidence for the genetic role of DNA is its transforming ability as observed in certain bacteria. Emphasizing the DNA aspect and ignoring such factors as cell morphology and variations between strains, we now present a simplified description of the production of a transformation for pneumococci:

1. Grow a culture of wild-type pneumococci cells.
2. To part of the culture add streptomycin, which kills all the cells except rare mutants, 1 cell in 10^7, which are drug-resistant.
3. Cultivate the drug-resistant mutant cells.
4. Extract and purify mutant DNA from the drug-resistant cells.
5. Add purified mutant DNA to a culture of wild-type pneumococci cells.

After addition of the mutant DNA to a wild-type culture, transformed (drug-resistant) cells appear to the extent of 1 cell in 10^2 to to 10^3, far exceeding the spontaneous mutation rate.

DNA is strongly implicated as the transforming principle because it is highly purified; proteolytic enzymes have no effect, and deoxyribonucleases, enzymes which digest DNA, prevent transformation. Replication of the added mutant DNA can occur, since it is possible to obtain more transforming principle than is added initially. However, newly drug-resistant cells divide slowly, and for several generations mutant DNA passes to only one daughter cell. Once mutant DNA replication has started, however, it continues in the progeny. Mechanical transfer of DNA yields results similar to those obtained from conventional gene transfer in dividing cells.

When the mutant cells undergo yet another mutation such that the drug-resistant strain can also ferment mannitol (which the wild type cannot do), two transformable genetic markers exist. Upon addition of purified DNA from the double-mutant cells to a wild-type culture, the majority of the cells are transformed for either streptomycin resistance or mannitol utilization. The frequency of cells transformed for both mutant characteristics is considerably greater than the product of the frequencies of the single transformations. Such results are genetically interpretable only as a linked transfer of two unit characters by a single event. In general, markers do not appear on the same piece of DNA.

Transformation has been observed in only a few classes of microorganisms, probably because of its sensitivity. Just how the DNA enters the cell is not yet clear. There are two other known methods for transferring genetic material between bacterial cells. In *transduction*, infective viruses carry genetic information from one cell to another. *Mating* is rare in bacteria, but when it does occur, direct contact allows passage of the greatest amount of genetic material. The quantity of DNA transferred is proportional to the amount of genetic material measured along a linear genetic map.

18-2 CHARGAFF'S RULES

Careful analyses of the base contents of DNA and RNA have led to the formulation of important generalizations known as Chargaff's rules. We represent the bases by their first letters (A for adenine, C for cytosine, G for guanine, T for thymine, and U for uracil); the following statements of experimental data then apply to DNA:

1. A + C = G + T, or the number of bases with 6-amino residues is equal to the number with 6-keto residues. This rule is the only one also applicable to most RNA when U replaces T.

2. C + T = A + G, or the sum of the pyrimidine bases is equal to the sum of the purine bases.

3. A/T = G/C = 1.0 within 10% for a variation of 0.4 < A/G < 2.7. Combination of the first two rules yields rule 3, which, however, is usually stated separately. Smaller ranges of A/G occur in plants (1.1 to 1.7) and animals (1.3 to 2.2) than the wider limits quoted for bacteria.

Exceptions and unusual bases occur, but the rules generally apply. Better agreement is obtained if C includes the sum of cytosine and 5-hydroxymethylcytosine. The latter usually occurs only in small amounts, but in the T-even phages it completely replaces cytosine.

18-3 SECONDARY STRUCTURE

Watson-Crick Structure. Figure 17-1 shows the covalent or primary structure of DNA. Further but weaker bonding determines the periodic backbone folding in space or the secondary structure. Several crystalline forms of DNA exist, but the B or high-humidity form is of the most interest because it occurs in vivo. Varying the humidity induces a reversible transition between the more crystalline low-humidity A form and the B form. Salts of DNA from several sources have been drawn into fibers of sufficient alignment to yield characteristically helical x-ray diagrams. The crystallographic repeat distance in the fiber direction is 34 A in the B form. A strong meridional reflection occurs at 3.4 A. Consideration of the twofold nature of the screw axis, unit-cell dimensions, density, and analysis of the strong reflections leads to the conclusion that there are two residues every 3.4 A in the B form.

A combination of the x-ray information due to Wilkins, Chargaff's rules, and exhaustive model building led Watson and Crick (1953) to propose for the B form of DNA a two-stranded helix comprised of two right-handed single helical chains running in opposite directions. The double helix has a pitch of 34 A with 10 residues per turn in each chain, and the phosphate residues are 9 A from the fiber axis, as shown in Fig. 18-1. Inside the helix, the bases are stacked 3.4 A apart, almost perpendicular to the fiber axis, and are specifically paired by hydrogen bonds: adenine on one chain with thymine on the other, and guanine on one chain with cytosine on the other, as shown in Fig. 18-2. These dimensions are consistent with the x-ray results for DNA; pairing of two pyrimidines or two purines would not fit easily. The overall dimensions are the same for both purine-pyrimidine base pairs in Fig. 18-2. The sequence of bases in one chain uniquely determines the sequence of the other; the chains are complementary. Unlike the α and β structures of proteins, in which the hydrogen bonds are situated between repeating features of the polypeptide backbone structure, the hydrogen bonds in DNA are placed between the side-chain residues or bases which are specifically paired on the inside of the chain. In proteins the amino acid side-chain residues are arranged irregularly on the outside of the chain.

The A form of DNA contains a double helix of 28 A pitch with 11 nucleotide residues per turn in each chain. The bases are tilted at an angle of about 20° to the fiber axis. The x-ray patterns of this form of DNA are similar to those obtained for soluble RNA (Sec. 20-4).

Because of the negative charges on the phosphate residues of DNA, it is necessary to work with salts. In more recent work the lithium salt has been used in preference to the sodium salt because, having fewer electrons, it offers less background scattering. The postulate of Watson and Crick seems secure, since theirs is the only structure which can account for the x-ray pattern of the B form. Details of the structure are being worked out as the analysis is extended to spots farther from the center of the x-ray picture to give finer resolution. Few

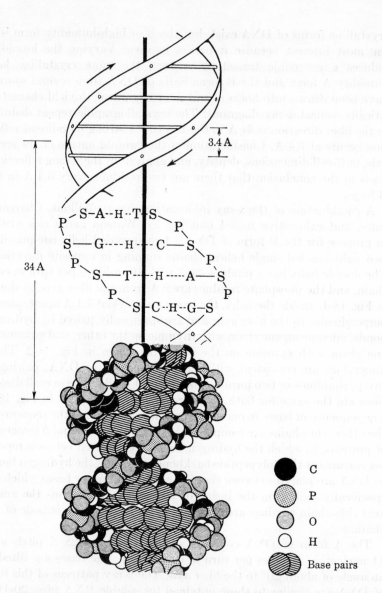

FIG. 18-1 Three representations of the two-stranded double-helical structure of DNA to same scale. Symbols are the usual chemical symbols and those for nucleic acid bases, with S for sugar and P for phosphate residues. Bottom: Space-filling model. Middle: Less detailed representation. Top: Schematic representation with the rungs in the twisted ladder depicting base pairs. Note the groove where a third strand of some polymer might be accommodated. (After C. P. Swanson, "The Cell," Prentice-Hall, Inc., Englewood Cliffs, N.J., 1960.)

hypotheses in the history of science have been as stimulating to further research as that of the double-helical structure of DNA. In recognition of their roles in developing the DNA structure, Watson, Crick, and Wilkins shared a Nobel prize in 1962.

Other Evidences of Secondary Structure. For nucleic acids, as for proteins, x-rays yield the most definitive information, but only with regard to ordered parts of a structure. Destructive interference of scattered radiation from disordered regions results in a pattern indica-

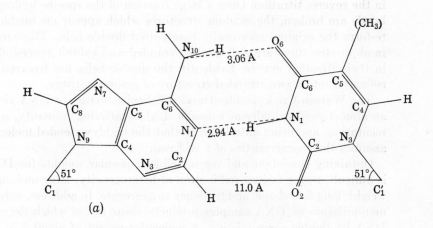

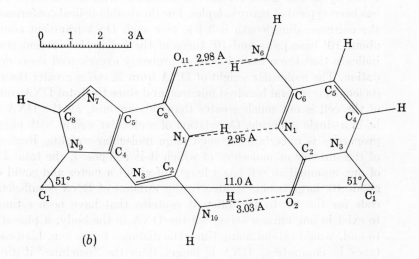

FIG. 18-2 Specific base pairing of nucleic acid bases in DNA. (*a*) Adenine and thymine. (*b*) Guanine and cytosine. Note the isosceles triangles. [After M. Spencer, *Acta Cryst.*, **12**, 66 (1959).]

tive only of those portions of the structure possessing a regular repeating electron density distribution. Since x-rays cannot accurately reveal the percentage of a structure that is ordered, other physical methods provide useful additional information concerning molecular weight and shape in solution. Recall the discussion of nucleic acid viscosity in Sec. 11-1.

The titration curve obtained upon addition of acid (to pH 2) or base (to pH 12) to a neutral solution of DNA is irreversible. This irreversibility can be interpreted as due to the breakup of hydrogen bonds upon ionization of the bases, which do not specifically pair in the reverse titration. Once a large fraction of the specific hydrogen bonds are broken, the random structures which appear are unable to re-form the original specifically base-paired double helix. These more random structures are still double-stranded and exhibit reversibility in their titration curves. Evidently the double helix has irreversibly collapsed into a two-stranded structure of greater entropy.

The Watson-Crick double-stranded helical structure of DNA yields an almost rigid cylinder as a model. Light-scattering, viscosity, sedimentation, and other data indicate that the highly extended molecule assumes the characteristics of a stiff coil.

Obtaining consistent and reproducible molecular weights for DNA is difficult, owing to its combination of heterogeneity, large molecular weight, long thin shape, and tendency to aggregate. In addition, normal manipulation of DNA samples produces shear forces which degrade DNA by double-chain scission. A molecular weight of about 7×10^6 has been typical of many samples. For the double-helical conformation, the corresponding length is 3.4 μ. One such DNA fragment contains about 10^4 base pairs and 10^3 turns of the helix. More recent studies indicate that these materials have probably experienced shear degradation. The molecular weight of DNA from *E. coli* is greater than 10^9, its length is several hundred microns, and since the total DNA content of the cell is not much greater than this amount, all the DNA may be in a single molecule. Correlation of molecular weight with physical properties is uncertain for such large molecular weights. Regardless of the number of molecules of which it is composed, the total DNA of one mammalian cell has a length of about a meter and could code about 10^3 large books. Evidently this amount of DNA is sufficient to code for the 10^4 to 10^5 different proteins that have been estimated to exist in one human being. All the DNA in the body, if placed end to end, would extend many times the distance to the sun. Like coding tapes in computers, DNA is longer than the "machine" it directs.

Deoxyribonucleases are enzymes which break specific covalent bonds in DNA. Simultaneous determination of the number of bonds split and the molecular weight indicates that the rate of decrease in molecular weight is close to zero initially but accelerates as the enzymatic reaction proceeds. This result is wholly inconsistent with a single-stranded structure but is the expected result for a double helix. As the enzymatic reaction proceeds and the number of breaks in the strands becomes greater, the probability increases that a break in one strand occurs near enough to a break in the other to reduce the molecular weight. A detailed analysis of the data shows that a separation of two pairs of nucleotides or less between breaks on complementary strands yields a scission of the double helix resulting in a molecular-weight decrease.

DNA absorbs ultraviolet light at about 260 mμ because the nucleic acid bases absorb in this region. The observed absorption of native DNA is about 40% less than is calculated from the nucleotide absorption for the known base content. The wavelength of maximum absorption is about 260 mμ in both cases. This marked hypochromic effect of the base absorption in the macromolecule is the result of light-induced dipole-dipole interactions among the horizontally stacked chromophores. Even a few base pairs, appropriately oriented, can produce a hypochromic effect.

In Sec. 16-3 we pointed out that the solvent may have an important role in helix stability. Water tends to disrupt organized structures in proteins because of its hydrogen-bonding properties, and we might expect that it would also weaken a DNA double-helical molecule. Deuterium exchange of nitrogen-bound hydrogens of pyrimidine and purine bases in DNA is rapid, perhaps due to general base catalysis of exchange. Numerous studies indicate that DNA is more stable in aqueous solutions than is reasonable to expect in view of high concentrations of the competitive hydrogen-bond acceptor and donor water. If in aqueous solutions hydrogen bonds supply little or none of the energy for the double-helical DNA structure, other explanations must be advanced for helix stabilization. Combination of cations at the negative phosphate residues would reduce charge repulsion. Interaction of the planar bases gives rise to a hypochromic effect in the ultraviolet absorption spectra, and this same interaction might provide a stabilizing effect. Addition of nonaqueous solvents to an aqueous solution weakens the structure of DNA. Since the denaturing abilities of these solvents are not related to their hydrogen-bonding abilities (urea is not especially effective), DNA is presumably stabilized by hydrophobic forces. Some of the bases along the interior of the molecule are quite insoluble in water, and their juxtaposition may account for considerable helix stabilization.

What emerges is an overall picture of DNA as a specific base-paired double-helical structure of two antiparallel right-handed helical strands. Hydrogen-bonded base pairs in the interior of the double helix provide selectivity but only a fraction of the stability, which is mainly due to electrostatic, van der Waals, and hydrophobic forces. When broken hydrogen bonds become clustered, the probability of rematching base pairs is small, and an open loop is frozen into the chain. A large number of such loops disorders a whole molecule, and denaturation occurs. Production and freezing of loops are abetted by high temperature.

Denaturation. Denaturation refers to the disorganization of the double-helical or secondary structure of DNA. In the past it has not always been clear whether this process necessarily implies strand separation. We can visualize a collapse of the double-helical structure of DNA without separation of the strands. Once disorganized, a molecule may have difficulty reforming with complementary base pairing and the appropriate helical pitch. Denaturing agents often cause more serious alterations; heating can result in depurination of bases along the chain.

The wavelength dependence of the effectiveness of light in inducing many biological alterations, the "action spectrum," is similar to the absorption spectrum of DNA. One effect of ultraviolet radiation in the 260-mμ region is to convert two suitably positioned thymine bases to a thymine dimer which is stable when subjected to acid and heat. When thymine dimers form between adjacent thymines on a single strand or between two strands of a DNA double helix, interference with specific base pairing occurs. Thymine dimers absorb more strongly at 240 mμ than at 260 mμ, and irradiation at the former wavelength produces monomers once again. Irradiation at 260 mμ reduces the transforming ability of DNA; it can be partially restored by irradiation at 240 mμ. Ultraviolet irradiation produces other changes in DNA and biological materials, but the formation of thymine dimers is thought to be one of the more significant effects.

Transformations from native to denatured DNA are accompanied by significant changes in solution properties. One such change is the large decrease in viscosity, the flow becoming newtonian for the denatured molecule, whereas native DNA exhibits nonnewtonian flow even to low shearing stress. Alterations in light-scattering behavior also occur. The large positive contribution to optical rotation due to helical content disappears upon denaturation. Another effect is a decrease in transforming ability. Most conveniently, DNA denaturation is followed by a 40% increase in light absorption at 260 mμ. This increase in absorption is the same as that observed when the molecule is hydrolyzed to component nucleotides. Indications are that hypochromism is a linear measure of helical content if there are at least eight residues in a helical region. Changes in these solution properties provide operational definitions of denaturation.

Denaturation can be effected by the addition of more than one equivalent of acid, owing to the breaking of hydrogen bonds and the repulsion of positively charged bases in the hydrophobic core. Decrease of ionic strength to less than 10^{-3} M or addition of base, urea, guanidinium salts, nonaqueous solvents, or heat also denatures. The causes of denaturation are interrelated; for instance, as the urea concentration increases, heat denaturation occurs at lower temperatures.

Heating a solution of native DNA produces little change in physical properties such as viscosity or ultraviolet absorption until a transition temperature is reached. At this temperature a decrease in viscosity and a 40% increase in absorption occur. The absorption increase takes place over a narrow temperature range indicative of a cooperative transition. This transition is similar to melting, except that the absorption versus temperature plot is irreversible. The temperature at the midpoint of the curve for native DNA in Fig. 18-4 is called the *transition* temperature. Decreasing the ionic strength broadens the temperature range and lowers the transition temperature nearly to room temperature, owing to the increased importance of electrostatic repulsion among the negative charges contained on each nucleotide residue. The addition of polyamines raises the transition temperature.

As the temperature of a solution of DNA is raised, imperfections occur in the strict Watson-Crick structure in the form of occasional sequences of unbonded base pairs forming open loops. Just below the transition temperature, the equilibrium condition is a fluctuating alternation of double-helical sections and loop sections of non-hydrogen-bonded base pairs. The fraction of the latter increases rapidly with temperature in the transition region, yielding an increase in ultraviolet absorption. At the transition temperature, the whole structure collapses. At a slightly higher temperature, strand separation takes place.

Transition regions would be even sharper if DNA were homogeneous. Samples of DNA are necessarily heterogeneous, because a cell contains several kinds of DNA molecules, differing at least in their base sequences. This diversity is to be expected of genetic material. The more complex an organism and its heredity, the more molecules of DNA it will contain, and the greater their heterogeneity. Thus calf-thymus DNA has a broader transition region than bacterial DNA. One cell nucleus of calf thymus contains several thousand molecules of DNA. Bacterial cells contain about 0.1% of the DNA contained in mammalian cells. In contrast to the frequent homogeneity of proteins, the inherent heterogeneity of DNA must always be considered in interpreting its physical properties.

Samples of calf-thymus DNA heated to a temperature within the

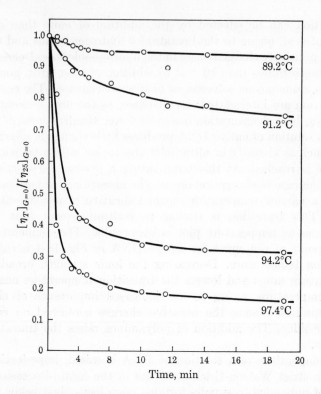

FIG. 18-3 Relative intrinsic viscosity of calf-thymus DNA at 25° after being held at the labeled temperature in the transition range for the indicated number of minutes. Limiting viscosity numbers are extrapolated to zero rate of shear. [From S. A. Rice and P. Doty, *J. Am. Chem. Soc.*, **79**, 3937 (1957).]

transition region exhibit a decrease in viscosity which levels off after about 20 min. Figure 18-3 shows that the limiting value is dependent upon temperature: lower plateau values of the intrinsic viscosity are obtained at higher temperatures. Since the denaturation is not reversible, only some of the DNA molecules are altered at a given temperature within the transition range. To denature the remainder, a higher temperature is required. A heterogeneous DNA sample contains molecules with a range of transition temperatures. At the transition temperature of the whole sample, half the molecules are double-helical and half single-stranded coils, rather than all the molecules being half coil and half helix. The all-or-none nature of the transition has been confirmed by direct examination with the electron microscope.

Bacteria provide samples of DNA with wide variations in guanine plus cytosine content (26 to 74%), though a single kind of bacteria has a narrow distribution of DNA molecules. Study of the DNA from many varieties of bacteria has demonstrated that the transition temperature is a linear function of the guanine plus cytosine content. At 0.15 ionic strength, extrapolation of the straight line to pure GC copolymer yields a transition temperature of 110°, while extrapolation to pure AT copolymer predicts a transition temperature of 69°. An observed transition temperature for the latter is 65°. High transition temperatures for DNA samples with high GC contents may be explained, at least in part, by the three hydrogen bonds between each G and C as opposed to only two between A and T. Coupled with the viscosity results of Fig. 18-3, the observed transition temperature is interpreted as the average value for the molecules in a heterogeneous DNA sample. Each molecule has its own transition temperature, dependent upon its GC content. The success of the correlation indicates that neither base pair is grouped along the chain and that the base pairs are distributed in such a manner that the transition temperature is a measure of the mean GC content of a whole molecule. Selective thermal deactivation of unlinked genetic markers occurring in DNA molecules of differing stability has been observed.

The density of a DNA sample, as measured by equilibrium sedimentation in a cesium chloride density gradient, is also a linear function of the GC content. Two effects, diffusion and heterogeneity of the sample, contribute to the equilibrium bandwidth in the density gradient. Since band broadening due to diffusion is dependent upon the molecular weight, its contribution to the bandwidth may be approximated. Broadening due to heterogeneity is found to be only a few mole percent in GC content, much less than the 50 mole percent GC content over which different bacterial samples range. Though a wide variation in GC content occurs in bacteria, a single specimen has a relatively narrow distribution of GC content among all the DNA molecules in the cell. As might be expected, a more complicated organism displays a wider distribution of GC content than a less complicated one, the distribution reaching the order of 10% in mammals.

When a heated solution of calf-thymus DNA is cooled to room temperature, the absorption decreases until it is about 10% higher than the room-temperature value obtained before heating. Evidently, some helical regions have re-formed. The high viscosity of the unheated sample is not attained, however, in the cooled solutions; therefore, the helical regions must be short. Reheating the cooled sample yields a broad transition region which is reversible through further heating and cooling cycles. The breadth of the transition indicates short, intra-chain helical regions of varying lengths and heterogeneity due to mis-matching of base pairs. Heating above the transition region causes strand separation. Subsequent cooling only allows formation of intrachain hydrogen bonds within a single strand and nonspecific interchain hydrogen bonding.

For a solution of native bacterial DNA, a transition region similar to but sharper than that of the more heterogeneous calf-thymus DNA is obtained on heating. When the solution is cooled to room temperature, the absorption of bacterial DNA is also about 10% higher than in the original unheated solution, as shown in Fig. 18-4. However, the curve obtained on reheating the cooled solution is dependent upon the rate of prior cooling. Upon reheating, slowly cooled samples exhibit a plateau and then an abrupt change in the transition region, indicating melting of double helix as in native DNA. Slow cooling permits re-formation of complementary strands, and the product is called *renatured* DNA. It differs from native DNA in being imperfectly united (as indicated by a 10% higher absorption), having a slightly lower molecular weight, and exhibiting only up to 50% of the transforming ability of the native molecule.

Quickly cooled samples of DNA have half the molecular weight of the native starting material when allowance is made for depolymerization at high temperatures and aggregation on cooling. This single-stranded material has almost no transforming ability and is called *denatured* DNA. On reheating, quickly cooled denatured bacterial DNA shows a maximum in the absorption curve, in Fig. 18-4, due to the melting out of short intrachain helices and the formation of interchain double-stranded helices, which then melt sharply in the same

FIG. 18-4 Heating curves of native bacterial DNA and quickly cooled and slowly cooled samples of native DNA previously heated at 100° for 10 min. Sodium citrate buffer with 0.27 M NaCl. (From Ref. 4.)

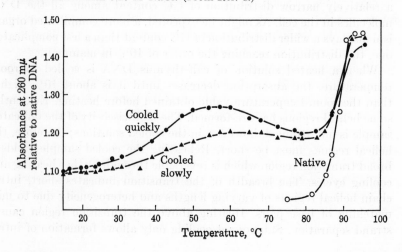

region as do slowly cooled samples. If quickly cooled denatured DNA is reheated and then slowly cooled ("annealed"), almost as much transforming ability is obtained as in the case of slowly cooled once-heated DNA.

Equilibrium sedimentation in a density gradient such as concentrated cesium chloride is a sensitive measure of density. Denatured DNA bands at a higher density than native DNA. Renatured DNA, however, has almost the same band position (and hence density) as the native material. Electron microscopy reveals a marked similarity in the appearances of native and renatured DNA (long thin rods), whereas that of denatured DNA is different from both (irregularly shaped coils). Thus two very different physical methods support the conclusions drawn from absorbance-temperature curves.

Strand separation and recombination are also verified by further density-gradient experiments with isotopically labeled bacterial DNA. When a mixture of N^{15} DNA and N^{14} DNA from the same species is heated and slowly cooled, intermediate bands appear, indicating the formation of mixed double helices. Of more interest, similar treatment of N^{15} with N^{14} DNA from a different but closely related species also gives hybrids. If the species are not closely related, or if the overall base compositions differ greatly, only homologous recombination occurs, without hybridization. This analysis can be sharpened by growing the heavy sample in a medium containing D_2O as well as $N^{15}H_4Cl$. These results have been verified by transformation experiments with genetic markers, indicating that the genetic information can be carried independently by each strand.

Although native DNA has over 10^3 turns per molecule, calculations indicate that unwinding of a DNA double helix may take only a few seconds. In practice, slow cooling of heated DNA lasts an hour or more and is therefore an equilibrium process throughout the temperature range. The reforming of a double helix during slow cooling involves the reunification of two complementary strands and will therefore increase in probability as the concentration increases. Noncomplementary strands of the heterogeneous DNA sample will also come together, but, due to mismatch of base pairs, the equilibrium constant for their forming a double helix is much less than for complementary strands. Since the whole process is in equilibrium throughout the slow cooling, mismatched strands will melt out in favor of complementary double helices of greater equilibrium constant. That such specific reunion is favored has also been verified by transformation experiments. The optimal temperature for reappearance of transforming activity is about 25° lower than the transition temperature of the native bacterial DNA.

In heated and slowly cooled solutions of DNA isolated from the thymus of calves, cells of which have 10^3 times as much DNA as bacteria, recombination to form double helices does not occur, because the concentration of complementary strands is much less than in the bacterial case, even though the total DNA concentration may be the same. Renaturation can take place, however, if the two strands of native mammalian DNA are chemically cross-linked at a few points along the double helix. Heating of the cross-linked material destroys the double helix without strand separation, and only cooling (no annealing) is required for renaturation to a double-helical structure.

We have interpreted the experimental observations reported in this section in terms of strand separation of double-helical DNA. Though widely held, this view is not universally accepted. As with other topics discussed in these chapters, further experiments may require modification of the viewpoints presented. It is partly for this reason that these fields are the subjects of such intense current research.

18-4 REPLICATION

If DNA is the genetic material, an important question arises: How does DNA replicate in an exact enough manner so that mistakes are seldom made in the transmission of hereditary characteristics? Since the DNA per haploid set is constant, a dividing cell must manufacture DNA. If the hereditary information contained in DNA is to be passed on faithfully, newly synthesized DNA apparently must be an exact replica of the original. In Fig. 18-5 we outline two suggested modes of DNA replication: conservative and semiconservative.

FIG. 18-5 Full arrows represent original antiparallel chains of DNA double helix; dashed arrows represent strands synthesized in succeeding generations.

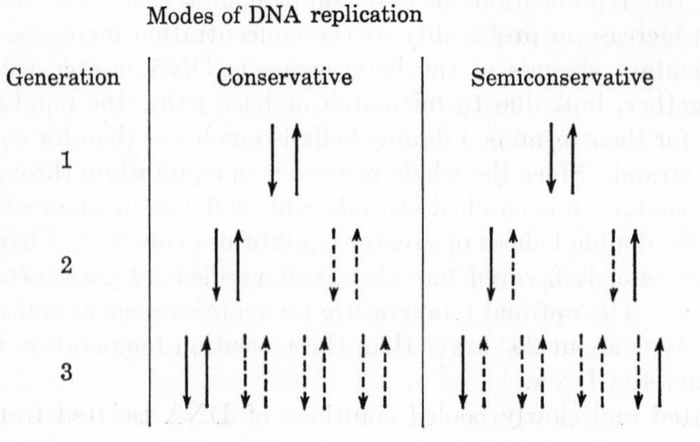

Modes of DNA replication

Generation	Conservative	Semiconservative
1		
2		
3		

In the conservative scheme the first-generation DNA remains intact during all replication processes; daughters are made solely of new DNA. In the semiconservative process half the parental DNA is passed on to each daughter during replication. Watson and Crick proposed a semiconservative scheme to accompany their DNA structure. They envisaged a mechanism whereby the complementary strands of the DNA helix unwind and serve as a template for the formation of new DNA. Other mechanisms of semiconservative modes of replication have also been suggested.

A third mode of replication (not illustrated) called dispersive replication includes the processes whereby parent DNA is fragmented among progeny DNA.

Of several experimental attempts to determine the mode of DNA replication, we shall consider only that of Meselson and Stahl. They grew *E. coli* for 14 generations in an N^{15} growth medium so that the DNA was predominantly labeled with heavy nitrogen. During the logarithmic phase of growth, the cells were switched to an N^{14} growth medium. DNA extracted from the cells after various numbers of generations in the N^{14} nutrient medium was spun in a CsCl density gradient in the ultracentrifuge. Banding of the DNA according to its density was followed by ultraviolet absorption optics until equilibrium was attained in about two days. Control experiments demonstrated that the density gradient is sufficiently sensitive to separate N^{14} and N^{15} DNA, which differ by only 0.014 g/cc.

The N^{15}-labeled DNA at zero time in the N^{14} nutrient medium yields a single band. A single band also appears after one generation, but at a density corresponding to equal amounts of N^{14} and N^{15} DNA. After two generations two bands appear, one at the same position as the N^{14}-N^{15} band, and the other at a new position corresponding to N^{14} DNA. For the same number of cells, both second-generation bands have half the absorption and hence half as much DNA as the zero- and first-generation bands.

Since bands rather than a distribution of densities are obtained, the results are inconsistent with a dispersive mode of replication. A conservative mode of replication requires that the N^{15} band remain throughout any number of generations. A semiconservative scheme fits the data very well. Evidently two pieces come apart during replication, but since there is no proof that it is the two antiparallel strands that do so, the Watson-Crick mechanism is not established. Unfortunately, in the experiment the DNA may have been aggregated. If aggregation did occur, a conservative scheme of replication is still possible, because we may be witnessing only such a process as the breakdown and re-formation of dimers. Other experiments make it likely, however, that strand separation is indeed the mechanism of replication. The precaution mentioned in the last paragraph of the previous section applies here also.

18-5 ENZYMATIC SYNTHESIS

The extracellular synthesis of DNA was first demonstrated by Arthur Kornberg, who shared a Nobel prize in 1959 for this work. Five reactants are essential for synthesis. An enzyme, polymerase, isolated from the colon bacterium *E. coli*, was obtained in a yield of about 10 mg from 1 kg of cells, which is about 20% of the possible yield since there are about 100 enzyme molecules per cell. Adenosine triphosphate (ATP) as an energy source, Mg^{++}, primer DNA, and the monophosphates of all four DNA nucleosides were also required. The deoxynucleoside monophosphates were shown to be converted to the corresponding triphosphate deoxynucleotides by kinase enzymes, and hence the deoxyribonucleotides were added in later experiments. The polymerase enzyme handles triphosphates. All four deoxyribonucleotides are essential for synthesis; if only one precursor is present, only a few bases are added to the deoxynucleoside end of the DNA primer chain.

Newly synthesized DNA is identified by labeling the innermost nucleotide phosphate with P^{32} and thymidine with C^{14}. Acid precipitation of DNA, followed by washing to rid the solid of any adhering soluble radioactive deoxyribonucleotides, yields radioactive DNA. This product contains all four deoxyribonucleotide residues linked by $3'$—$5'$ diester bonds as in DNA. Ten-to twentyfold increases of DNA, yielding over 90% synthesized polymer, have been obtained. Sedimentation and viscosity studies on native and denatured material, as well as the absorption increment on DNase digestion, all show comparable results on the primer and synthetic product. DNA from animal, plant, bacterial, and viral sources is effective in synthesis, but deoxyribonucleoside diphosphates, ribose instead of deoxyribose sugars, RNA, acid-denatured DNA, and DNase-treated DNA are all ineffective. Synthesis proceeds normally when ribonuclease is added, but it is inhibited by the addition of pyrophosphate, owing to augmentation of the reverse of the synthesis reaction:

$$\begin{matrix} n_1 TP^*PP \\ n_1 dAP^*PP \\ n_2 dCP^*PP \\ n_2 dGP^*PP \end{matrix} \underset{\rightleftharpoons}{\text{DNA}} \left[\begin{pmatrix} TP^* \\ dAP^* \end{pmatrix}_{n_1} \begin{pmatrix} dCP^* \\ dGP^* \end{pmatrix}_{n_2} \right] + 2(n_1 + n_2)PP \qquad (18\text{-}1)$$

The small d indicates deoxyribose sugar. This symbol is unnecessary before thymidine triphosphate because only the deoxyribosenucleotide occurs naturally, the corresponding ribonucleotide being uridine triphosphate. The asterisk indicates that the innermost phosphate is radioactive. On the right-hand side of the equation, the brackets represent synthesized DNA. Analysis of the product bases yields results in conformity with Chargaff's rules (except that adenine and thymine are sometimes high). Moreover, the base ratios correspond to those of the primer and are not related to the ratios of the deoxynucleotide precursors despite wide variations in the latter. Evidently, primer DNA is determining the composition of the synthetic polymer product.

Heat-denatured DNA is frequently a better primer than the native material. A naturally occurring single-stranded DNA from the tiny bacteriophage ΦX174 is also an excellent primer. In both cases the product DNA is two-stranded.

When no primer DNA is added to an otherwise complete reaction mixture, the polymerase enzyme produces a copolymer of the deoxyadenylate and thymidylate precursors. Sequence and physical analyses indicate a double-helical structure of two base-paired strands with alternating residues:

```
· · · ATATAT · · ·
· · · TATATA · · ·
```

Production of the copolymer proceeds autocatalytically; during an initial lag period of several hours, copolymer appears and aids in the synthesis of more of itself. If this AT copolymer is used as a primer in the usual way, no lag period ensues, but more AT copolymer is produced even when all four DNA precursors are present. No guanine or cytosine is found in the synthetic polymer under these conditions. Thus the importance of the primer is strikingly confirmed. There is nothing to prevent this reaction from occurring in experiments in which native DNA is used as a primer. Its occurrence accounts for the high values for adenine and thymine incorporation cited above.

A *de novo* polymer is also obtained from a reaction mixture containing polymerase, dGPPP, dCPPP, and Mg^{++} without primer, but greater enzyme and substrate concentrations are required than for initiation of AT copolymer. In contrast to the equivalent amounts of bases occurring in the AT copolymer, equivalent amounts of guanine and cytosine bases are not always found. The product consists of polydeoxyguanylate chains hydrogen-bonded to polydeoxycytidylate chains of lengths which are not necessarily equal:

```
· · · GGGGGG · · ·
· · · CCCCCC · · ·
```

Thus the product is not a copolymer but consists of two homopolymer chains hydrogen-bonded together. The formation of dGdC polymer is also autocatalytic.

Analogues of the four DNA precursors may be incorporated into the synthetic product by the polymerase enzyme if their hydrogen-bonding side is not altered (Fig. 17-2), consistent with the double-helical structure of DNA. Deoxycytidine triphosphate may be replaced by the 5-bromo or 5-methyl derivatives, thymidine triphosphate by the 5-bromo or 5-methyl (deoxyuridine) derivatives, and deoxyguanosine by deoxyinosine (no 2-amino group). All these replacements are specific; the derivative bases substitute only for the bases mentioned. Presumably because the absence of the 2-amino group permits only two hydrogen bonds to cytosine instead of the usual three when guanine is present, the last replacement is the least effective. Of the five substitutions mentioned above, only the two bromo derivatives may be incorporated as monophosphates, because the kinase enzyme can convert only these two to triphosphates.

In addition to incorporation of analogue bases in primed DNA, polymers analogous to dAT and dGdC can be prepared. These synthetic analogues are useful for delineating many special aspects of properties that may be associated with DNA. For instance, although replication of dAT incorporates no guanine, the latter appears in a chain when the analogous copolymer primer $dA\overline{BU}$ (where $\overline{BU}$ represents 5-bromouracil) is used. Nearest-neighbor frequencies (discussed in the next section) indicate, however, that simple mismatching with bromouracil is not an adequate explanation for guanine incorporation. Unlike those of DNA, the thermal transitions of dAT copolymer are reversible. Slow cooling of a previously heated mixture of double-helical dAT and $dA\overline{BU}$ copolymers can yield a hybrid double helix $dAT:dA\overline{BU}$, of intermediate melting temperature and density. Hybrid double helices can also be produced by priming, with dAT, a reaction mixture containing dAPPP and $d\overline{BU}PPP$ substrates. If the reaction is continued for an extended time, $dA\overline{BU}$ copolymer predominates. A converse procession of polymers occurs if $dA\overline{BU}$ copolymer is used to prime a dAPPP and TPPP substrate mixture.

18-6 NEAREST-NEIGHBOR BASE-SEQUENCE FREQUENCIES

Analyses of base sequences in DNA molecules containing 10^4 or more bases present a far more formidable problem than determination of sequences of 10^2 amino acids in proteins. Due to this difficulty, we must be content for now with less than complete information on the base sequences of nucleic acids. The frequency of nearest-neighbor sequences can be determined by utilizing the directional sense of a nucleic acid chain and employing the clever stratagem of enzymatically splitting the chain on the opposite side of a radioactive phosphate residue from which the polymerase enzyme has catalyzed the synthesis of the molecule. As shown in Fig. 18-6, the polymerase enzyme builds the nucleic acid molecule from 5'-deoxyribonucleotides, while digestive enzymes break every bond on the 5' side of the phosphate residue, yielding 3'-deoxyribonucleotides.

Primer DNA is mixed with the four labeled and unlabeled deoxyribonucleotide precursors in four ways, in each of which only one of the four deoxyribonucleotide precursors is labeled with P^{32} as the innermost of the three phosphorus atoms. In Reaction 1 only the adenine-containing deoxyribonucleotide is labeled with P^{32}; in Reaction 2 thymidine triphosphate is labeled; in Reaction 3 only guanine deoxyribonucleotide is labeled; in Reaction 4 only cytosine deoxyribonucleotide.

The polymerized components of Reaction 1 are digested to yield the 3'-deoxyribonucleotides, which are isolated by paper electrophoresis. Radioactive P^{32} will appear combined with each of the four possible nucleotides in an amount which corresponds to the frequency with which the adenine nucleotide was linked to the 3' position of each of the neighboring nucleotide residues in the newly synthesized chains. By similar determinations on all four reaction mixtures, the relative frequencies of all 16 nearest-neighbor sequences may be determined. The sum of the relative frequencies for any one reaction mixture must correspond to the frequency with which the base with the labeled

FIG. 18-6 Left: Polymerase-catalyzed synthesis of DNA from 5'-deoxyribonucleotides. Right: Enzymatic digestion of same nucleic acid chain to yield 3'-deoxyribonucleotides. (From Ref. 6.)

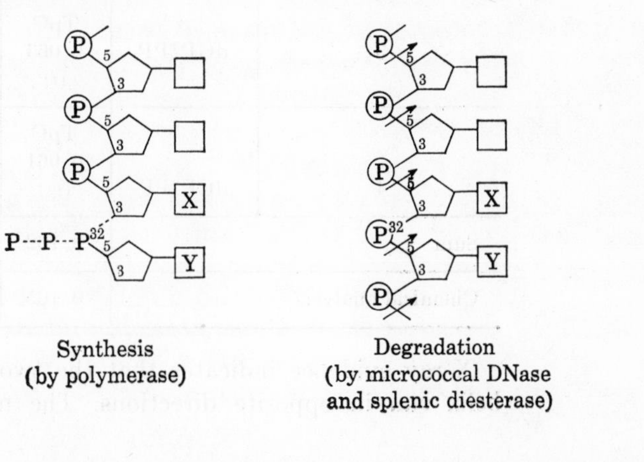

Synthesis
(by polymerase)

Degradation
(by micrococcal DNase
and splenic diesterase)

deoxyribonucleotide precursor occurs in the DNA molecule, as previously determined by standard techniques. Thus in Reaction 1 the sum of the nearest-neighbor frequencies of adenine with all four bases must equal the frequency with which it has already been determined that adenine appears in this particular DNA. This comparison provides a check on the accuracy of the experiments.

Table 18-1 shows the results of an experiment with DNA from *M. phlei* used as a primer. The relative frequencies were evaluated by an algebraic method made possible by (1) the complete recovery of the 3'-deoxyribonucleotides from the enzymatic digest and (2) a knowledge of the specific radioactivity of each labeled precursor, even though the amount of newly synthesized DNA is a variable fraction of the primer DNA added initially. The sums of the bottom of Table 18-1 check with the chemical analysis of the primer DNA, an agreement which confirms faithful replication of the overall composition of primer DNA in the synthesized product. These figures are also consistent with Chargaff's rules and the base-pairing scheme of the Watson-Crick double-helical structure of DNA.

TABLE 18-1 *Nearest-neighbor Frequencies of M. phlei DNA (After Ref. 6)*

Reaction number	Labeled triphosphate	Isolated 3'-deoxyribonucleotides			
		Tp	Ap	Cp	Gp
1	dAP*PP	TpA 0.012 (a)	ApA 0.024 (b)	CpA 0.063 (c)	GpA 0.065 (d)
2	TP*PP	TpT 0.026 (e)	ApT 0.031 (f)	CpT 0.045 (g)	GpT 0.060 (h)
3	dGP*PP	TpG 0.063 (i)	ApG 0.045 (j)	CpG 0.139 (k)	GpG 0.090 (l)
4	dCP*PP	TpC 0.061 (m)	ApC 0.064 (n)	CpC 0.090 (o)	GpC 0.122 (p)
Sum		0.162	0.164	0.337	0.337
Chemical analysis		0.165	0.162	0.335	0.338

X-ray evidence indicates that the two strands of a DNA double helix run in opposite directions. The nearest-neighbor frequencies

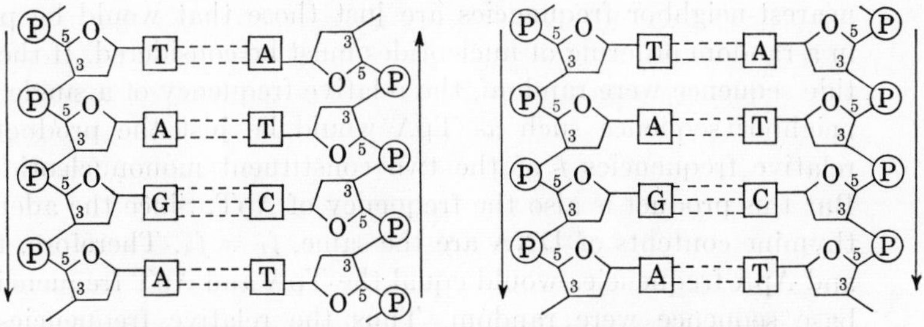

Opposite polarity

TpA (0.012) = TpA (0.012)
ApG (0.045) = CpT (0.045)
GpA (0.065) = TpC (0.061)

Similar polarity

TpA (0.012) = ApT (0.031)
ApG (0.045) = TpC (0.061)
GpA (0.065) = CpT (0.045)

FIG. 18-7 Newly synthesized chains of DNA combined to form complementary strands of a double helix of opposite polarity (left) and similar polarity (right). The two models predict different matchings of nearest-neighbor frequencies. Only the predicted matched pairs of the model for opposite polarity are consistent with all the results of Table 18-1. (After Ref. 6.)

expected to be matched for two chains running in opposite directions are in some cases different from the matchings predicted for both chains running in the same direction. Thus the matching sequences predicted by the two models are different. This difference may be clarified by reference to Fig. 18-7, where newly synthesized strands of a DNA double helix are shown.

Consider the first example of Fig. 18-7; the sequence TpA would be expected to have a relative frequency matching only its own if the strands were of opposite polarity. If the strands were of the same polarity, the TpA frequency would be about the same as that for ApT. As Table 18-1 indicates, only the former situation occurs. In general, we predict that for strands of opposite polarity the relative frequencies of the following pairs of squares of Table 18-1 should be matched: $a = a$, $b = e$, $c = i$, $d = m$, $f = f$, $g = j$, $h = n$, $k = k$, $l = o$, and $p = p$. For strands of the same polarity, the following matches are expected: $a = f$, $b = e$, $c = h$, $d = g$, $i = n$, $j = m$, $k = p$, and $l = o$. Inspection of the relative frequencies of Table 18-1 reveals that all predicted pairs of the first list are matched within experimental error, whereas serious mismatchings occur for four of the six pairs in the second list which are not also in the first list. Thus the nearest-neighbor frequencies are consistent only for a double-helical model with specific base pairing between chains running in opposite directions.

A single bacterium such as *M. phlei* contains on the order of 10^7 base pairs. Due to the large numbers involved, the possibility that the nearest-neighbor frequencies are just those that would be predicted in a random ordering of nucleotides must be considered. If the nucleotide sequence were random, the relative frequency of a single nearest-neighbor sequence such as TpA would be just the product of the relative frequencies f of the two constituent mononucleotides: $f_T f_A$. But this product is also the frequency of ApT. Since the adenine and thymine contents of DNA are the same, $f_T = f_A$. Therefore, the TpT and ApA frequencies would equal the TpA and ApT frequencies if the base sequence were random. Thus the relative frequencies of the following squares of Table 18-1 should be identical: $a = b = e = f$. Similar arguments for the other bases predict that for random sequences of nucleotides the nearest-neighbor frequencies of the following sets of squares of Table 18-1 should be equal: $c = d = g = h$, $i = j = m = n$, $k = l = o = p$. Thus a random sequence of bases predicts that the relative frequencies of the four squares in each quadrant of Table 18-1 should be identical. This is clearly not the case, and we therefore conclude that the base sequence of the DNA is nonrandom and unique. Comparison of the lists of relative frequencies for the three cases considered reveals that the list for two strands of similar polarity is contained within the random list and that matches occur in the list for two strands of opposite polarity which do not appear in either of the other two lists.

Conclusions derived from the results described for the particular case of DNA from the bacterium *M. phlei* have been verified on DNA from mammalian, animal, plant, viral, and other bacterial sources when they were used as primers. The numbers of Table 18-1 are, of course, different, but the relationships among the nearest-neighbor frequencies are the same. Further experiments with the same technique have shown that if the newly synthesized DNA, rather than native DNA, is used as a primer in an additional experiment similar to those described above, identical results are obtained. DNA that has been denatured by heating for 30 min at 100°, when used as a primer, yields the same nearest-neighbor frequencies as does native DNA. Within experimental errors, DNA samples isolated from different tissues and tumors in a given species are the same.

When the technique is applied to the AT copolymer of the previous section, every deoxyadenylate residue has a thymidylate as a nearest neighbor, and vice versa. Thus the perfect alternation of the two kinds of residues in this copolymer is strikingly confirmed. In the dGdC polymer, on the other hand, the homopolymeric nature of each chain is attested by nearest-neighbor frequencies. Interestingly, a minor light DNA component from crab testis exhibits alternating A and T or T and A residues in 93% of its sequences, even though all 16 possible sequences occur to some extent.

Single-stranded DNA from the small virus ΦX174 presents a unique nearest-neighbor-sequence situation. This DNA does not contain equivalent amounts of adenine and thymine or guanine and cytosine. Since newly synthesized strands attached to the primer in a double helix and identified by their P³² content exhibit base contents complementary to the primer, the inference is that the observed nearest-neighbor frequencies in limited replication are just the reverse of those in the primer. Unlike the limited case, in unlimited replication, matching of complementary nearest-neighbor frequencies is observed. The values are close to those predicted from limited replication on the assumption that both strands of the double helix function as primers.

SELECTED BIBLIOGRAPHY

1 E. Chargaff and J. N. Davidson (eds.), "The Nucleic Acids," vols. 1 to 3, Academic Press Inc., New York, 1960.

2 F. H. C. Crick and J. D. Watson, The Complementary Structure of Deoxyribonucleic Acid, *Proc. Roy. Soc. London*, **A223**, 80–96 (1954); *Nature*, **171**, 737–738 and 964–967 (1953).

3 M. H. F. Wilkins et al., The Molecular Configuration of Deoxyribosenucleic Acid, *J. Mol. Biol.*, **2**, 19–64, (1960); *Science*, **140**, 941–950 (1963).

4 J. Marmur, P. Doty, et al., Strand Separation and Specific Recombination in Deoxyribonucleic Acids, *Proc. Natl. Acad. Sci. U.S.*, **46**, 453–476 (1960).

5 A. Kornberg, "Enzymatic Synthesis of DNA," John Wiley & Sons, Inc., New York, 1962.

6 J. Josse, A. D. Kaiser, and A. Kornberg, Frequencies of Nearest Neighbor Base Sequences in Deoxyribonucleic Acid, *J. Biol. Chem.*, **236**, 864–875 (1961).

7 E. Freese, The Arrangement of DNA in the Chromosome, *Cold Spring Harbor Symp. on Quant. Biol.*, **23**, 13–18 (1958).

QUESTIONS

18-1 One of your classmates insists that DNA forms an α helix and that certain fibrous proteins form a double-helical structure. What arguments could you marshal in an attempt to set him straight?

18-2 How would substitutions on the hydrogen-bonding and non-hydrogen-bonding sides of the bases of Fig. 17-2 affect the DNA structure?

18-3 It has been estimated that there are 5 billion nucleotide pairs per human cell. What is the total length of DNA in one human cell?

18-4 If the human body contains 10^{15} cells, what is the total length of DNA in the body?

18-5 Predict the effect of ionic strength on the transforming ability of slowly cooled denatured DNA.

18-6 What bands would appear in a density-gradient experiment upon heating and quickly cooling a mixture of N^{15} DNA with N^{14} DNA from the same species?

18-7 Point out the features of the enzymatic synthesis of DNA which support the Watson-Crick structure.

18-8 Two species exhibit nearly identical base compositions in their DNA. How might you distinguish the two kinds of DNA?

18-9   A polymer of guanine and cytosine deoxyribonucleotides does not transfer a phosphate residue in the experiments described in the last part of this chapter. Propose a structure for the polymer, and account for the fact that the polymer does not necessarily have equal amounts of guanine and cytosine.

18-10   Single-stranded ΦX174 DNA contains the following mole-fraction base contents: adenine, 0.25; thymine, 0.33; guanine, 0.24; cytosine, 0.18. Predict the base compositions of the first newly synthesized complementary strand and of those after unlimited replication.

18-11   Describe the changes observed in the frequencies of the four sequences TpA, ApT, CpG, and GpC after limited and unlimited replication in ΦX174 DNA.

19 | Polyribonucleotides

Even if given the appropriate base composition, ribonucleic acid could not assume the double-helical conformation described for DNA in Sec. 18-3 because of the interference of the additional 2'-hydroxy group in the ribose ring. Partly due to the difficulty of aligning RNA chains into an oriented fiber, it is more difficult to obtain sharp x-ray patterns for RNA than for DNA. The characteristically helical diffraction patterns show a repeat of about 27 A on the fiber axis and strong meridional reflections at about 3.3 and 3.9 A. Though similar to the pattern of DNA in some ways, these reflections have not yielded a definitive structure. In biological systems RNA conformation is frequently determined by that of associated protein. In tobacco mosaic virus (TMV), for instance, free TMV protein has the virus shape, while free TMV-RNA does not. These nucleoprotein complexes are discussed further in the next chapter. This chapter is concerned with the conformation in solution of protein-free RNA and related polyribonucleotides. With polyribonucleotides as with proteins, when the native material is difficult to analyze, investigators turn their attention to synthetic polymers of known compositions which often contain only a single repeating residue. Through the study of synthetic polyribonucleotides, more amenable to investigation on many counts, a reasonable structure for free RNA has been deduced.

19-1 ENZYMATIC SYNTHESIS

The synthesis of polyribonucleotides was first performed by Svero Ochoa, who in 1959 shared a Nobel prize for this work with Arthur Kornberg, whose extracellular synthesis of DNA was described in Sec. 18-5. Ochoa, in cooperation with M. Grunberg-Manago, by observing a rapid exchange of labeled phosphate, discovered in 1955 an enzyme which converts nucleoside-5'-diphosphates into polyribonucleotides in the presence of magnesium according to the equation

$$nX - R - P - P \rightleftarrows (X - R - P)_n + nP \tag{19-1}$$

where n is an integer, X is a nucleic acid base, R stands for ribose, and P stands for phosphate. The polymer product of 5′-nucleoside mono-phosphate units linked to one another through 3′-phosphoribose ester bonds has the same backbone as RNA and is susceptible to similar enzymatic attack.

Reaction (19-1) is reversible, equilibrium being attained when about 70% of the orthophosphate is liberated. Addition of the enzyme system to polyribonucleotides results in phosphorolytic cleavage to yield nucleoside-5′-diphosphates until the equilibrium position is reached (when forward and reverse reaction rates are equal). This system is analogous to the reversible synthesis and breakdown of polysaccharides from glucose-1-phosphate catalyzed by the enzyme phosphorylase. For this reason the enzyme of the Ochoa system is called polynucleotide phosphorylase. Several monomer units are possible in the system. Polynucleotide phosphorylase was originally found in bacteria and has since been found in both plants and animals. It differs from the enzyme of the DNA system by working on diphosphates instead of triphosphates, and the polymeric products tend to reflect substrate rather than primer composition. More recently, enzymes which cata-lyze the synthesis of RNA from ribonucleoside triphosphates have been discovered. The requirements for these systems are similar to those for DNA polymerase, even to the necessity for DNA. The synthesized RNA has the same base composition and nearest-neighbor base frequencies as the DNA used. Such systems are discussed in Sec. 19-5.

Polyribonucleotide phosphorylase catalyzes the synthesis of the homopolymers poly A, poly C, poly U, poly T, and poly I from the corresponding nucleoside-5′-diphosphates in the presence of Mg^{++}. Poly I represents polyinosinic acid, which contains the purine base hypoxanthine (6-ketopurine or guanine without the 2-amino group).

Poly G is made only with difficulty. Guanine, however, will enter a mixed nucleotide of poly AGUC formed from a mixture of the nucleoside-5'-diphosphates.

As purer preparations of the enzyme were used, a lag period developed in the formation of polyribonucleotides. Apparently a primer for the polymer synthesis existed in the cruder enzyme preparations. Results of careful studies of primer requirements for synthesis of polyribonucleotides catalyzed by polynucleotide phosphorylase from nucleoside-5'-diphosphate substrates are collected in Table 19-1. All polyribonucleotides act as primers for themselves. Poly C is a universal primer and is the only primer for the synthesis of poly C. Poly AU is a random copolymer made from a substrate mixture of ADP and UDP. Poly AGUC has the activity of the RNA of the system in which it is synthesized. RNA is primed only by itself; either natural or synthetic RNA is effective.

TABLE 19-1 *Synthesis of Polyribonucleotides: Effect of Primers on Substrates*†

	Primer					
Substrate	Poly A	Poly U	Poly C	Poly I	Poly AU	Poly AGUC or RNA
ADP	+	−	+	0	+	+
UDP	−	+	+	0	+	+
CDP	−	−	+			−
IDP	−	0	+	+		
ADP + UDP					+	
ADP + UDP + CDP + GDP	0	0	+			+

† Abbreviations: ADP, adenosine diphosphate; UDP, uridine diphosphate; CDP, cytidine diphosphate; IDP, inosine diphosphate; GDP, guanosine diphosphate; +, primes; −, inhibits; 0, no effect.

Priming by shorter sequences, oligonucleotides, is less specific. Thus triadenylic acid primes the syntheses of poly A and poly U. For the latter, pApApA$\vert$pUpU $\cdots$, the addition of the uridine groups is to the right end of the primer, which is to the left of the vertical dashed line. Small p represents a phosphate residue in the structure. The dimerization of trioligonucleotides is not catalyzed, but transnucleotidation (disproportionation) does occur when no P or ADP is present. Whole chains are primed by some process other than adding to preformed chains, as in oligonucleotides. The biological role of reactions catalyzed by polynucleotide phosphorylase is uncertain; it is possible that the reverse of Eq. (19-1), the breakdown of RNA, is the significant reaction.

19-2 PHYSICAL PROPERTIES

Molecular weights of synthetic polyribonucleotides vary from 30×10^3 to $2,000 \times 10^3$. The maximum value is of the same order of magnitude as naturally occurring RNA samples.

Polyriboadenylic acid gives a highly crystalline x-ray fiber diagram with a strong 3.8-A meridional reflection. These results indicate a molecular structure comprised of a parallel-chain double helix with eight residues per turn in each chain and a pitch of 30 A. Since the amino group of adenine in the double-helical structure does not react with formaldehyde, the amino group is presumably involved in hydrogen bonding. The meridional reflection is larger than that obtained for DNA (3.4 A), owing to the necessity of tilting the hydrogen-bonded bases in the double helix.

Poly AU and poly AGUC give x-ray patterns resembling that of RNA. Owing to the random nature of these synthetic polymers,

FIG. 19-1 Hydrogen bonding between hypoxanthine bases of the three-stranded helical polyinosinic acid. [From A. Rich, *Biochim. Biophys. Acta*, **29**, 502 (1958).]

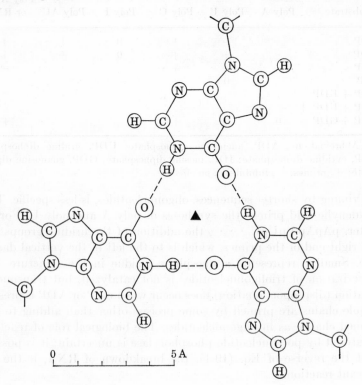

0   5 A

specific base pairing such as occurs in DNA is ruled out in the case of RNA.

In solution, poly A can exist in two forms: random coil and double helix. Formation of the helical form is favored at low pH because protonation of the bases produces a positive charge which forms an inner salt with a negative phosphate group on the other strand. The sharp helix-coil transition is conveniently followed by measuring optical rotation or ultraviolet absorption spectra. X-ray patterns similar to those of the solid have been obtained in dilute solutions of the helical form. This similarity supports the contention that study of the x-ray patterns of solids has meaning relative to the structure of molecules in solution. Except at temperatures near freezing, poly U exhibits little or no secondary structure in aqueous solution.

Polyinosinic acid has an unusual x-ray pattern in that the first layer line is at a very low 9.8 A rather than the usual 30 A or more. A second layer line occurs at 5.2 A, and a third, intense, meridional layer line occurs at 3.4 A. No simple integral relationship exists between these values (for example, $3 \times 3.4 \neq 9.8$). This fact, coupled with the nonmeridional first and second layer lines, implies a helical conformation. The results are interpreted as a triple helix of three parallel chains with the hypoxanthine bases hydrogen-bonded as in Fig. 19-1. The threefold rotation axis reduces the fiber-axis repeat distance to 9.8 A instead of 29.4 A. Stacking of the hypoxanthine bases normal to the fiber axis accounts for the 3.4-A meridional reflection. Poly G is also multistranded.

19-3 MIXED HELICES OF POLYRIBONUCLEOTIDES

When neutral, dilute salt solutions of poly A and poly U are mixed, immediate and dramatic increases in viscosity and sedimentation coefficients are observed, as well as a decrease in ultraviolet absorption, as compared with the results expected through additivity of the properties of the unmixed solutions. If the poly A and poly U are mixed in the appropriate proportions, a single component with the characteristics of neither reagent polymer appears in sedimentation and electrophoresis experiments. Ultraviolet absorption, as a function of mole percent poly U, is shown in Fig. 19-2. In the absence of Mg^{++}, a minimum occurs at 50 mole percent, indicating the formation of a 1:1 complex of poly A and poly U, denoted as poly (A + U).

The x-ray pattern of the solute poly (A + U), recovered from a 50 mole percent solution, is similar to that of neither reactant, but rather to that of DNA, both being helical in character and having an identical layer-line spacing of 34 A at 78% relative humidity. The results are inter-

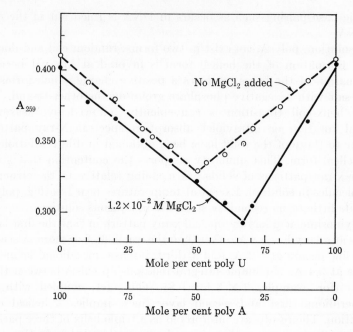

FIG. 19-2 Ultraviolet absorption at 259 mμ as a function of mole percent poly U at constant total moles of polymer (poly A + poly U). All solutions are 0.1 M in NaCl and at neutral pH. [After G. Felsenfield and A. Rich, *Biochim. Biophys. Acta*, **26**, 457 (1957).]

preted as a double helix, one chain of poly A linked to one of poly U by hydrogen bonds, with 10 residues per turn in each strand and a pitch of 34 A as in DNA. The planar bases are stacked nearly at right angles to the fiber axis, but the diameter of the helix is 6 A greater than in DNA, owing to the additional ribose OH group on each residue. No space is available for the additional 2'-ribose oxygen in the DNA structure; therefore the poly (A + U) complex differs slightly from the DNA structure. The similarities of the two structures, however, are much greater than the differences.

Formation of the poly (A + U) complex demonstrates that ribose, as well as deoxyribose chains, can form double helices when specific base pairing can occur. Since the formation of the poly (A + U) double helix is rapid, winding (and presumably unwinding) of a double helix in short time intervals is possible. This experimental result has an important implication for the Watson-Crick scheme of DNA replication, because it indicates that rapid coiling and uncoiling of long-chain, double-helical molecules is not as improbable as might have first appeared.

Figure 19-2 also shows that in the presence of Mg^{++} the absorption minimum is obtained at 67 mole percent poly U. This percentage corresponds to a poly (A + 2U) species in which the additional poly U chain can fit into the helical grove of the DNA-like poly (A + U) structure. The two poly U chains are not equivalent in this structure. X-ray evidence implies that the additional poly U strand is hydrogen-bonded only to poly A. Since the three-stranded helix will also form in 0.7 M NaCl, apparently the function of salts is to overcome the electrostatic repulsion of negatively charged phosphate groups, divalent Mg^{++} being considerably more effective than Na^+.

Thymine (5-methyluracil) may be substituted for uracil in the mixed helices just described. This substitution should cause no difficulties, because the methyl group is substituted on the non-hydrogen-bonding side of the uracil (see Fig. 17-2). Poly (A + U) will not add a third chain of poly A or poly C. Poly A, however, forms double and triple helices with poly I. Figure 19-3 shows the proposed specific hydrogen bonding between the base pairs of poly (A + I). Poly (I + C) exists in two forms, a crystalline A form resembling DNA, except that the bases are tipped at 7° to the fiber axis, and a B form closely resembling RNA. A summary of the results is provided in Table 19-2. Since aqueous solutions of DNA undergo rapid deuterium exchange, it would be of interest to investigate the rate of deuterium exchange in three-stranded helices, which presumably lack the helical groove of DNA.

Two-stranded poly (A + I) is formed from poly A and poly I at an

FIG. 19-3 Hydrogen bonding between adenine and hypoxanthine bases of poly (A + I). [From A. Rich, *Nature*, **181**, 521 (1958).]

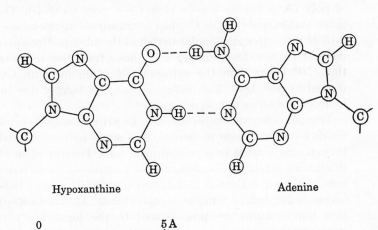

Hypoxanthine   Adenine

0 |___|___|___|___| 5 Å

increasing rate as the ionic strength is raised. At zero ionic strength no combination occurs, because charge repulsion is stronger than the forces responsible for complex formation. Divalent cations are about 100 times as effective as monovalent cations in bringing about the formation of the two-stranded helix. Polyamines, which also neutralize negative phosphate charges, are about as effective as divalent cations. Poly (A + I) has a greater molecular weight than the sum of the molecular weights of its constituents, poly A and poly I. Therefore, overlapping of strands must occur in this double helix.

T A B L E 1 9 - 2 *Double and Triple Helices of Homopolyribonucleotides*†

	A	I	U(T)	C
A	A + A low pH	A + 2I	A + 2U	NONE
		high salt or Mg^{++}	
I	A + I low salt	3 I	NONE	I + C
U(T)	A + U low salt	NONE	U + U low temperature	NONE
C	NONE	I + C	NONE	C + C

† The triple helices A + I + U, A + I + T, and A + T + U also form, but A + T does not add a third strand of A, C, or I.

As in the case of DNA, the increase in ultraviolet absorption may be used to follow helix-coil transitions and to determine transition temperatures. Transition temperatures increase in the order poly (I + I + I) < poly (A + I + I) < poly (I + C) < poly (A + U). The last and most stable, poly (A + U), has a transition temperature of 61° at 0.15 M ionic strength, similar to that of the adenine-thymine copolymer discussed in Sec. 18-5. Poly (I + C) has a transition temperature more than 50° lower than the extrapolated value for pure GC polymer quoted in Sec. 18-3. This difference may be largely due to the third hydrogen bond in the copolymer.

Transition temperatures decrease as pH increases, because negative charges become more numerous, and some hydrogen bonds may be broken and ionized to give hydrogen ions. Denaturation thus occurs in alkaline solutions. Acidification of neutral solutions reduces charge repulsion, and, if there is no interference with hydrogen bonding, new, higher-order helical complexes may form. At constant pH, transition temperatures are proportional to the logarithm of the NaCl concentration.

Experiments with mixed helices of copoly AU and poly U or poly A provide further evidence of the nature of base pairing. Single-stranded copoly AU consists of a nucleic acid chain with adenine and uracil bases succeeding in a random fashion. Samples of copoly AU with varying A:U ratios have been prepared. In every case, formation of a mixed helix with either poly A or poly U yields a minimum in ultraviolet absorption when equal numbers of complementary bases occur in the copolymer and homopolymer, but not when the number of molecules of both polymers is the same. The 1:1 correspondence is between complementary bases in the two polymers, instead of between moles of polymer molecules. Consistent results are obtained for the three-stranded helix AU + U + U; the number of uracil bases in the homopolymer is twice the number of adenine bases in the copolymer. Evidently, mismatched bases such as uracil in copoly AU in the last example must loop out of the two- or three-stranded helix. Model building indicates loops are even possible for only one residue. Such loops are thought to be important in the RNA structure and may provide the mechanism whereby unpaired bases produced by additions or deletions in the sequence of nucleotides are remedied in the DNA double-helical structure.

19-4 RIBONUCLEIC ACID

At ionic strengths greater than 0.01 M, RNA exhibits a low limiting viscosity number ($[\eta] \sim 1$ deciliter/g) for the molecular weight as compared with the high intrinsic viscosity ($[\eta] \sim 10^2$ deciliters/g) for the molecular weight in DNA. Sedimentation studies confirm that RNA behaves hydrodynamically as tightly coiled and somewhat contracted single chains. Relatively strong intramolecular interactions must be responsible for the contracted state, because an RNA chain contains repeating negative charges at each phosphate residue. These intramolecular bonds are broken by increasing the temperature or removing salt, as demonstrated by an accompanying viscosity increase as well as an increased ultraviolet absorption, which indicates that the bases are involved.

The hypochromicity, or reduced absorption of the contracted polymer compared to the random coil or sum of absorptions of constituent nucleotides, is shown in Fig. 19-4 to be a function of temperature. Unlike those of native DNA, these curves are almost completely reversible. The steepest slope and sharpest transition is observed in the most homogeneous RNA sample, that from tobacco mosaic virus (TMV-RNA). The transition temperatures of the three samples increase as the product of the mole fractions of the triply hydrogen-bonded GC base pair increases.

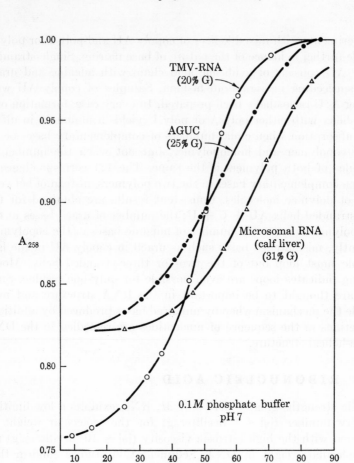

FIG. 19-4 Ultraviolet absorption of synthetic and natural RNA samples as a function of temperature. TMV is tobacco mosaic virus. Microsomal RNA is RNA from the ribosomes described in Sec. 20-3. The %G in parentheses is the molar percent guanine. (From Ref. 3.)

Hydrogen-bonding and base-pair interactions are implicated by further experiments. Addition of 6 M urea displaces the curves of Fig. 19-4 about 25° to the left as compared with a similar 18° displacement in DNA. Formaldehyde reacts three times faster with the amino groups of TMV-RNA at 45° as compared with 25° than is inferred from measurements on nucleotide monomers at the same two temperatures. On the other hand, formaldehyde, though it does not react with double-helical DNA, does react with a single-stranded bacteriophage DNA. The increase in rates of enzymatic phosphorolysis at 40°

as compared with those at 25° is linearly related to the ultraviolet absorption and proceeds about twice as fast for poly AGUC and microsomal RNA as for the non-hydrogen-bonded poly U. For TMV-RNA, the relative rate is five times faster than for poly U, consistent with its greater homogeneity and structural regularity. All these experiments, mentioned only briefly, implicate base-pair and hydrogen-bond interactions in samples of RNA and indicate that change in ultraviolet absorption is a useful and convenient measure of these interactions.

Augmentation of the ultraviolet absorption of 20 to 30% (compared with 40% in DNA) on proceeding from a more to less ordered conformation is great enough to require an explanation other than the disruption of randomly paired bases. Indeed, random pairing probably could not account for the hypochromic effect, which is due to effects in the stacking of nucleotide bases and not to hydrogen bonding alone.

FIG. 19-5 Correspondence of changes in optical density (solid line) and optical rotation (open circles) through the transition region of RNA from tobacco mosaic virus. (From Ref. 3.)

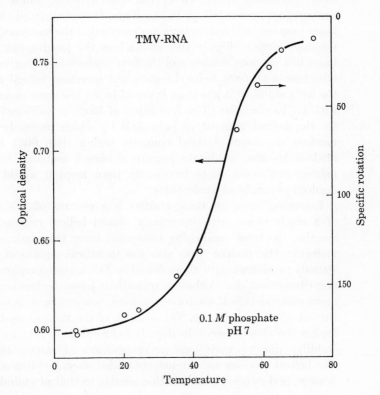

Thus, single-stranded helical regions must exist in RNA. This conclusion is supported by the correspondence between changes in ultraviolet absorption and optical rotation. This correspondence is illustrated for TMV-RNA in Fig. 19-5. We have seen in Sec. 16-4 that optical rotation is a sensitive measure of helix formation in proteins. The fact that the increase in ultraviolet absorption through a transition region of RNA parallels the decreases in optical rotation is evidence that absorption changes are a measure of alterations of helical content. A similar congruence of absorption and optical-rotation changes is observed in other polyribonucleotides such as poly $(A + U)$, where a 35% decrease in absorption is accompanied by an increase of $275°$ in specific optical rotation. Thus we might predict that the 21% decrease in absorption for TMV-RNA should be accompanied by a $275 \times {}^{21}\!/_{35} = 165°$ increase in specific rotation. This is nearly the change in Fig. 19-5. In addition, TMV-RNA and poly $(A + U)$ have the same specific rotation in the less ordered form.

It can be shown that a random sequence of the four nucleotides would have a helical content of less than 20%. Yet the estimated helical contents of polyribonucleotides are as follows: poly AGUC, 62%; ribosomal RNA, 78%; TMV-RNA, 88%. These high helical contents are accounted for in two ways. It is postulated that unpaired bases loop out of the structure, as described in the last paragraph of the previous section. Figure 19-6 shows how the looping out of unpaired bases in a random sequence of the four nucleotides can give a probable structure with 58% helix. Looping out increases helical content, but the helix stability is less than it would be for the same percentage helix with no looping out. The formation of loops is sufficient to account for the helical content of poly AGUC, which probably consists of random sequences. Helical contents higher than 60% in polyribonucleotides also evidently require a biased sequence so that base pairing can occur more frequently than looping would allow in a random sequence of nucleotides.

Emerging from all these studies is a picture of RNA consisting of a single chain with irregularly placed helical regions of varying lengths, the total comprising somewhat more than half of the whole molecule. Hairpinlike turns give rise to helical regions of antiparallel strands consistent with those found in DNA and complexes of homopolyribonucleotides. Although transitions from the less ordered to the more ordered helical conformations are reversible, it is not known if the same regions regroup. The breadth of the transitions is accounted for by the short, unevenly distributed helices of varying length and stability due to variations in proportions of strong base pairing. The helical sections are extensively folded over, yielding a contracted, flexible, and swollen conformation similar to that of globular proteins.

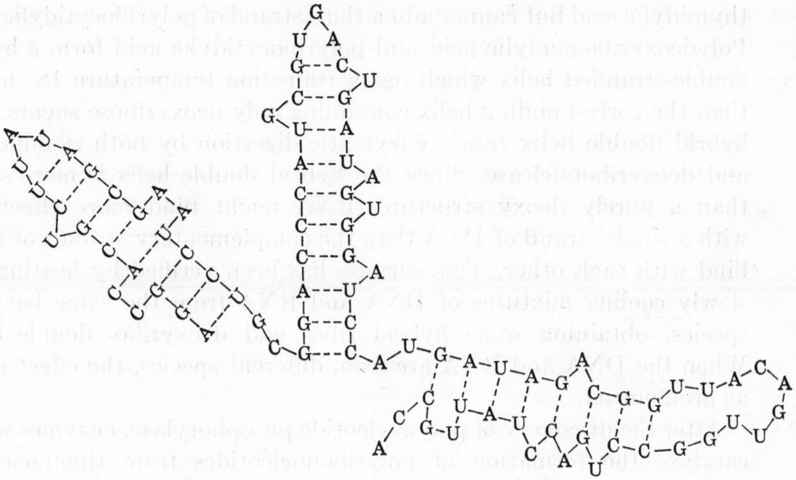

FIG. 19-6 A probable arrangement of an RNA-like chain containing equimolar quantities of four nucleotides in a random sequence. The helical character of the three base-paired regions is not depicted. (From Ref. 5.)

Helical regions of RNA, however, are much more stable than those of proteins, because no protein could withstand the electrostatic repulsion arising from one negative charge for each phosphate residue at neutral pH. Divalent cations effectively reduce this electrostatic effect in RNA. In contrast to the situation for proteins, in RNA the sequence is far more important than the conformation. Although RNA occurs naturally in combination with proteins, as described in the next chapter, there is evidence that the ordered form described above also exists in vivo.

19-5 HYBRID HELICES OF RIBONUCLEOTIDES AND DEOXYRIBONUCLEOTIDES

With the demonstration of the formation of double and triple helices of polyribonucleotides such as poly (A + U) and poly (A + 2U), the question arises as to whether it is possible to make double helices containing both ribose and deoxyribose sugars. Polydeoxyribothymidylic acid does, indeed, form 1:1 and 2:1 complexes with polyriboadenylic acid, but not with polyribo U, I, or C. A two-stranded helix of polydeoxyribothymidylic acid and polyriboadenylic acid can add a third strand of polyribouridylic, polyriboinosinic, or polyribothymidylic acid but cannot add a third strand of polyribocytidylic acid. Polydeoxyriboguanylic acid and polyribocytidylic acid form a hybrid double-stranded helix which has a transition temperature 18° higher than the corresponding helix containing only deoxyribose sugars. This hybrid double helix resists enzymatic digestion by both ribonuclease and deoxyribonuclease. Since the hybrid double helix is more stable than a purely deoxy structure, RNA might bind more effectively with a single strand of DNA than the complementary strands of DNA bind with each other. This surmise has been verified by heating and slowly cooling mixtures of DNA and RNA from the same bacterial species, obtaining some hybrid ribo- and deoxyribo- double helix. When the DNA and RNA are from different species, the effect is not as pronounced.

After the discovery of polynucleotide phosphorylase, enzymes which catalyze the formation of polyribonucleotides from ribonucleoside triphosphates were found in several plant, animal, bacterial, and viral systems. In addition to polyribonucleic acid, inorganic pyrophosphate is a product. Requirements for synthesis are the enzyme RNA polymerase, all four nucleoside triphosphates, a divalent cation Mg^{++} or Mn^{++}, a sulfhydryl-containing compound, and primer. For cases in which DNA is the primer, the frequencies of the 16 nearest-neighbor base sequences for primer and synthetic polyribonucleotide are very close.

Experiments with synthetic deoxyribonucleic acids emphasize the role of the primer in determining both composition and sequence of the polyribonucleotide products. Poly dT homopolymer primes only the incorporation of AMP, even when other nucleoside triphosphates are present. The copolymer dAT incorporates AMP only in the presence of UTP, and, conversely, UMP is incorporated only when ATP is available to yield a ribonucleotide polymer with alternating adenine and uracil bases. Only GMP and CMP units are incorporated in the presence of polymeric dGdC.

Highly purified preparations of DNA polymerase from *E. coli*, incubated with deoxyribonucleoside and ribonucleoside triphosphates, Mn^{++}, and a primer DNA, yield mixed deoxyribonucleotides and ribonucleotides on the same strand. The mixed polymeric product reflects sequences in the primer. Since enzymes and even alkali cleave specifically, depending upon the sugar present, the mixed polymer is useful in sequence analysis of the primer.

RNA synthesized in the bacterium *E. coli* after infection by bacteriophage T2 complexes with phage DNA but not with DNA from other sources. Single-stranded DNA from bacteriophage ΦX174, when utilized as a primer, yields an RNA of complementary base composition. At least in laboratory solutions, the indications are that both strands of

DNA can prime the formation of ribonucleic acids. The ribonucleic acids synthesized in these systems presumably consist, at least in part, of messenger RNA, to be discussed further in Sec. 20-4.

SELECTED BIBLIOGRAPHY

1 R. F. Steiner and R. F. Beers, "Polynucleotides," Elsevier Publishing Company, Amsterdam, 1961.

2 A. Rich, Molecular Structure of the Nucleic Acids, *Revs. Mod. Phys.*, **31**, 191–199 (1959), reprinted in J. L. Oncley (ed.), "Biophysical Science—a Study Program," p. 191, John Wiley & Sons, Inc., New York, 1959. See also the other articles in this volume.

3 P. Doty et al., Secondary Structure in Ribonucleic Acids, *Proc. Natl. Acad. Sci. U.S.*, **45**, 482–99 (1959).

4 J. R. Fresco and B. M. Alberts, The Accommodation of Noncomplementary Bases in Helical Polyribonucleotides and Deoxyribonucleic Acids, *Proc. Natl. Acad. Sci. U.S.*, **46**, 311–321 (1960).

5 J. R. Fresco, B. M. Alberts, and P. Doty, Some Molecular Details of the Secondary Structure of Ribonucleic Acid, *Nature*, **188**, 98–101 (1960).

QUESTIONS

19-1 Why should phosphate buffers be avoided in the enzymatic synthesis of polyribonucleotides?

19-2 What are the differences between poly AU and poly (A + U)?

19-3 How can the role of Mg^{++} in producing mixed helices of poly A and poly U be rendered consistent with structures held together by hydrogen-bonded bases?

19-4 Propose the hydrogen bonding between the specific base pairs of each helix in Table 19-2.

19-5 How does poly (A + U) differ from the adenine-thymine copolymer of Sec. 18-5?

19-6 In the center base-paired helical structure of Fig. 19-6, change each uracil to cytosine and each cytosine to uracil. Then pair the bases to achieve maximum helical content of the chain fragment.

19-7 Why are sharper x-ray fiber diagrams obtained from polyribonucleotides than from RNA?

19-8 Why is it that RNA does not form a DNA double helix?

20 | Nucleoproteins

Nucleic acids usually associate with some basic protein to form a functional unit. DNA is often combined with basic proteins, protamines, and histones. Viruses contain either DNA or RNA in association with protein. The multiplication of viruses occurs only in metabolizing host cells. While the nucleic acid is responsible for virus heredity, the protein coat determines the kind of cell entered by the virus particle. For instance, whole polio virus infects only man and monkey, but free polio-virus RNA can also infect mouse and chicken embryos. Ribosomes, components of many cells, consist of RNA and protein and are involved in the synthesis of proteins. We shall consider each of these nucleoproteins in turn and conclude with the role of nucleic acids in protein synthesis.

20-1 PROTEINS ASSOCIATED WITH DNA

Protamines. Except for a stronger first layer line, oriented sperm heads of cuttlefish and squid have x-ray diffraction patterns similar to the B form of DNA. Thus, this form of DNA, described in Sec. 18-3, exists in live sperm heads and is not an artifact of the preparative methods used for the isolation of DNA. The stronger first layer line in the sperm heads may be accounted for by the presence of protamine in a groove of the B form of DNA.

Protamines, basic proteins found in the generative cells and consisting mainly of arginine and lysine, have a molecular weight of about 5,000. Deoxyribonucleoprotamines contain about 70% DNA and 30% protamine, almost exactly the ratio required for charge neutralization. The positively charged side chains on the protein are thought to be systematically matched with negative phosphate residues in DNA. Nonbasic amino acids in protamines seem to occur in pairs and can be conveniently looped out of the associated structure (unlike a single amino acid), permitting a 1:1 correspondence of phosphate and basic residues. The x-ray patterns of DNA plus polylysine or polyarginine are similar to those obtained from sperm heads. DNA seems to determine the conformation of the protein with which it is combined, in contrast to RNA-protein combinations, in which the conformation of the protein determines that of the RNA.

Histones. Histones are basic proteins (less basic than protamines) found in somatic cells; nucleohistones are the major constituents of chromosomes in higher organisms. Several varieties of histones occur, and the molecular weights range from 10,000 to 20,000. Histones may possess a secondary structure of their own. Since DNA which is fully complexed as a nucleohistone is inactive in DNA-primed RNA synthesis, it has been suggested that histones are regulators of gene activity. Studies on protamines and histones are still in a preliminary stage.

20-2 SMALL VIRUSES

Viruses are conveniently classified according to the host into three groups: plant, animal, and bacterial. Plant viruses contain only RNA and protein; animal viruses, either RNA or DNA and protein; bacterial viruses or bacteriophage, usually DNA and protein. All known viruses contain protein and genetically homogeneous nucleic acids. Several larger viruses also contain lipids and carbohydrates. We shall be concerned, however, with small viruses whose structures have been relatively well described. These small viruses are usually thin rods of particle weight about 40×10^6, or approximate spheres of particle weight of the order of 5×10^6. Whatever the particle weight of the virus, the total RNA molecular weight is usually about 2×10^6.

Tobacco Mosaic Virus (TMV). Of all viruses, the plant virus TMV is the most extensively studied. Yet what is now known is probably only a fraction of the potentially available information to be gained from studies of this virus. According to several physical measurements, TMV is a thin rod about 3,000 A long and 150 A in diameter, with a particle weight of 39×10^6. Five percent of the virus is an RNA chain with a sedimentation constant of 27 S and a molecular weight of 2.0×10^6. If extended, the RNA would reach about ten times the length of the virus; therefore, it must be wound in some way. The remaining 95% of the virus is protein composed of about 2,130 identical subunits, each containing 158 amino acids and having 17,420 molecular weight. The tobacco mosaic virus protein subunit is the third protein, following insulin and ribonuclease, for which the complete amino acid sequence has been delineated. Each subunit is a single polypeptide chain with an acetylated N-terminal serine, one of the few cases in which the N terminus is so altered. Various strains of the virus have

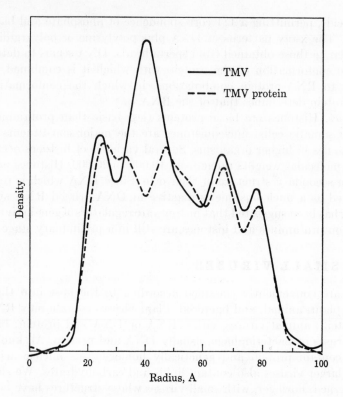

FIG. 20-1   Mean electron density in excess of that due to water as a function of distance from the center of the TMV rod (solid line) and from the center of aggregated protein only (dashed line). (From R. E. Franklin, A. Klug, and K. C. Holmes, in "The Nature of Viruses," p. 39, Ciba Foundation, Churchill Ltd., London, 1957.)

different amino acid compositions. All strains studied have one cysteine residue; some strains lack methionine and histidine.

Intact RNA may be separated from protein by addition of detergent followed by fractional precipitation, by extraction of the protein with phenol, or by heating in the presence of salt. Without RNA, the protein alone polymerizes at low pH, forming rods of the same diameter as the whole virus, but of variable length.

X-ray studies of oriented gels indicate that the repeating unit of TMV virus is only 69 A long. Since the rod is about 3,000 A in length, the existence of subunits is again implied. The protein subunits are arranged in a helical array, $16\frac{1}{3}$ per turn or 49 in three turns of the helix, giving a pitch (rise per turn) of 23 A. Planes of nitrogen bases of the RNA are approximately parallel to the rod axis. Isomorphous replacement (see Sec. 15-1) with Pb and Hg has been used to determine the signs of the reflections. The method would not be applicable to so large a particle except for the existence of identical subunits in a regular repeating pattern, nearly all of which are replaced similarly by the heavy-metal atom. From the observed amplitudes the computed Fourier synthesis yields the radial electron density distribution or the average electron density as a function of the distance from the center of the rod, as shown by the solid line in Fig. 20-1. A minimum occurs at the center, implying a hollow core which is probably filled with water. Companion studies on polymerized TMV protein which is free of RNA give a very similar radial electron density distribution, except for the absence of the peak at 40 A, as shown by the dashed line in Fig. 20-1. The difference between the solid and dashed curves of Fig. 20-1 indicates that the RNA of TMV is embedded in the protein component of the virus 40 A from the rod axis. The inner peak at 24 A must be due to protein. A cross section along the length of the rod of tobacco mosaic virus is shown in Fig. 20-2. The nucleic acid does not run through the protein subunits, but between them. Chemical analyses indicate an integral number of bases (three) per protein subunit, permitting a systematic repeat. Density and packing considerations suggest that the particle is grooved. The analysis of so complex a structure is a remarkable achievement and is made possible by the occurrence of repeating subunits.

A combination of the results of three different techniques may be used to calculate the particle weight of TMV. The light-scattering radius of gyration and electron-microscopy results reveal rodlike particles 3,000 A in length. X-ray patterns indicate 49 subunits per 69 A length, yielding $49 \times 3,000/69 = 2,130$ subunits per particle. Amino acid analysis gives the molecular weight of each protein subunit as 17,420. The molecular weight of protein per particle is therefore $2,130 \times 17,420 = 37.2 \times 10^6$. Since 5% of the particle is RNA, the weight of the whole particle is $37.2 \times 10^6/0.95 = 39 \times 10^6$. This value agrees well with the results obtained from light-scattering, sedimentation and diffusion, and sedimentation-equilibrium studies.

Infection of a tobacco leaf by TMV involves the stripping of the protein coat from the RNA, followed by multiplication of virus RNA in the cell nucleus. Virus protein is then formed in the cytoplasm under the control of TMV-RNA. Combination of the synthesized RNA and protein yields a new, complete virus particle. Normally only 1 in 10^6 virus particles is effective in initiating infection. This one infective particle results in about 10^5 virus particles in one day. Infectious TMV-RNA has been synthesized in cell-free systems, isolated from plants, to which have been added the four ribonucleoside triphosphates and Mg^{++}.

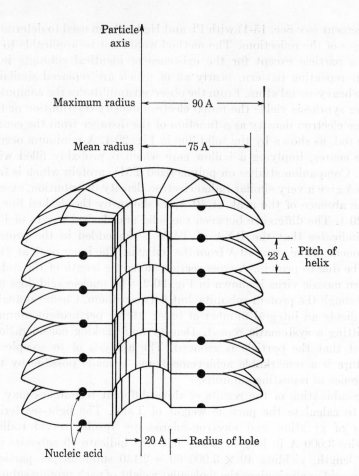

FIG. 20-2 Cross section a short distance along the length of the rod of tobacco mosaic virus. The RNA helix is shown at a radius of 40 A. (From R. E. Franklin, A. Klug, and K. C. Holmes, in "The Nature of Viruses," p. 39, Ciba Foundation, Churchill Ltd., London, 1957.)

Virus RNA and protein can be separated and recombined to give reconstituted virus with up to 80% infectivity. TMV protein may combine with RNA from other sources, and even with polyriboadenylic acid, to yield noninfectious rods. Free RNA of a strain of the virus, with methionine and histidine in the protein, was reconstituted with the protein of another virus strain which contained neither of the two mentioned amino acids. Progeny protein of the mixed virus contained methionine and histidine, demonstrating that the RNA rather than the protein carries the genetic information. It is not known how a single-chain RNA virus replicates. Owing to the directional sense of a nucleic acid chain, the product of a base-pairing scheme would yield another protein unless the base sequence of RNA was very unusual.

Revealing experiments have been performed using the separated components of TMV, protein and RNA. TMV protein is not infectious in the absence of RNA, while the isolated RNA has a low infectivity but one-third less latent period. The fact that greater infectivity is not attained is attributed to the instability of the free RNA. Infectivity is not due to trace amounts of DNA or protein because only RNase, and neither DNase nor proteolytic enzymes, destroys infectivity. Only high-molecular-weight RNA is infectious, especially the whole piece of molecular weight 2×10^6. Although free virus RNA is vulnerable to digestion by RNase, in the virus the protein coat protects RNA from enzymatic attack. The infectivity of viral nucleic acids rather than protein has been proved to be a general phenomenon in both RNA and DNA viruses.

A knowledge of the amino acid sequence of so simple a nucleoprotein as TMV makes possible many experiments significant to the discovery of the relations among chemistry, heredity, and amino acid sequences. If the nucleotide sequence of the RNA were also known, the code by which the RNA base sequence determines the amino acid sequence could almost certainly be broken. The RNA, however, contains about 6,000 bases, about 40 for each amino acid of the protein subunit. Since the RNA base sequence is not known, more indirect experiments are required.

Introduction of 5-thiouracil or 5-fluorouracil into TMV-RNA has no effect on virus activity. This alteration of structure occurs on the non-hydrogen-bonding side if the intrachain RNA hydrogen bonds are similar to the interchain hydrogen bonds of DNA. Formaldehyde and nitrous acid, however, cause alterations on the hydrogen-bonding side of the nucleic acid bases. Nitrous acid converts amino to keto groups (by tautomerization of the alcohol):

$$
\begin{array}{ccc}
\underset{\underset{\displaystyle N}{|}}{\overset{\displaystyle NH_2}{\underset{\displaystyle \diagdown}{\overset{\displaystyle |}{C}}}} & + \; HNO_2 \rightarrow & \underset{\underset{\displaystyle |}{|}}{HN}\overset{\displaystyle O}{\underset{\displaystyle \diagdown}{\overset{\displaystyle \|}{C}}} \; + \; N_2 + H_2O
\end{array}
$$

This reaction changes the naturally occurring adenine to hypoxanthine, guanine to xanthine, and cytosine to uracil. The last alteration is particularly significant, because one naturally occurring nucleic acid base is converted to another. If the base sequence is a code for amino acid sequence, the message is changed when cytosine is transformed to uracil. Hypoxanthine can presumably pass as guanine, again changing the message. The formation of xanthine might destroy the code, yielding noninfective material, or it might revert to guanine upon replication. Of more than 100 mutants induced by nitrous acid, about one-quarter exhibit one amino acid replacement and a few possess two amino acid replacements in the protein coat subunit. The majority of the mutants display no recognizable difference in the main protein component. This result implies that some of the TMV-RNA encodes other proteins (enzymes) required for viral infection and reproduction.

TMV-RNA that has been treated with nitrous acid and reconstituted with native protein usually yields noninfectious material; most deaminations induced by nitrous acid are lethal. Occasionally mutants which differ in amino acid content from the native protein are obtained. In one such case the nitrous acid mutant contained a leucine, an alanine, and a serine in place of a proline, an aspartic acid, and a threonine residue in the native protein. The C-terminal sequence of TMV protein is —Gly—Pro—Ala—Thr. The proteolytic enzyme carboxypeptidase cleaves one amino acid at a time from the C-terminal end of proteins. Since carboxypeptidase cannot pass a proline residue, the enzymatic action ceases after removal of the threonine and alanine residues from native TMV protein. In the nitrous acid mutant just mentioned, carboxypeptidase continued past the third residue, liberating leucine. Thus the action of nitrous acid on TMV-RNA produced a mutant virus with 3 of 158 amino acids altered, one of them the replacement of proline by leucine, three amino acids from the C terminus. This alteration is presumably caused by a specific cytosine-to-uracil conversion somewhere along the RNA chain of 6,000 bases. An analysis indicates that an alteration of only one of these bases may be mutagenic. How the nucleic acid determines the amino acid sequence is not known. Tobacco mosaic virus provides one of the simplest systems for unraveling the correspondence between amino acid and nucleotide sequences.

Spherical Viruses. Small spherical viruses have particle weights of 5 to 10×10^6 and the percentage of nucleic acid necessary to yield an RNA molecular weight of about 2×10^6. Thus 6,000 nucleotides and at least 25,000 amino acids are contained in the virus particle. Because the base to amino acid ratio of 1:4 is too small to allow individual coding of each amino acid, the protein component must be composed of identical subunits. Like TMV, whole spherical viruses are resistant to ribonuclease; therefore, the protein subunits must encompass the virus nucleic acid. We assume that the packing of the subunits is not random, but organized in some regular way.

Owing to the translational element, a screw axis generates asymmetric units indefinitely and hence cannot occur in a finite system such as that of spheres. Spheres with optically active subunits have only rotational symmetry. Unlike space-group symmetry, which is not limited by the size of the crystal lattice, point-group symmetry is finite in extent and clusters around a point. The relations among the parts of a spherical virus particle are epitomized by the five regular platonic solids described by Euclid. Arrangements of protein subunits to yield icosahedral viruses have been inferred from x-ray patterns and observed directly with the electron microscope. The hollow protein shell, which can exist independently of the RNA, may exhibit a symmetry different from that of the whole virus particle.

Bacteriophage. We shall consider briefly the T-even phages of the bacterium *E. coli* as representative examples of bacterial viruses. Several T phages exist, but those with even numbers, T2, T4, and T6, have many common characteristics. A schematic representation of a T2 phage is shown in Fig. 20-3. The structure is more complex than those of the viruses previously considered, and the particle weight is about 240×10^6. About 25 to 50% of the particle is DNA, and most of the remainder is protein. In place of cytosine, the DNA of T-even phages contains hydroxymethylcytosine, the major part of which appears as a glucosyl derivative. Since the host bacteria have cytosine-containing DNA, a convenient marker is available for studying phage infection. T-odd phages contain cytosine, but no hydroxymethylcytosine.

Hexagonal phage heads consist of a protective protein sheath enclosing DNA combined with polyamines. In T2, the DNA is all one piece, of 130×10^6 molecular weight and about 60 μ long. If the DNA is labeled with P^{32}, and the protein with S^{35}, and if the phage particles are equilibrated in salt solution, upon quick placement of the particles into distilled water the osmotic shock separates the double label, so that the S^{35} remains in the phage ghosts which contain no DNA.

Phage attach themselves to the much larger bacteria by means of tail fibers. In doubly labeled phage the P^{32} DNA is injected into the bacteria, and the S^{35} protein remains outside. Bacteriophage function as molecular syringes. Immediately after injection, the synthesis of host DNA, RNA, and protein ceases, and phage DNA directs the synthetic machinery in the cell. Within 2 min, phage-specific RNA appears; at 4 min, new proteins are observed; 6 min after infection, phage DNA is synthesized about five times faster than is host DNA in uninfected cells. In 20 min, about 100 phage progeny are produced and released from the cell. The protein ghost lacks any genetic role; ghosts can attach themselves to the cell walls, inhibit RNA and protein synthesis in the host, and kill and lyse the cell, but they cannot produce progeny phage.

Phage behave genetically like an organism with a single haploid

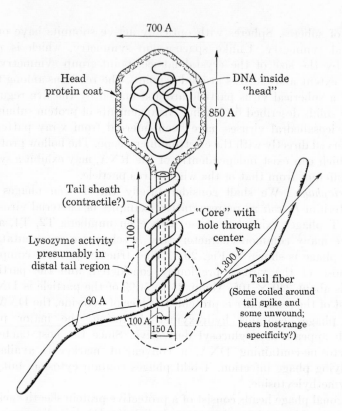

FIG. 20-3 Bacteriophage T2. The whole particle weight of 240×10^6 is one piece of DNA. Some of this DNA is oriented parallel to the tail. The enzyme lysozyme catalyzes the rupture of cell walls. (From C. B. Anfinsen, "The Molecular Basis of Evolution," John Wiley & Sons, Inc., 1959.)

chromosome. Geneticists have constructed maps of the genetic traits of many organisms. The mapping of phages is similar to that of larger organisms, except that the combination of mutants does not proceed directly, but rather by the simultaneous infection of a single bacterium with two mutant phage strains. Mutant characteristics are separated on a linear genetic map by distances proportional to the recombination frequencies observed when crosses are made. The more frequent the crossover, the farther apart the mutant loci on the genetic map. Map distances can be worked out quantitatively and often checked. A very large number of mutants of bacteriophage T4 have been mapped. One particular region of the genetic map has been examined in detail; the distance between the most closely linked loci is estimated to be equivalent to that of a few base pairs in DNA. An important result is that a linear genetic map with no branching is sufficient to account for all the data. The classical gene lacks precision for this kind of analysis, and new units are defined operationally.

Bacteriophage ΦX174, which is 240 A in diameter, is about one-fortieth as heavy as T2 phage. There is one DNA molecule of 1.7×10^6 molecular weight per virus particle of 6.2×10^6 particle weight. This DNA lacks a complementary base composition, reacts with formaldehyde even in the intact virus, is flexible according to light-scattering data, and is hydrolyzed by DNase as expected for a single-stranded structure. Much information concerning the replication of the more usual double-stranded DNA may be forthcoming from a study of this single-stranded, apparently cyclic virus DNA, which is active as a primer in the polymerase system described in Sec. 18-5.

20-3 RIBOSOMES

Inside a cell wall, there is usually a nucleus surrounded by cytoplasm. Most cellular DNA is found in the chromosomes of the nucleus. The cytoplasm is a complex structure. Relatively large mitochondria generate utilizable chemical energy by oxidative phosphorylation to yield ATP. To a lipoprotein network in animal cells, called the *endoplasmic reticulum*, are attached quite small particles composed of ribonucleoprotein. These particles, found free or attached to walls in bacterial cells, are involved in the synthesis of protein and are now referred to as *ribosomes*.

Ribosomes contain about 85% of the cellular RNA and are themselves about 40 to 65% RNA, with the remainder protein, the percentage depending upon the source. Ribosomes from bacterial, plant, and animal sources all have a sedimentation constant of 70 to 80 S and a particle weight of 2.6×10^6 to 4×10^6. The RNA content corresponds to a molecular weight of 2×10^6, similar to that in many viruses.

Ribosomal particles sediment with sharp boundaries in the ultracentrifuge; the sedimentation coefficients depend upon ionic strength and divalent cation concentration. Added polyamines also maintain particle integrity. In the particular case of ribosomes from *E. coli*, the 70-S particle of weight 3×10^6 dissociates at 10^{-4} M Mg^{++} into a 30-S and a 50-S particle with weights of 1×10^6 and 1.8×10^6, respectively. The 30-S particle contains 16-S RNA (0.55×10^6 molecular weight), while the 50-S particle contains 23-S RNA (1.1×10^6 molecular weight). The amino acid contents of the two dissimilar particles are not distinguishable. At about 10^{-2} M Mg^{++} the 70-S particle dimerizes to yield a 100-S particle of weight 5.9×10^6. Electron micrographs confirm the inferences from sedimentation and diffusion studies. Protein synthesis appears to occur in aggregates of ribosomes.

Within the ribosomes, the distribution of protein and antiparallel RNA chains seems different from that in the spherical viruses as inferred from x-ray studies. Like the viruses, ribosomes are RNase-resistant, but once freed the RNA is enzymatically cleaved. The RNA within the ribosomes shows the same hypochromicity as does free RNA, implying some base stacking in the ribosome. Labeling experiments indicate that only a fraction of ribosomal protein is involved directly in protein synthesis; the major portion provides a structural matrix for RNA, similar to the situation in the viruses. Like the histones, the proteins of the ribosomes are heterogeneous and basic, with molecular weights of about 25×10^3.

20-4 PROTEIN SYNTHESIS

Ribosomes are implicated as the major site of protein synthesis in the cell because ribosomal protein is the first labeled when C^{14} amino acids are supplied to the medium. In addition, ribosomes can function extracellularly if supplemented with amino acids, nucleotides, an energy source, and Mg^{++}. Such isolated systems have incorporated labeled amino acids into protein. The RNA contents of the tissues of an organism correlate well with the rate of protein synthesis of those tissues. High RNA contents are found in embryonic tissues and exocrine glands of pancreas and tumors. In bacteria, the growth rate is approximately proportional to the average RNA content.

Enzymes mediate practically all the reactions of intermediary metabolism that have been so well delineated by biochemists. If we consider a priori how proteins are synthesized, the attribution of the synthesis of specific protein sequences to enzymes is clearly inadequate, because enzymes are themselves proteins. Even a bacterium has about 1,000 enzymes. If the exact sequence of amino acids in each protein is ascribed to a set of enzymes (or even one enzyme), the proliferation of enzymes becomes very great indeed. We are faced with the problem of determining how many more enzymes are required to synthesize the already numerous known enzymes, so that astronomical numbers are quickly reached. For this reason it is necessary to assume that proteins are synthesized on some kind of template on which the amino acids are somehow arranged in the correct sequence and then joined together. RNA is thought to be the template, and the ribosome the site of combination of the amino acids.

Further consideration of the problems of protein synthesis makes it unlikely that amino acids are attached directly to ribosomal RNA and simply zippered together. In the first place, it is difficult to understand how only four bases in RNA, regardless of the molecular geometry, could function as a direct template to provide the information for the sequential arrangement of 20 amino acids. It seems necessary to postulate adaptor molecules that, on one hand, combine specifically with the amino acids and, on the other, ferret out the appropriate positions on the template. Secondly, as discussed in Sec. 2-4, the equilibrium position for the synthesis of proteins from amino acids favors the amino acids. Since an energy source must be available to drive the endergonic reaction to completion, only activated amino acids may be linked to form proteins. Both adaptor molecules and activated amino acids have been found experimentally as components of protein synthesis.

Protein synthesis originates only from single amino acids; other proteins or peptides are degraded to amino acids before being built into new protein. If one essential amino acid is missing, no synthesis occurs. In the cell fluid surrounding the ribosomes, activating enzymes in the presence of Mg^{++} catalyze the reaction of amino acids with adenosine triphosphate (ATP) to yield activated amino acid adenylate enzyme complexes and pyrophosphate:

$$
\begin{array}{c}
\overset{\displaystyle NH_3^+}{\underset{\displaystyle |}{}} \\
R\text{—CH—COO}^- + ATP + \text{enzyme} \rightleftarrows
\end{array}
$$

$$
\begin{array}{c}
\overset{\displaystyle NH_3^+}{\underset{|}{}} \quad \overset{\displaystyle O}{\underset{\parallel}{}} \quad \overset{\displaystyle O^-}{\underset{|}{}} \\
PP + \text{(enzyme) R—CH———C—O—} \overset{}{\underset{\displaystyle O_-}{P^+}} \text{—O—C}_5{}'\text{—ribose—adenine}
\end{array}
$$

$$(20\text{-}1)$$

Activating enzymes are found in bacteria, plants, and animals. At least 20 such enzymes exist, one for each L-amino acid.

The complex formed in Reaction (20-1) reacts further with the *soluble* RNA of the cell fluid to yield an amino-acyl RNA and adenosine monophosphate (AMP):

(enzyme) amino acid adenylate + sRNA $\rightleftarrows$
$$\text{amino-acyl RNA} + AMP + \text{enzyme} \quad (20\text{-}2)$$

About 10% of cellular RNA is soluble RNA (sRNA) of the cell fluid. Just as each amino acid has its own specific activating enzyme, so there is at least one specific amino acid acceptor RNA for each amino acid. The various soluble RNA molecules have sedimentation coefficients of about 4 S and molecular weights of about 25,000, much less than the total of about 2×10^6 for the cellular RNA found in the ribosomes described above. The eighty or so nucleotides of amino acid acceptor RNA's obey Chargaff's rules and, at the same time, contain a few percent of uncommon bases, both features in striking contrast to ribosomal RNA. The unusual bases are probably formed from the common ones after synthesis of the RNA chain. X-ray analysis of sRNA yields a typically helical diffraction pattern similar to the A form of DNA, indicating that a molecule may be folded back on itself and may undergo complementary base pairing. Consistent with this view is the relatively greater resistance of sRNA to ribonuclease. Complete sequence analyses of sRNA for each amino acid by x-ray-diffraction techniques may be possible.

All *amino acid acceptor* RNA molecules have the same three bases (- - - - cytosine-cytosine-adenine) at the end of the RNA chain at which the amino acid is attached and have guanosine-5′-mono phosphate as the terminal nucleotide on the nonacceptor end. The specificity of the soluble RNA for a particular amino acid therefore begins at least four residues from the amino acid end, where differences begin to occur. The three bases are added enzymatically and specifically to the soluble RNA that lacks them:

$$\text{ATP} + 2\text{CTP} + \text{sRNA} \rightleftarrows \text{sRNA—pCpCpA} + 3\text{PP}$$

The amino acid in the amino-acyl RNA is attached to the 2′ or 3′ position of the terminal ribose attached to adenine:

$$\begin{array}{c}
\text{NH}_2 \\
| \\
\text{C} \\
\text{N—C} \quad \text{N} \\
\text{HC} \\
\text{N—C} \quad \text{CH} \\
\text{N} \\
\text{CH}
\end{array}$$

$$\text{—CH—O—P}^+\text{—O—CH}_2\text{—CH——CH—O—C—CH—NH}_3{}^+$$

The sum of Reactions (20-1) and (20-2) is

$$\text{Amino acid} + \text{ATP} + \text{RNA} \rightleftarrows \text{amino-acyl RNA} + \text{AMP} + \text{PP} \quad (20\text{-}3)$$

Reaction (20-3) has an equilibrium constant of about 0.4 at pH 7. Since the left-hand side contains ATP with a known high group-transfer potential (Sec. 2-5), and AMP and PP are not high-energy compounds, the amino-acyl-RNA compound must be activated to account for an equilibrium constant of the order of unity. This compound exhibits a higher group-transfer potential than ordinary esters under biological conditions, mainly owing to ionization of more acidic carboxylic acid groups in amino acids (Sec. 2-3 and Question 2-13).

Reactions (20-1) and (20-2) are mediated by the same enzyme, resulting in considerable economy, for 20 less enzymes are required. In the few cases that have been studied, an amino-acyl-RNA synthetase is more discriminating in Reaction (20-2) than in Reaction (20-1). Although a second amino acid may be slowly activated in Reaction (20-1), no amino-acyl RNA appears. An amino-acyl-RNA synthetase also exhibits some species specificity in the second reaction. For example, a bacterial enzyme will catalyze Reaction (20-2) for other bacterial, but not animal, sRNA. Similarly, an activating enzyme from animals will catalyze transfer to sRNA isolated from other animals, but not from bacterial sources. Indications are that the interchangeability of activating enzymes and sRNA samples depends upon both the organisms and the particular amino acid. Radioactive amino acids are incorporated more rapidly onto soluble RNA than into protein.

All of Reaction (20-3) occurs in the cell fluid. We have previously given evidence that protein synthesis occurs in the ribosomes but requires both activated amino acids and adaptor molecules. The amino-acyl-RNA product of Reaction (20-3) is an adaptor molecule containing an activated amino acid. It is necessary to transfer this product to the ribosome and to assemble the protein on some kind of template RNA. This transfer step is catalyzed by an enzyme which displays little specificity. The transfer enzyme from bacteria catalyzes the transfer of amino-acyl RNA from any source to bacterial, but not to animal, ribosomes. Likewise, the transfer enzyme from rabbits can catalyze the transfer of amino-acyl amino acid acceptor RNA from bacteria to yield hemoglobin in rabbit-reticulocyte ribosomes. Thus the transfer enzyme seems somewhat specific for the ribosomes but much less so for the intermediates.

Up to this point the low-molecular-weight (25,000) RNA of the cell fluid has been called by its operational name, soluble RNA, or by a functional name, amino acid acceptor RNA. At least part of the amino acid acceptor RNA enters the ribosome carrying an activated amino acid. The functional name *transfer* RNA may be used to denote the low-molecular-weight RNA that enters the ribosome. Transfer RNA contains no sequence information; it is only able to combine with a single, specific amino acid. Having entered the ribosome, transfer RNA is attached to template RNA, perhaps by means of specific base pairing. Attachment presumably occurs in such a manner that the activated amino acids are oriented in a stereochemically favorable position for linking to form protein. Guanosine triphosphate is essential for one of the processes just described. After transfer RNA has performed its function and donated its activated amino acid to the growing polypeptide chain in the ribosome, it reenters the cell fluid to repeat the process.

At one time it was thought that the stable ribosomal RNA might be the template upon which amino-acyl transfer RNA's link to form protein. However, only a weak correlation exists between base compositions of DNA and ribosomal RNA. In addition, bacteria cannot synthesize a protein when the corresponding gene has been destroyed. Incorporation of unusual bases into RNA results in rapid alteration of protein and synthesis of unaltered protein stops. These three points are not a final refutation, but they serve to illustrate the difficulties in postulating stable ribosomal RNA as the template RNA.

Evidence now exists that the cytoplasm-residing ribosomes are non-specialized structures which receive genetic information from nuclear DNA via yet another kind of RNA, *messenger* RNA. Messenger RNA is unstable and has a base composition corresponding to the relevant DNA (with the provision that uracil is equivalent to thymine), and not to ribosomal or sRNA.

When *E. coli* are infected with T2 phage, no new ribosomes appear, and net RNA synthesis ceases. However, a new RNA with rapid turnover and base composition corresponding to that of phage DNA rather than bacterial DNA is added to the preexisting cellular ribosomes, where synthesis of phage proteins then takes place. This messenger RNA is found associated with aggregated 70-S ribosomal particles, as demonstrated by experiments with radioactive labels. Upon phage infection, cellular messenger RNA is no longer synthesized and, owing to its instability, soon disappears.

Messenger RNA seems heterogeneous and comprises 2 to 4% of all RNA in a cell. It has a sedimentation coefficient of about 8 to 14 S, implying a molecule of the order of 10^3 nucleotides, perhaps long enough to encode a peptide chain of several hundred amino acids. Messenger RNA isolated from phage-infected cells forms a hybrid complex when heated with phage DNA and slowly cooled. No hybrid complex is formed with DNA from other sources. A hybrid RNA-DNA complex also occurs naturally. Unlike amino acid acceptor RNA, which seems to be reused cyclically, messenger RNA is used only a few times. Ribosomal RNA, on the other hand, is a stable, nonspecialized structure. An RNA component with a base composition corresponding to the DNA has also been found in other organisms, including mammals. It has been shown that in bacteria all three kinds of RNA hybridize with portions of homologous DNA, suggesting that RNA molecules have their origin in DNA. Evidently not all of a long DNA molecule is copied by RNA at once, and if this feature of the transcription process is carried over to replication, entanglement problems due to winding and unwinding of very long strands are eliminated.

Much remains to be learned concerning the final stage of protein synthesis: assembly of protein in the ribosomes. Messenger RNA seems to promote aggregation of 70-S ribosomes. Experiments with labeled amino acids in rabbit reticulocytes indicate that it requires about 1 to 2 min for a hemoglobin chain to grow in a linear fashion from the amino-terminal end. Many more details are still to be worked out in this and other steps of protein synthesis. Our exposition here has been a cursory examination of a complex field involving many workers.

20-5 CODING

We have indicated that the base sequence of the genetic carrier DNA in some way determines the amino acid sequence of proteins. Just how a sequence of four bases accounts for the arrangement of the 20 amino acids that normally occur in proteins may be treated as a purely formal problem, apart from any particular mechanism of synthesis. If the code is a doublet, apparently only $4 \times 4 = 16$ amino acids may be coded. For this reason, three-letter or triplet codes have often been considered.

Since only one amino acid is changed in some TMV mutants, an overlapping code in which one base codes for two or more adjacent amino acids is unlikely. The intercession of an adaptor molecule that eliminates the need for direct contact between the amino acid and nucleic acid bases permits nonoverlapping codes. Detailed analysis of mutants in bacteriophage T4 indicates that the code is probably a triplet, begins at a fixed starting point, and contains little nonsense. The last stipulation means that most three-letter combinations code for an amino acid. Since a triplet code yields $4 \times 4 \times 4 = 64$ possibilities, several combinations evidently code for the same amino acid; i.e., the code is degenerate. This conclusion is in agreement with the discovery of two leucine-specific amino acid acceptor RNA molecules. Degeneracy of the genetic code may promote the survival of organisms. A mistake in DNA replication or transcription might yield a nonsense syllable in a nondegenerate code and a sense syllable for another amino acid in a degenerate code. If the former should yield no protein or incomplete peptide chains, an organism would be at a disadvantage as compared to one containing the protein with a single amino acid replacement, which is likely to have no significant consequences.

The discovery and the indicated role of messenger RNA provide a tool for cracking the genetic code. Native messenger RNA is large enough so that studies are more easily performed on synthetic messengers of known compositions. What would happen if a synthetic polyribonucleotide of the kind discussed in Chap. 19 were added to a cell-free protein-synthesizing suspension? M. W. Nirenberg and J. H. Matthei added poly U to a washed ribosomal system from *E. coli* and observed a thousandfold stimulation of incorporation of L-phenylalanine into polymer, and no stimulation with 17 other amino acids. Evidently polyphenylalanine is synthesized, and the code for phenylalanine is a succession of uracil bases of uncertain length. In agreement with the transient character of messenger RNA, added poly U is rapidly degraded. Undegraded tritiated poly U was found associated with ribosome aggregates along with newly incorporated C^{14}-labeled phenylalanine. These results support the view that poly U is a synthetic messenger and that messenger RNA plays a role somewhat similar to that described in the last section. Addition of poly A to this system results in binding of poly U in mixed double- and triple-stranded helices with no phenylalanine incorporation, indicating that a single-stranded messenger is required.

Copolymers of uracil with one or two other bases lead to augmented incorporation of other amino acids. Addition of a copolymer of poly UC containing five times as much uracil as cytosine yields a ratio of stimulation of incorporation of phenylalanine to that of serine of 4.4:1. Incorporation of other amino acids is not stimulated appreciably. If we assume a triplet code of unspecified sequence, the code letters for serine can be evaluated by the following argument: For random sequences in the UC copolymer, the UUU/UCC ratio is 25, and the UUU/UUC ratio is 5. Since the latter ratio is nearest to the amino acid incorporation ratio of 4.4, the code letters for serine are evidently UUC. By applying this sort of argument to a series of copolymers, a whole set of code letters has been constructed.

Code letters for amino acids determined in bacterial systems are in agreement with those found from mammalian studies; generality is thus implied for the code. In both kinds of systems leucine is degenerate, coded by CUU or UGU triplets. From bacterial systems, the code letters for proline are CUC. As mentioned in Sec. 20-2, a nitrous acid–induced mutant of TMV contains leucine in place of proline. This substitution is consistent with deamination of cytosine to give uracil in the above coding letters. Also in conformity with the code letters obtained in nonviral systems, phenylalanine appears but never disappears in nitrous acid–induced mutants of TMV. Nitrous acid–treated synthetic polyribonucleotide copolymers yield deaminated derivatives which, when added to a bacterial protein-synthesizing system, also give results concordant with those above. For instance, nitrous acid treatment of the poly UC copolymer discussed in the previous paragraph results in overall decrease of activity, nearly complete loss of ability to incorporate serine, and retention of phenylalanine-incorporating activity. The universality of the genetic code is indicated by these and other results.

Recognition that synthetic polynucleotide copolymers stimulate the incorporation of amino acids has permitted a test of the adaptor hypothesis for amino acid acceptor RNA. Poly UG stimulates the incorporation of cysteine, but not alanine, into polypeptides. Cysteine attached to soluble RNA and then desulfhydrated yields alanine still fixed on cysteine amino acid acceptor RNA. Under these conditions poly UG stimulates the incorporation of alanine, indicating that, once attached to a soluble RNA, the amino acid no longer participates in coding, and poly UG recognizes the specific cysteine amino acid acceptor RNA regardless of the amino acid attached. Thus amino acid acceptor RNA has all the attributes of an adaptor molecule discussed in the previous section. In a similar experiment, alanine was incorporated into a peptide fragment from the α chain of hemoglobin which normally carries cysteine but not alanine. This result assures that soluble RNA functions as a specific adaptor in protein synthesis.

20-6 AN OVERALL VIEW

Consider the following facts:

1. Sequence studies of proteins indicate exactness of protein synthesis and specificity for similar proteins in different animals. Amino acid analogues are incorporated into proteins only with difficulty. Proteins consist of nonbranched, single polypeptide chains with cross-linking mainly by disulfide linkages.

2. Abnormal human hemoglobins which are genetically allelic, i.e., in which alteration occurs at the same genetic locus, have one amino acid substituted at the same position on a polypeptide chain. Substitution of a neighboring amino acid is nonallelic.

3. Transformation experiments provide evidence for DNA as the hereditary material. RNA can function as a genetic carrier as in TMV or in protein synthesis.

4. Genetic mapping of bacteriophage requires only linear maps down to a resolution involving distances no longer than a few base pairs in DNA. The Watson-Crick structure for DNA is linear.

If a section of a DNA molecule (a gene in classical biology) determines, by means of the base sequence, one polypeptide chain, many of the above facts fit together. Thus the implications of the maxim "one gene—one enzyme" are apparent. Until nucleic acid sequences are determined with greater facility, it will be impossible to relate the sequence information of proteins to nucleic acids directly.

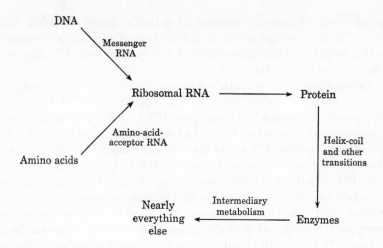

FIG. 20-4 General scheme for relationships between molecules considered in this book.

Relationships between proteins and nucleic acids, the macromolecules considered in this book, are diagrammed in Fig. 20-4. Whatever the detailed mechanism, replication of DNA is a much simpler problem than protein synthesis, because proteins are not synthesized from other proteins, but rather from nucleic acids. The mechanism by which four or so nucleic acid bases are transformed into 20 or more amino acids in a protein is of necessity more complex. Messenger RNA is probably synthesized from singly stranded DNA. Since the antiparallel, complementary DNA strands each contain the same genetic information, albeit in different forms, possibly only one DNA strand is utilized in vivo for transcription to RNA. Mixed two- and three-stranded helices of polyribonucleotides and polydeoxyribonucleotides can be formed as described in Sec. 19-5. Helix-coil transitions are the subject of Sec. 16-3. Enzymes are involved everywhere in biological systems, including the steps that lead to protein. Intermediary metabolism is the subject matter of standard courses in biochemistry. The "nearly everything else" of Fig. 20-4 includes the compounds which feed back into the cycle and provide subunits for synthesis of the macromolecules.

SELECTED BIBLIOGRAPHY

1   E. Chargaff and J. N. Davidson (eds.), "The Nucleic Acids," vol. 3, Academic Press Inc., New York, 1959.

2 A. Klug and D. L. D. Caspar, The Structure of Small Viruses, *Advan. Virus Res.*, **7**, 225–325 (1960).

3 F. M. Burnet and W. M. Stanley (eds.), "The Viruses," 3 vols., Academic Press Inc., New York, 1959.

4 M. F. Perutz, "Proteins and Nucleic Acids," Elsevier Publishing Company, Amsterdam, 1962.

5 H. Chantrenne, "The Biosynthesis of Proteins," Pergamon Press, New York, 1961.

6 J. D. Watson, Involvement of RNA in the Synthesis of Proteins, *Science*, **140**, 17–26 (1963).

7 S. Brenner, F. Jacob, and M. Meselson, An Unstable Intermediate Carrying Information from Genes to Ribosomes for Protein Synthesis, *Nature*, **190**, 576–581 (1961). See also the succeeding article.

8 F. H. C. Crick, L. Barnett, S. Brenner, and R. J. Watts-Tobin, General Nature of the Genetic Code for Proteins, *Nature*, **192**, 1227–1232 (1961).

QUESTIONS

20-1 Nucleic acids have an isoelectric point in the pH range 1 to 2. What may be inferred about the isoelectric point of a protein that neutralizes the nucleic acid charge at pH 7? What possibilities exist for the composition of this protein?

20-2 Account for the fact that concentrations of NaCl greater than 1 M dissociate deoxyribonucleoprotamines.

20-3 How many turns of the helix are there in one TMV particle?

20-4 Is there a directional sense to the TMV rod?

20-5 What conditions must be met for successful isomorphous replacement in a spherical virus?

20-6 Estimate the minimum depth of the phage head of Fig. 20-3 required to hold T2 DNA.

20-7 How much longer than the diameter of the virus is the extended DNA strand of bacteriophage ΦX174?

20-8 Give the similarities and differences between the spherical viruses and ribosomes.

20-9 Compare the conformations of RNA when free in solution with those when it is combined with protein.

20-10 Assuming that the various RNA's of this chapter behave similarly when free, find the dependence of the sedimentation coefficient on molecular weight for this type of molecule.

20-11 Amino acid acceptor RNA has also been called soluble RNA, transfer RNA, shuttle RNA, and translational RNA. Justify terms by reference to the properties or functions of the RNA.

20-12 Enumerate the molecules with which sRNA combines specifically.

20-13 Messenger RNA has also been called informational RNA, transcript RNA, template RNA, and translatable RNA. Justify these terms by reference to the properties or functions of the RNA.

20-14 What base-pair changes, due to the action of nitrous acid on parent TMV-RNA, would you predict for succeeding generations?

20-15 When placed in a cell-free protein-synthesizing suspension, a copolymer poly UA containing five uracils for each adenine stimulates the incorporation of phenylalanine and tyrosine in a 4:1 ratio. Under the assumption of a triplet code, what are the code letters for tyrosine?

20-16 What are the possible consequences for resultant protein due to the alteration of one nucleic acid base in DNA?

20-17 Suppose that, in order to study the origin of optical activity,† you set out to synthesize a world of nucleic acids with L-ribose and proteins with D-amino acids. How might you proceed, and at what stages would you expect to encounter stumbling blocks?

† Among the suggestions concerning the origin of optical activity in living matter, no one seems to have considered the world's most salient unidirectional event. The absolute sense of direction which is derived from the enduring rotation of the earth might provide the necessary asymmetry for the origin of optical activity. The mechanism whereby one-directional rotation results in a favoring of one optical antipode over another is a matter for further inquiry.

21 | Enzymes

Biological reactions occur under a narrow range of conditions near neutrality and 300° abs. Organic chemists often promote reactions with extreme acidic or alkaline conditions, high temperatures, and potent oxidizing or reducing agents. Such reagents are not appropriate in biological systems, where a delicate balance must be maintained between diverse components. To attain equilibrium rapidly where and when required, living organisms contain catalysts. These catalysts, called enzymes, are either mainly or wholly protein. Nonprotein parts of enzymes may be metal ions, some vitamins or coenzymes, or other prosthetic groups. No matter what their makeup, enzymes speed the attainment of equilibrium by increasing forward and reverse reaction rates by the same proportion. Enzymes and other catalysts do not alter the equilibrium condition, which is independent of the path taken from reactants to products; they provide a more rapid path for the reaction. Because it is often essential to accelerate some reactions without affecting others, enzymes are usually highly specific, interacting only with one or a few similar compounds or substrates. Protein conformation is presumably important in determining enzyme specificity.

Enzymes are catalysts *par excellence*, and enzyme-catalyzed reactions were important in the development of the idea of a "catalytic force" by Berzelius in 1836. He found that an enzyme mixture from potatoes degraded starch more rapidly than a sulfuric acid solution. Though the rates and specificities of enzyme-catalyzed reactions have never been reproduced in the laboratory with smaller-molecule catalysts, they are being approached, and the mechanisms of catalysis are becoming better understood. In this chapter we shall avoid detailed discussion of any mechanisms but shall consider enzyme kinetics in general and the relationship of enzyme activity to some properties of proteins discussed previously.

21-1 ENZYME - SUBSTRATE INTERMEDIATES

When the initial velocity v of an enzyme reaction is plotted against varying initial substrate concentrations (S), a curve similar to that of Fig. 21-1 is obtained. At low substrate concentrations, velocity is of the first order in (S); at high substrate concentrations, it is of zero order in (S). The order indicates the power to which a reactant appears in the rate expression. Simple nonenzymatic reactions are only first-order in substrate concentration. Enzyme-catalyzed reactions are almost always first-order in enzyme concentration.

Early workers usually followed the conversion of reactants to products by following the change of reactant concentration with time for a given initial substrate concentration. This method was complicated by changes of pH during a run, inhibition by products formed, and alterations in enzyme activity. Many attempts were made to formulate general equations which would fit the observations. In 1902, A. Brown proposed that enzyme E and substrate S react to form an enzyme-substrate intermediate:

$$\text{E} + \text{S} \underset{k_2}{\overset{k_1}{\rightleftarrows}} \text{ES} \overset{k_3}{\rightarrow} \text{E} + \text{products} \tag{21-1}$$

Though his proposition is qualitatively correct, Brown did not formulate any rate expressions. In 1903, V. Henri derived the kinetic consequences of enzyme-substrate theory for the relatively complex case including product inhibition. Henri assumed an equilibrium between concentrations of reactants and intermediate:

$$\frac{k_2}{k_1} = K_{\text{eq}} = \frac{(\text{E})(\text{S})}{(\text{ES})} \tag{21-2}$$

The total enzyme concentration (E) is the sum of the free-enzyme concentration (E) and that combined in an enzyme-substrate intermediate (ES):

$$(E) = (\text{E}) + (\text{ES}) \tag{21-3}$$

We assume that the substrate concentration greatly exceeds the small catalytic amount of enzyme present; the substrate in (ES) is negligible compared to the initial free-substrate concentration (S). Substitution of Eq. (21-2) into Eq. (21-3) yields

$$(E) = \left[1 + \frac{K_{\text{eq}}}{(\text{S})}\right](\text{ES}) \tag{21-4}$$

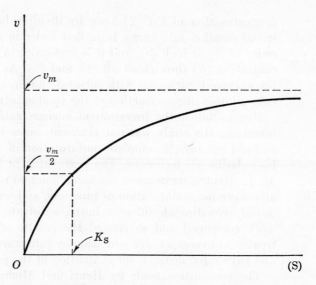

FIG. 21-1 Initial velocity of an enzyme-catalyzed reaction versus initial substrate concentrations at constant total enzyme concentration. The substrate concentration at the velocity of half-maximum, $v_m/2$, yields the substrate-dependent constant K_S.

The initial rate of formation of products is given by

$$v = \frac{d(\mathrm{P})}{dt} = k_3(\mathrm{ES}) = \frac{k_3(E)(\mathrm{S})}{(\mathrm{S}) + K_{eq}} \tag{21-5}$$

The second equality results from the substitution of Eq. (21-4). An equation of the same form as Eq. (21-5) may be derived by considering the heterogeneous equilibria of absorption and desorption of substrate on an enzyme surface.

Equation (21-5) accounts for the character of the curve of Fig. 21-1. At low substrate concentrations, $(\mathrm{S}) \ll K_{eq}$, yielding

$$v_l = \frac{k_3(E)(\mathrm{S})}{K_{eq}}$$

at high substrate concentrations, $(\mathrm{S}) \gg K_{eq}$, which gives the maximum velocity at constant total enzyme concentration:

$$v_m = k_3(E) \tag{21-6}$$

If a series of experiments is performed over a range of total enzyme concentrations, the initial velocity v may be adjusted according to the proportionality of Eq. (21-5) or by dividing both sides by (E). The initial reaction rate varies from first order in (S) at low (S) to zero order in (S) at high (S), and it is first-order in the total enzyme concentration (E) throughout all (E) and (S). At high (S), virtually all the enzyme is saturated with substrate and present as ES, but this is only an insignificant fraction of the total substrate concentration (S).

Henri studied the inversion of sucrose catalyzed by the enzyme invertase. His study was not clear-cut, since he did not control pH and did not permit complete mutarotation of the product glucose in his polarimetric technique. Ten years later, in 1913, L. Michaelis and M. L. Menten reexamined the same reaction at controlled pH, made allowance for mutarotation of products, and used only the method of initial velocities at different initial substrate concentrations. Their work confirmed and sharpened the results of Henri, extended the treatment to competitive inhibition by substances other than products, and gave some methods for evaluation of the parameters.

The assumption made by Henri and Michaelis and Menten that an equilibrium exists between reactants and enzyme-substrate intermediate is unnecessarily and dangerously restrictive. The less restrictive steady-state assumption was applied to the mechanism in Eq. (21-1) by G. E. Briggs and J. B. S. Haldane in 1925. According to Eq. (21-1), we may write

$$-\frac{d(S)}{dt} = k_1(E)(S) - k_2(ES) \tag{21-7}$$

$$\frac{d(P)}{dt} = k_3(ES) \tag{21-8}$$

$$-\frac{d(E)}{dt} = \frac{d(ES)}{dt} = k_1(E)(S) - (k_2 + k_3)(ES) \tag{21-9}$$

By the steady-state assumption, when the substrate is in great excess over the enzyme, after a brief induction period, the rate of appearance of enzyme-substrate intermediate is equal to its rate of disappearance. Consequently the rate of change of (ES) with time is zero, or $d(ES)/dt = 0$. Applying this result, we obtain from Eq. (21-9),

$$k_1(E)(S) = (k_2 + k_3)(ES) \tag{21-10}$$

By comparison with Eqs. (21-7) and (21-8),

$$-\frac{d(S)}{dt} = \frac{d(P)}{dt} \tag{21-11}$$

A substrate-dependent constant K_S is defined by rearranging Eq. (21-10):

$$K_S = \frac{k_2 + k_3}{k_1} = \frac{(E)(S)}{(ES)} \tag{21-12}$$

Comparison with Eq. (21-2) reveals that K_S is an equilibrium constant only when $k_2 \gg k_3$. Combination of Eqs. (21-3), (21-12), (21-6), and (21-7) or (21-8) yields

$$v = \frac{d(\mathrm{P})}{dt} = \frac{k_3(E)(\mathrm{S})}{(\mathrm{S}) + K_S} = \frac{v_m(\mathrm{S})}{(\mathrm{S}) + K_S} \qquad (21\text{-}13)$$

Equation (21-13) reduces to Eq. (21-5) (derived from the more restrictive equilibrium considerations) only when $k_2 \gg k_3$ so that $K_S = K_{eq}.$†

In the vast literature on enzyme reactions, instances are reported in which the enzyme-substrate intermediate decomposes to products quickly enough so that $k_3 > k_2$ and K_S is not an equilibrium constant. Also reported is the condition in which $k_2 \gg k_3$ so that an equilibrium exists between E + S and ES. Unless shown to be otherwise, it must not be assumed that K_S is an equilibrium constant, but rather that it is the more complex collection of rate constants represented by Eq. (21-12). Unfortunately, the relative values of k_2 and k_3 cannot be evaluated directly by steady-state methods (rate of disappearance of reactants or appearance of products). Either indirect arguments are used or the constants are evaluated directly by fast-reaction techniques. The nature of the constant K_S has been determined for some subtrates of the proteolytic enzyme α-chymotrypsin with the result that K_S is an equilibrium constant for most substrates, including proteins. Even with the same enzyme, relative values of k_2 and k_3 may become inverted, depending upon the substrate. Since many synthetic substrates are employed in studies of enzyme reactions, a wide range of rates is obtained.

Group-transfer, oxidation-reduction, and hydrolytic reactions all involve a second substrate. Sometimes the second substrate is bound to the enzyme so that a ternary complex is formed, as in the hydrolysis of peptide and ester bonds by α-chymotrypsin. This enzyme is particularly effective in hydrolyzing the peptide bond on the carboxyl sides of aromatic amino acid residues in proteins. In such a reaction, water, a second substrate, is apparently bound at a site neighboring the substrate binding site. In other cases such as that of catalase, in which two molecules of hydrogen peroxide are converted to water and oxygen, there is no evidence for ternary complex formation. To discuss the details of these and other cases would take us too deeply into the intricacies of the mechanisms of the numerous enzyme reactions.

† It is common practice to denote K_S as K_M in honor of Michaelis. This identification is historically inadmissible. If homage is necessary, it would seem more appropriate to ignore the priority of Henri and denote K_{eq} as K_M. Because of this confusion, K_M is not used for either K_{eq} or K_S in this book.

Transient-state studies on the buildup of enzyme-substrate complex in α-chymotrypsin yield values of $k_1 > 10^6$ molar^{-1} sec^{-1} for all substrates studied. Combination of enzyme and substrate apparently occurs on nearly every collision, because the rate constant approaches that expected of a diffusion-controlled reaction. This rapid initial buildup of ES assures the validity of the steady-state assumption when $(S) \gg (E)$, for the induction period is very short, of the order of milliseconds.

The course of conversion of reactants to products according to Eq. (21-1) is illustrated in Fig. 21-2. The reactants at some arbitrary level of free energy on the left are thermodynamically driven toward products at a lesser energy on the right. The rate of transition from reactants to products depends upon the height of the intervening barriers. In the absence of a catalyst, this barrier height might be as

FIG. 21-2 The course of conversion of reactants to products in an uncatalyzed reaction (dashed curve) and a catalyzed reaction (solid curve) with a single enzyme-substrate intermediate ES.

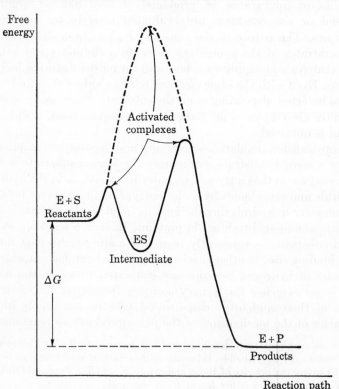

indicated by the dashed curve. Enzymes lower the free energy of activation by providing alternative pathways with lesser barrier heights. Peaks in the curve correspond to activated complexes, having only a fleeting existence, from which the reaction components slide down the hills to valleys on either side. The enzyme-substrate intermediate is not an activated complex but, as indicated by the valley, is metastable with a finite lifetime. In the example of Fig. 21-2, $k_2 > k_3$ because the barrier height is greater for ES going to products than to reactants.

The equilibrium position between reactants and products is determined by the relative positions of reactants and products on the free-energy axis. Rates of conversion of reactants to products, and vice versa, are determined by the barrier heights. Catalysts lower barrier heights but do not change the energy levels of reactants and products. Introduction of a catalyst replaces a high barrier with a lower one, speeding up the forward and reverse reaction rates in the same proportion but leaving the final equilibrium balance unaltered.

By studying the temperature dependence of reaction rates, the free energies of activation in Fig. 21-2 may be analyzed into heat and entropy terms. Usually a catalyst lowers the heat of activation compared to an uncatalyzed reaction, while the entropy of activation is either unchanged or increased. Because of the often indeterminate number of enzyme-substrate intermediates, temperature variations refer to complex ratios of both rate- and K_S-type constants. In addition, enzyme conformation itself will be temperature-dependent, and a decreased reaction rate may be due to increased unfolding. For these reasons the temperature variations of enzyme-catalyzed reactions comprise a complex subject which is beyond the scope of this book.

So far only a single enzyme-substrate intermediate has been considered. In many cases several intermediates may exist,

$$ E + S \rightleftarrows ES \rightleftarrows ES' \rightleftarrows ES'' \rightleftarrows \cdots \rightleftarrows E + P $$

with a corresponding increase in the number of activated complexes. In the steady-state methods considered here, only disappearance of reactant or appearance of product is observed, so that it is not possible to determine the number of intermediates or reaction parameters aside from those in Eq. (21-13) without resorting to auxiliary techniques and measurements. For this reason the constants determined by the methods to be described are often complex combinations of several rate constants depending upon the number of intermediates.

Only the two apparent constants of Eq. (21-13), v_m and K_S, may be evaluated by steady-state methods. By studying rates over a wide range of substrate concentrations, we may obtain a curve similar to that of Fig. 21-1, evaluate the maximum velocity v_m from the asymptotic limit at high (S), and evaluate K_S from the substrate concentration when $v = v_m/2$ according to Eq. (21-13). However, more convenient and accurate methods are available for the determination of v_m and K_S. By taking the reciprocal of Eq. (21-13), we obtain

$$\frac{1}{v} = \frac{1}{v_m} + \frac{K_S}{v_m(S)} \tag{21-14}$$

If the reciprocal of the initial velocity is plotted against the reciprocal of the initial substrate concentration, a straight line of slope K_S/v_m and ordinate intercept $1/v_m$ is obtained. Division of the slope by the intercept yields K_S. This method has the disadvantage that points are frequently inconveniently bunched unless care is taken in choosing initial substrate concentrations.

Equation (21-14) may be multiplied through by (S) to give

$$\frac{(S)}{v} = \frac{(S)}{v_m} + \frac{K_S}{v_m} \tag{21-15}$$

Figure 21-3 shows a plot of $(S)/v$ versus (S) from which K_S may be determined by dividing the ordinate intercept by the slope or by extrapolating the data to the abscissa intercept. Determination of K_S by the latter method also provides a visual estimate of the error in K_S. No matter how determined, a larger uncertainty appears in K_S than in v_m; the uncertainties attending an extrapolation illustrate this fact. This method of plotting tends to space points more equally on the abscissa, and Eq. (21-15) is more amenable to a least-squares calculation.

The rate equation (21-13) may also be integrated to yield

$$-\left[1 + \frac{K_S}{(S)}\right] \int_{(S_0)}^{(S)} d(S) = v_m \int_0^t dt$$

where (S_0) is the substrate concentration at zero time. Performing the indicated integrations, we obtain

$$(S_0) - (S) + K_S \ln \frac{(S_0)}{(S)} = v_m t$$

The combination of the first two and last terms is characteristic of an integrated zero-order rate equation, while the third and last terms are typical of an integrated first-order rate equation. A plot of $(1/t) \ln [(S_0)/(S)]$ versus $[(S_0) - (S)]/t = (P)/t$ yields a slope of

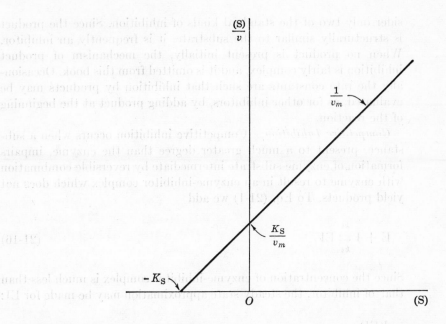

FIG. 21-3 $(S)/v$ versus (S) for determination of the parameters v_m and K_S for an enzyme-catalyzed reaction at constant enzyme concentration. When determinations are made at several enzyme concentrations, accommodation may be made in v according to Eq. (21-13).

$-1/K_S$ and an intercept of v_m/K_S. Integrated rate expressions permit consideration of greater extents of reaction than do interpretations of initial reaction rates. We have not considered, however, the back reaction of enzyme and product in Eq. (21-1). Further analysis indicates that the discussion here is only valid when the ratio of the product concentration (P) to the substrate constant for the product K_P is much less than unity.

21-2 INHIBITION

Enzymes, though large protein molecules, usually contain only one or a few active sites which are the seats of enzymatic conversion of substrate to products. Other substances, in addition to substrate, may interact at or near the active sites and alter the kinetic character of enzyme-catalyzed reactions. These substances, often structurally similar to substrates, are called *inhibitors* if they slow the noninhibited reaction in some way. Some substances such as metal ions may act either as inhibitors or activators. In the following discussion we consider only two of the standard kinds of inhibition. Since the product is structurally similar to the substrate, it is frequently an inhibitor. When no product is present initially, the mechanism of product inhibition is fairly complex, and it is omitted from this book. Occasionally the rate constants are such that inhibition by products may be evaluated, as for other inhibitors, by adding product at the beginning of the reaction.

Competitive Inhibition. Competitive inhibition occurs when a substance, present to a much greater degree than the enzyme, impairs formation of enzyme-substrate intermediate by reversible combination with enzyme to result in an enzyme-inhibitor complex which does not yield products. To Eq. (21-1) we add

$$\mathrm{E} + \mathrm{I} \underset{k_6}{\overset{k_5}{\rightleftarrows}} \mathrm{EI} \tag{21-16}$$

Since the concentration of enzyme-inhibitor complex is much less than that of inhibitor, the steady-state approximation may be made for EI:

$$\frac{d(\mathrm{EI})}{dt} = 0 = k_5(\mathrm{E})(\mathrm{I}) - k_6(\mathrm{EI})$$

Therefore,

$$\frac{k_6}{k_5} = \frac{(\mathrm{E})(\mathrm{I})}{(\mathrm{EI})} = K_\mathrm{I}$$

The inhibitor constant K_I, unlike the substrate constant K_S, is always an equilibrium constant. The total enzyme concentration is now given by

$$(E) = (\mathrm{E}) + (\mathrm{ES}) + (\mathrm{EI}) = \frac{K_\mathrm{S}(\mathrm{ES})}{(\mathrm{S})} + (\mathrm{ES}) + \frac{(\mathrm{E})(\mathrm{I})}{K_\mathrm{I}}$$
$$= (\mathrm{ES})\left[\frac{K_\mathrm{S}}{(\mathrm{S})} + 1 + \frac{K_\mathrm{S}(\mathrm{I})}{K_\mathrm{I}(\mathrm{S})}\right] = \frac{(\mathrm{ES})}{(\mathrm{S})}\left[K_\mathrm{S} + (\mathrm{S}) + \frac{K_\mathrm{S}(\mathrm{I})}{K_\mathrm{I}}\right]$$

from which we obtain, for the initial reaction rate,

$$v = k_3(\mathrm{ES}) = \frac{k_3(E)(\mathrm{S})}{(\mathrm{S}) + K_\mathrm{S}[1 + (\mathrm{I})/K_\mathrm{I}]} \tag{21-17}$$

Equation (21-17) indicates that $v_m = k_3(E)$ is unaffected by the presence of a competitive inhibitor. This result is expected because, in principle, sufficiently high substrate concentrations would virtually eliminate any effect of enzyme-inhibitor interaction. A competitive inhibitor retards the reaction by withdrawing some of the total enzyme concentration into a form EI which is not accessible for combination with substrate. A competitive inhibitor does not alter any rate constants.

Upon casting Eq. (21-17) into the form suitable for an $(S)/v$ versus (S) plot,

$$\frac{(S)}{v} = \frac{(S)}{v_m} + K_S \frac{1 + (I)/K_I}{v_m} \tag{21-18}$$

we see that the effect of maintaining a given concentration of enzyme and competitive inhibitor, as the substrate concentration is varied, is to increase the ordinate intercept with unchanged slope for each successively greater inhibitor concentration, as shown in Fig. 21-4. Each increased inhibitor concentration yields another parallel line of greater intercept. A second plot of the abscissa intercepts of Fig. 21-4 versus (I) should yield a straight line of slope $-K_S/K_I$. Since K_S is known

FIG. 21-4 Competitive inhibition. The effect of specific concentrations of a competitive inhibitor on an $(S)/v$ versus (S) plot according to Eq. (21-18). In the figure, inhibitor concentrations decrease in the order $(I_3) > (I_2) > (I_1) > 0$.

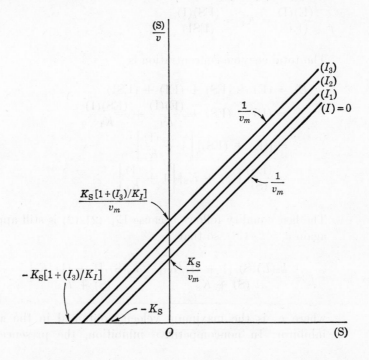

from the case in which (I) = 0, K_I may be evaluated. K_I values are even less precisely known than K_S values.

Two important criteria exist for competitive inhibition: K_I must be independent of (I), and K_I must also be independent of the particular substrate used in its evaluation. For a case in which similar values of K_S and K_I are obtained for structurally similar substrate and inhibitor, an indirect inference is that K_S is an equilibrium constant, since K_I always is.

Noncompetitive Inhibition. In this case an inhibitor present to a much greater degree than the enzyme combines with the enzyme in a reversible manner in such a way that combination with substrate is unaffected and only the inhibitor-free complex yields products. In addition to Eq. (21-1), we have

$$E + I \rightleftarrows EI \tag{21-19}$$

and

$$ES + I \rightleftarrows ESI \tag{21-20}$$

In this simplified treatment we shall assume that the inhibitor equilibrium constant for Eq. (21-19) also applies to Eq. (21-20):

$$\frac{(E)(I)}{(EI)} = K_I = \frac{(ES)(I)}{(ESI)}$$

The total enzyme concentration is

$$
\begin{aligned}
(E) &= (E) + (ES) + (EI) + (ESI) \\
&= (E) + (ES) + \frac{(E)(I)}{K_I} + \frac{(ES)(I)}{K_I} \\
&= [(E) + (ES)]\left[1 + \frac{(I)}{K_I}\right] \\
&= \frac{(ES)}{(S)}[(S) + K_S]\left[1 + \frac{(I)}{K_I}\right]
\end{aligned}
$$

The last equality follows because Eq. (21-12) is still applicable. Once again $v = k_3(ES)$, so that

$$v = \frac{k_3(E)(S)/[1 + (I)/K_I]}{(S) + K_S} = \frac{v_m(S)/[1 + (I)/K_I]}{(S) + K_S}$$

where v_m is the maximum velocity obtained in the absence of an inhibitor. In noncompetitive inhibition, the presence of inhibitor

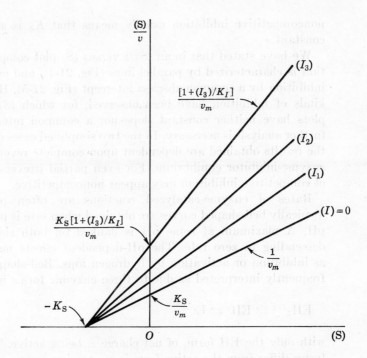

FIG. 21-5 Noncompetitive inhibition. The effect of specific concentrations of a noncompetitive inhibitor on an $(S)/v$ versus (S) plot according to Eq. (21-21). In the figure, inhibitor concentrations decrease in the order $(I_3) > (I_2) > (I_1) > 0$. The maximum velocity v_m is that obtained at high substrate concentration in the absence of inhibitor.

does not alter the K_S value. The $(S)/v$ versus (S) plot of Fig. 21-5 is represented by the equation

$$\frac{(S)}{v} = \frac{[1 + (I)/K_I](S)}{v_m} + \frac{K_S[1 + (I)/K_I]}{v_m} \qquad (21\text{-}21)$$

which shows that both the slope and ordinate intercept are increased by the presence of a noncompetitive inhibitor. The ratio of intercept to slope and the abscissa intercept remain unaffected.

Our analysis of noncompetitive inhibition is incomplete because it assumed that the equilibrium constants $1/K_I$ for the formation of EI and ESI complexes are identical, which may not be true. Furthermore, an alternative path exists for the formation of a ternary complex: $EI + S \rightleftarrows EIS$. A complete steady-state analysis has been performed on this system, with the important result that the occurrence of noncompetitive inhibition usually means that K_S is an equilibrium constant.

We have stated that in an $(S)/v$ versus (S) plot competitive inhibition is characterized by parallel lines (Fig. 21-4), and noncompetitive inhibition by a common abscissa intercept (Fig. 21-5). However, other kinds of inhibition have been observed, for which $(S)/v$ versus (S) plots have neither constant slope nor a common intercept, so that further analysis is necessary. In the two simplified cases discussed here, the results obtained are dependent upon complete reversibility of the enzyme-inhibitor equilibrium. For even partial irreversibility, a case of competitive inhibition may appear noncompetitive.

Rates of enzyme-catalyzed reactions are often pH-dependent. Typically bell-shaped curves are obtained when rate is plotted against pH. A maximum at some pH is flanked on both sides by curves descending to zero rate. The pH-dependent effects may be treated as inhibition or activation by hydrogen ions. Bell-shaped curves are frequently interpreted as due to three enzymic forms in equilibrium,

$$EH_2^{z+1} \rightleftarrows EH^z \rightleftarrows E^{z-1}$$

with only the EH form, of net charge z, being active. The other two forms differ from the active form in containing one more and one less proton than EH near the active site; either alteration upsets the fine balance required for a catalytic site. The pH at the midpoint of a descent from the maximum then corresponds to the pK_a of the acid-base group involved. Since the number of groups of given pK_a in proteins is limited (Table 5-1), an indication of the amino acid residues at an active site is obtained. Unfortunately, there are uncertainties inherent in this approach. Dependent upon the details of the mechanism, descending curves on a rate versus pH plot may be due to complex combinations of rate and equilibrium constants or due only to rate constants. Both have been observed for small molecules, and their occurrence in enzymes, in which a great diversity of mechanisms is possible, is likely.

21-3 CONCLUSIONS

Much information is made available by substrate and inhibition studies of enzyme reactions. It would take us far afield to review any of these studies in detail, but some general conclusions, complementary to other ideas in this book, may be drawn. Consider first only the enzyme itself: activity is generally dependent upon maintenance of tertiary structure. Denaturing agents which alter the enzyme conformation reduce or destroy activity. In at least one case, ribonuclease, enzyme conformation is maintained by bound substrates even in the presence of agents that are otherwise denaturing. On the other hand, not all the primary sequence is necessary for activity. Three-fifths of the proteolytic-like enzyme papain has been systematically whittled away without loss of activity. The active fragment remains sensitive to denaturing agents, indicating that an appropriate tertiary structure is necessary for activity. Such results cause one to wonder why enzymes are so large. Evidently only a small part of an enzyme functions as an active site, but the remainder may be helpful, if not necessary, in the precise and efficient production and maintenance of an enzymatically active conformation, a necessary product of evolutionary development, or an incidental result of blundering and inefficient evolutionary processes. The course of evolution is marked by much stumbling, akin to the process of discovery by scientists.

Amino acid sequence studies of an enzyme are necessary but not sufficient for elucidation of an active site. Several proteins have similar sequences about a serine residue at the active site. These enzymes catalyze a diverse group of transfer reactions, providing a simplification and a challenge to the chemist interested in mechanism. There is strong evidence that α-chymotrypsin has a histidine as well as serine residue at the active site. Amino acid residue sequence studies reveal that the nearest histidine is at least 50 residues from the reactive serine, conclusively demonstrating the importance of conformation in producing an active enzyme.

The importance of conformation is further revealed when substrate specificity is considered. Proteolytic enzymes transfer groups (water in hydrolysis) almost exclusively with L substrates, yet D substrates are often bound more strongly and are inhibitory. Apparently, a reactive substrate makes a three-point landing on an enzyme, for if only two points were critical, there would be no difference between L and D substrates. Because of their own optical activity, those enzymes catalyzing synthetic processes can produce an optically active product from optically inactive substrates.

The functions of enzymes are to bind substrates in a manner favorable to a particular reaction and to lower the free energy of activation so that the reaction occurs at a suitable rate under biological conditions. The most complementary structures between enzyme and substrate may not occur in the enzyme-substrate intermediate but in an activated complex. Enzyme conformation is sometimes slightly altered by binding of substrates and inhibitors. Though enzyme-substrate intermediates are implied by the kinetic results, little is learned of the succession of structures of such intermediates without further experiments on varieties of substrates and inhibitors, as well as considerations of chemical-reaction mechanisms. In the formulation of detailed mechanisms, consideration must be given to the free-energy changes associated with the postulated reactions, as well as to the return of the enzyme to its initial state. All net reactions must be thermodynamically feasible. This chapter is the only one in this book primarily concerned with reaction pathways and initial and final equilibrium states. Because kinetics is concerned with the path taken as well the initial and final states, it is a much more complicated subject than thermodynamics.

SELECTED BIBLIOGRAPHY

1 M. Dixon and E. C. Webb, "Enzymes," Academic Press Inc., New York, 1958.

2 P. D. Boyer, H. Lardy, and K. Myrback (eds.), "The Enzymes," 2d ed., vol. 1, Academic Press Inc., New York, 1959. Most of the subjects discussed in this chapter are included in volume 1, which is followed by chapters on specific enzymes in subsequent volumes.

QUESTIONS

21-1 Describe how you would determine the order with respect to enzyme concentration in an enzyme-catalyzed reaction.

21-2 Derive Eq. (21-13) from Eq. (21-8) and from Eq. (21-7).

21-3 By adding a k_4 step to Eq. (21-1) with only a single ES intermediate, show that if K_S for the forward reaction is an equilibrium constant, the corresponding constant for the reverse reaction cannot be an equilibrium constant.

21-4 With reactants, intermediate, and products at the same relative levels of free energy, redraw Fig. 21-2 for $k_3 > k_2$.

21-5 Redraw Fig. 21-2, with ES less stable than either reactants or products, for $k_3 > k_2$ and for $k_2 > k_3$.

21-6 If the energy levels for reactants and products in Fig. 21-2 are at the same level, what drives an initial solution of reactants to equilibrium with products?

21-7 Draw a figure similar to Fig. 21-2 for a case in which two enzyme-substrate intermediates occur. Label clearly all activated complexes.

21-8 An enzyme of molecular weight 20,000 is studied as a catalyst at a concentration of 1 mg/ml and at constant pH and ionic strength. At substrate concentrations of 1.0, 2.0, 4.0, 8.0, 12.0, 16.0, and 20.0×10^{-3} M, the initial rates of reaction are 7.1, 13, 20, 29, 33, 36, and 38×10^{-5} sec^{-1}, respectively. Calculate v_m, k_3, and K_S.

21-9 If the molecular weight of the enzyme in Question 21-8 is really 22,000 instead of 20,000, how are v_m, k_3, and K_S affected?

21-10 A third method of obtaining a linear plot from Eq. (21-13) is to plot v versus $v/(S)$. How would v_m and K_S be found from such a plot?

21-11 What is the significance of the abscissa intercept of a $1/v$ versus $1/(S)$ plot?

21-12 Describe the effects of a competitive inhibitor on a $1/v$ versus $1/(S)$ plot.

21-13 Describe the effects of a noncompetitive inhibitor on a $1/v$ versus $1/(S)$ plot.

21-14 How could you find K_I for a case of noncompetitive inhibition?

...

22 | Metal Ions in Biological Systems

Every biological system contains a variety of metal ions. At the
pH values of many biological tissues, some of these metal ions would
precipitate as hydroxides if they were not strongly bound by molecules
in the system. The vital importance of many of these combination
interactions has long been recognized; for others it is just beginning
to be appreciated. Table 22-1 lists the metal ions frequently occurring

TABLE 22-1   *Some Metal Ions Found in Biological Systems*

Metal ion	Occurrence
Sodium	Blood
Potassium	Tissues
Magnesium	Chlorophyll, enzyme cofactor as in ATP reactions
Calcium	Enzyme cofactor, bone
Manganese	Enzyme cofactor
Iron	Oxygen transport and storage, electron transport, oxidation reactions
Cobalt	Trivalent ion in vitamin B_{12}
Copper	Oxygen carrier, oxidative enzymes
Zinc	Cofactor in hydrolysis and dehydrogenase enzymes
Molybdenum	Enzyme cofactor

in biological systems and some of their functions. In this chapter we
present a brief general discussion of metal ions of biological significance; specific topics are considered in the references listed at the
end of the chapter. In contrast to the previous chapter on enzymes,
which included a discussion of rates, we assume in this chapter that,
unless specifically stated otherwise, all reactions are sufficiently rapid
so that only the equilibrium condition need be considered.

22-1   FORMATION CONSTANTS

Which of the numerous groups or ligands in biological systems might
bind a metal ion is indicated by many studies of metal-ion interactions

with small molecules. This information is usually expressed in terms of a formation constant K_1 between a metal ion and the conjugate base of a ligand. For an acid-base system and a metal cation, two equilibrium expressions may be written. For example, for an amine-charge-type ligand,

$$HA^+ \rightleftarrows H^+ + A \qquad K_a = \frac{(H^+)(A)}{(HA^+)} \qquad (22\text{-}1)$$

$$M^{++} + A \rightleftarrows MA^{++} \qquad K_1 = \frac{(MA^{++})}{(M^{++})(A)} \qquad (22\text{-}2)$$

If species A is a weak base such as chloride ion, our concern is solely with the second equation. Comparison of Eqs. (22-1) and (22-2) reveals that the acid ionization constant K_a for the combination of a hydrated proton with a conjugate base is analogous to the reciprocal of the formation constant for combination of a metal ion with the same base. Reciprocals of formation constants are often called *dissociation* constants. Since both acid ionization constants and metal ion formation constants are often reported in logarithmic form, pK_a and log K_1, respectively, taking the reciprocal simply changes the sign of the function. Metal ions often combine more avidly with ligands than protons and displace protons from conjugate acids, which otherwise are not appreciably ionized:

$$M^{++} + HA^+ \rightleftarrows MA^{++} + H^+ \qquad (22\text{-}3)$$

Equation (22-3) follows from Eqs. (22-1) and (22-2). All three equations are incomplete as written, since the ligand is replacing one or more water molecules from the inner hydration sphere of the metal ion.

Formation constants are evaluated by measuring proton displacements according to Eq. (22-3), conductometrically, spectrophotometrically, potentiometrically, by determination of the free metal ion concentration, and in other ways. Standard procedures are available for all the methods; Table 22-2 lists some of the results that have been obtained. In many metal-ion reactions, charges are created or destroyed, and a strong ionic strength dependence is expected. Most of the constants recorded in Table 22-2 are concentration rather than thermodynamic constants because, though the ionic strength has usually been held constant with inert salt, the equilibrium formation constants have not been extrapolated to zero ionic strength. Since the values recorded in Table 22-2 have been determined under a variety of conditions of ionic strength and temperature, they may vary by as much as a log unit and are not strictly comparable. Nevertheless, certain general trends may usefully be discussed.

TABLE 22-2 *Logarithms of Formation Constants*

Ligand	H^+	Mg^{++}	Ca^{++}	Mn^{++}	Fe^{++}	Co^{++}	Ni^{++}	Cu^{++}	Zn^{++}
Acetic acid	4.7	0.5	0.5				0.7	2.0	1.0
Oxalic acid	4.2	3.4	3.0	3.9	4.7	4.7	5.3	6.2	4.9
Ammonia K_1	9.3		−0.2			2.1	2.8	4.2	2.4
K_2						1.6	2.2	3.5	2.4
Ethylene-diamine	10.1			2.7	4.3	5.9	7.7	10.6	5.7
Imidazole	7.0		0.1	1.7		2.4	3.3	4.3	2.6
Histidine	9.2			1.8		6.9	8.7	10.4	6.6
Glycine	9.7	3.4	1.4	3.4		5.2	6.2	8.6	5.5
Glutathione (sulfhydryl only)	8.9			1.9		3.7	4.0		5.0
Mercaptoacetic acid	10.6			4.4	5.5	5.8	7.0		7.8
Mercaptopro-pionic acid	10.4						5.2		6.8
2-Mercapto-ethylamine	10.8				6.2	10.2	10.1		9.9
Cysteine	10.5			4.1	6.2	9.3	10.5		9.9

Metal ions have more than one position for ligand bonding: typically two positions in a linear array, four with the metal ion the center of a tetrahedron (zinc) or plane (cupric), and six with the metal ion the center of an octahedron with a ligand donor atom at each of the six corners (the other metal ions of Table 22-2). For this reason successive formation constants are defined, one for each ligand group that adds to the complex. In writing such equilibria, it is assumed that coordination positions not occupied by ligands are taken up by solvent. We may write, in addition to Eq. (22-2),

$$MA^{++} + A \rightleftharpoons MA_2^{++} \qquad K_2 = \frac{(MA_2^{++})}{(MA^{++})(A)}$$

$$MA_2^{++} + A \rightleftharpoons MA_3^{++} \qquad K_3 = \frac{(MA_3^{++})}{(MA_2^{++})(A)}$$

and so on for as many steps as are necessary. For n ligand groups that have become attached, we have

$$M^{++} + nA \rightleftharpoons MA_n^{++} \qquad K_1 K_2 K_3 \cdots K_n = \frac{(MA_n^{++})}{(M^{++})(A)^n}$$

In general $K_1 > K_2 > K_3 > \cdots$, especially in those cases in which the basic form of the ligand carries a charge, for then each successive ligand is increasingly repelled electrostatically by those already coordinated in a complex. Because zinc ion is six-coordinate in water and only four-coordinate with most ligands such as ammonia, values of successive formation constants may increase, reflecting a change in coordination number. Successive formation constants are illustrated in Table 22-2 for ammonia.

Two or more coordinate positions about a metal ion may be occupied by a single ligand with two or more donor groups to form a chelate compound. An example is the bidentate ligand ethylenediamine,

$$
M^{++}
\begin{array}{c}
\diagup NH_3 \\
\diagdown NH_3
\end{array}
\qquad
M^{++}
\begin{array}{c}
\diagup NH_2 \\
\quad \diagdown CH_2 \\
\quad \diagup CH_2 \\
\diagdown NH_2
\end{array}
$$

which is similar to two ammonia molecules joined by methylene groups. Vacant coordinate positions are assumed to be occupied by water molecules. Though Werner recognized the first of the chelate compounds in 1901, their special character went unappreciated until 1904, when Ley studied the chelate complex of cupric ion and glycine. Its low conductivity in solution indicates that the complex must be uncharged overall, according to the structure

$$
\begin{array}{c}
O \qquad O \text{------} NH_2 \\
\diagdown \quad \diagup \quad \diagdown \\
C \qquad \qquad CH_2 \\
\diagup \quad | \quad \diagdown \\
CH_2 \quad Cu \quad C \\
\diagdown \quad \diagup \quad \diagup \\
NH_2 \text{------} O \qquad O
\end{array}
$$

with cupric ion near the center of a plane which has two nitrogen and two oxygen atoms at its corners. Using conductance as a tool, Ley found that the relative strengths of glycinate complexes is $Cu^{++} > Ni^{++} > Co^{++}$. By noting that amino acids of increasing length decreased the conductance of solutions of copper acetate most in the order glycine > β-alanine > γ-aminobutyric acid, with no significant drop for the last amino acid, Ley also demonstrated that five-membered chelate rings are more stable than six-membered rings and that ligands favor binding by a single donor group rather than chelation in a seven-membered ring.

Since this early work, there has appeared a vast literature on coordination compounds, from which some generalizations of biological interest may be enumerated. Many of these statements are illustrated by the selected list of compounds in Table 22-2.

The stability sequence of several divalent metal ions with a given ligand is, for almost every ligand,

$$Mg < Mn < Fe < Co < Ni < Cu > Zn$$

This series is broken when coordination numbers exceed 4, partly because cupric and zinc ions tend to be only four-coordinate with ligands other than water. Usually $Cu > Ni > Zn$, but with sulfhydryl ligands Zn tends to be promoted to give $Cu > Zn > Ni$.

The stability of alkaline earth-metal complexes is almost entirely due to a favorable entropy term resulting from charge neutralization and release of water on coordination. A favorable heat term also appears with the transition-metal ions. Except when its small size precludes its complete coordination with large ligands, Mg^{++} binds ligands more strongly than Ca^{++}.

The sum of two formation constants for a monodentate ligand is less than the corresponding single constant for a bidentate ligand. Thus, in Table 22-2, for ammonia, $\log K_1 + \log K_2 < \log K_1$ for ethylenediamine. Similarly, glycine values are greater than the sum of the ammonia and acetic acid constants. Analysis reveals that this chelate effect is based largely in the entropy term, rather than the heat term, and can be ascribed to an entropy of dilution. By suitable choice of standard states, the discrepancy can be made to vanish or nearly so. Nonetheless, in dilute aqueous solutions, wherein lies our primary concern, the chelate effect is important.

In chelated ligands, five-membered rings are usually favored over six-membered rings; compare mercaptoacetate and mercaptopropionate in Table 22-2. Seven-membered chelate rings are little more stable than the ligand acting as a monodentate ligand. Larger rings may form, however, if rotational freedom about several bonds is restricted, as it may be in macromolecules.

With the exceptions of histidine and cysteine, most amino acids exhibit formation constants similar to those of glycine.

Imidazole binds metal ions slightly more strongly than ammonia, despite the fact that the latter is a hundred times stronger as a base. This result illustrates the importance of π acceptor properties in imidazole, and π bonds generally, for metal-ion binding.

Mg^{++}, Ca^{++}, and Mn^{++} tend to coordinate with charged oxygen ligands. An exception is chlorophyll, in which coordination with nitrogen donors seems to be influenced by the abundance and small size of Mg^{++}.

Fe^{++}, Co^{++}, and Ni^{++} prefer mixed oxyanion-nitrogen ligands.

Note an inversion of relative stabilities at about Fe^{++} when comparing formation constants of ethylenediamine with oxalic acid, glycine, or mercaptoacetic acid.

Cu^{++} and Zn^{++} prefer sulfur and nitrogen ligands. Although they combine with oxyanions more strongly than Mn^{++} for example, Cu^{++} and Zn^{++} bind so many times more strongly to sulfur and nitrogen ligands that they are expected to be found at these locations in biological systems.

22-2 FACTORS AFFECTING METAL ION SPECIFICITY

Although the formation constants of Table 22-2 are useful, they do not by themselves supply all the information necessary for assessing relative binding strengths under physiological conditions. As Eq. (22-3) indicates, hydrogen and metal ions compete for ligands. The extent to which metal ions are bound to one of several ligands present in excess varies with pH. To estimate the influence of pH on the fraction of metal ions bound to ligands, we calculate the free metal ion concentration when half of all ligand present is bound to metal ions, i.e., when

$$(MA^{++}) = (A) + (HA^+)$$

Only the first formation constant is considered, because ligands are assumed to be present in excess. Combination with Eqs. (22-1) and (22-2) yields

$$(M^{++})_{1/2} = \frac{1 + (H^+)/K_a}{K_1} \tag{22-4}$$

Equation (22-4) shows that at high pH $[K_a \gg (H^+)]$ the negative logarithm of the free metal ion concentration at half saturation of ligand is

$$pM_{1/2} = \log K_1$$

while at low pH, where $(H^+) \gg K_a$,

$$pM_{1/2} = \log K_1 + pH - pK_a$$

Only for ligands with $pK_a \ll pH$ will the formation constants of Table 22-2 be effective. When $pK_a \gg pH$, the difference $\log K_1 - pK_a$ is a better measure of relative effective formation constants among different ligands.

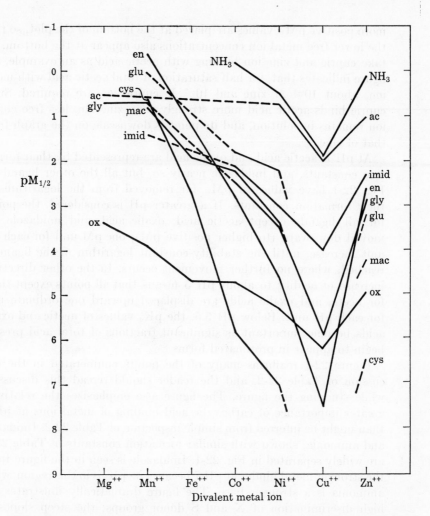

FIG. 22-1 Negative logarithm of free metal ion concentration at pH 7 and half saturation of ligand by metal ion versus divalent metal cation. The lower free metal ion concentrations are at the bottom of the graph. The following symbols are used: NH_3, ammonia; ac, acetic acid; imid, imidazole; en, ethylenediamine; gly, glycine; glu, glutathione sulfhydryl group only; mac, mercaptoacetic acid; ox, oxalic acid; cys, cysteine. Cupric ion is reduced by sulfhydryl groups, so that its formation constant with sulfhydryl-containing ligands is seldom known.

In biological systems interest often centers on pH values near 7. In Fig. 22-1, $pM_{1/2}$ values at pH 7 are plotted against several divalent cations for a variety of model ligand groupings. In constructing this figure, hydrolysis (association of the metal ion with hydroxide ion) has been ignored; it is probably unimportant in all cases. The more positive $pM_{1/2}$ values are placed at the bottom of the plot, so that the lower free metal ion concentrations also appear at the bottom. To take cupric and zinc ion binding with acetic acid as an example, the figure indicates that, for half saturation of total acetic acid with metal ion, about 10^{-1} M zinc and 10^{-2} M cupric ion are required. Since cupric binds acetic acid more strongly than zinc ion, less free cupric ion remains in solution, and its point is downscale on the graph from that of zinc.

At pH 7, acetic acid and oxalic acid are represented by their formation constants, and imidazole nearly so, but all the other ligands in Fig. 22-1 have values of $pM_{1/2}$ far removed from the logarithms of their formation constants. If a greater pH is considered, the points for all ligands except acetic acid, oxalic acid, and imidazole are moved downward (to higher positive pM), one pM unit for each pH unit increase, until the stability-constant logarithm of the ligand is reached, where no further movement occurs. In the other direction, increase of acidity to about pH 5 means that all points except those for acetic and oxalic acids are displaced upward one ordinate unit for each pH unit. Below pH 5.5, the pK_a values of acetic and oxalic acids become important as significant fractions of total acid present begin to appear in protonated forms.

Figure 22-1 reaffirms many of the points enumerated in the discussion of Table 22-2, and the reader should reread this discussion while studying the figure. The figure also emphasizes the relatively greater importance of carboxylic acid binding of metal ions at pH 7 than might be inferred from simple inspection of Table 22-2. Imidazole and ammonia, shown with similar formation constants in Table 22-2, are widely separated in Fig. 22-1. Imidazole is seen in the figure to be the stronger metal binder at pH 7 because its pK_a is in this region, while ammonia is a stronger base. The figure dramatically illustrates the high discrimination of N and S donor groups; the steep slopes of ethylenediamine and cysteine are readily apparent. Oxyanion ligands exhibit much less selectivity among metal ions.

Phosphate binding might be represented by a relatively horizontal line at $pM_{1/2}$ values of 2 to 4. Thus, in ribonucleic acids, we expect the metal ions on the left-hand side of Fig. 22-1 to be bound mainly to phosphate residues, and those on the right-hand side to be bound to the nitrogen atoms of the bases. Significant amounts of divalent metal ions occur naturally with ribonucleic acids, and their part in forming double- and triple-helical polyribonucleotides was mentioned in Sec. 19-3. The presence of metal ions increases the temperature at which helix-coil transitions occur, and they may play a role in stabilizing the helix conformation by providing intramolecular cross-linkages in addition to reducing charge repulsion between phosphate residues. In the double-helical structure of DNA, the nitrogen bases are not as exposed to the ambient medium, and metal ion association at phosphate groups is relatively more favorable than in RNA. Some experiments indicate that cupric ion disrupts the helix by reacting at the bases and, consequently, lowers the transition temperature. Other divalent transition-metal ions and alkaline earths raise the DNA transition temperature, presumably owing to charge neutralization at phosphate residues. Some evidence exists for the binding of metal ions such as ferrous to specific sites in nucleic acids. Relatively few studies have been made on metal ions in nucleoproteins.

The nature of the donor atoms and pH have been shown to affect metal-ion selectivity. The effect of pH is heightened by the different pH values in various parts of living organisms. In addition, metal ions in a charged form can pass the lipoprotein network of cell walls only with difficulty. Uncharged chelate complexes diffuse through such membranes more rapidly than charged complexes or free metal ions. Selectivity is also influenced by the geometry of chelating ligands and steric hindrance. Since it increases formation constants of several metal ions by about the same factor, chelation by itself does not add materially to metal-ion selectivity. The occurrence of more than one spin state and its effects on selectivity are discussed in the next section.

In enzyme-catalyzed reactions rate as well as equilibrium properties are important. A discussion of metal-ion selectivities in biological systems would be incomplete without noting that metal ions may participate by altering the nature of the activated complex and hence the rate of a reaction. A simple example is the base-catalyzed hydrolysis of glycine ethyl ester. As shown in Table 22-3, the hydrolysis

TABLE 22-3 *Rate Constants for Glycine Ethyl Ester Hydrolysis in M^{-1} sec^{-1} at 25.0° and 0.2 Ionic Strength*

Reaction	Rate constant
$NH_2CH_2COOC_2H_5 + OH^-$	0.78
$NH_3^+CH_2COOC_2H_5 + OH^-$	32
$Cu^{++}(NH_2CH_2COOC_2H_5) + OH^-$	100,000

rate of the protonated ester is about 40 times that of the uncharged form. This difference is consistent with the expected electrostatic effect of positively charged nitrogen on negative hydroxide ion attack at the carbonyl carbon. (Compare with the microconstants of glycine discussed in Sec. 4-4.) The 1:1 ester-to-cupric complex, however, hydrolyzes 3,000 times more rapidly than the protonated ester, indicating the effects of chelation through the carbonyl oxygen in promoting hydrolysis. Examples such as the last, where the rate is greatly augmented by placing a positive charge at a point on the molecule at which a proton is unlikely to be found, have been referred to as *super-acid* catalysis. A metal ion often performs this acidlike function in neutral and alkaline solutions.

Metals, of course, do not always behave as super acids. Many, but not all, metal-ion-catalyzed oxidation-reduction reactions involve a more profound role for the metal ion. Ferrous-ferric valence changes occur in the cytochrome series of enzymes. The heme enzymes catalase and peroxidase normally contain ferric ion and may become quadrivalent during the course of enzyme function. Several copper enzymes pass through a cupric-cuprous cycle while functioning as oxidases.

When the equilibrium properties of metal ions are considered, it is appropriate to compare their formation constants with a given ligand. A formation constant may be considered to be the ratio of a forward rate constant for combination of metal ion with ligand to a reverse rate constant for decomposition of complex. Two metal ions may have similar formation constants with a given ligand, but the individual rate constants may differ greatly as long as the ratios of forward and reverse rate constants are similar. In the formation reaction with adenosine triphosphate (ATP), calcium ion reacts about 100 times more rapidly than magnesium, yet their equilibrium formation constants are nearly identical, slightly favoring Mg^{++}. The rate-controlling step in the formation of Mg^{++} and Ca^{++} complexes is dissociation of water from the inner hydration sphere of the metal ion. Since this water-dissociation rate is about 100 times slower for Mg^{++} than for Ca^{++}, the rate difference observed on formation of ATP complexes is a general property of Mg^{++} and Ca^{++} aqueous chemistry. This difference in formation rates might account for the observed differences between Mg^{++} and Ca^{++} in ATP reactions. However, the complex-formation reaction is so fast in both cases that other explanations for the difference between the reactivities of Mg^{++} and Ca^{++} should be sought. Two other possibilities depend upon the relative sizes of Mg^{++} and Ca^{++}. Due to its smaller size, Mg^{++} offers a greater concentration of charge than Ca^{++} and has a greater ability to polarize labile bonds, abetting subsequent decomposition. Bulky ligands also will have difficulty in becoming fully coordinated to the small Mg^{++}, so that the less highly chelated Mg^{++} ion will leave unbound groups which may react, depending upon the requirements of a particular reaction, more or less rapidly than the more highly chelated Ca^{++} complex. The vacant positions in the coordination sphere of Mg^{++} are presumably occupied by water, which may be important in hydrolysis reactions.

22-3 METAL ION BINDING IN PROTEINS

Cysteine has three ligand groups capable of chelating with a metal ion. For steric reasons, all three groups do not chelate simultaneously. Thus there are three possibilities for chelation between two groups in cysteine, through O and S, O and N, or N and S groups:

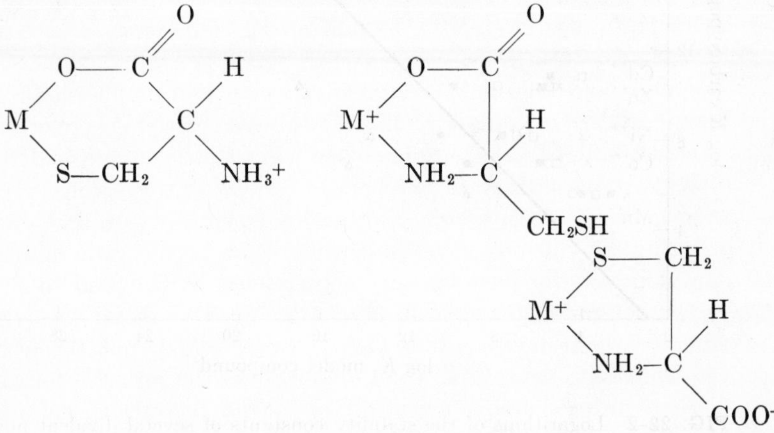

Different metals favor one or the other of the above structures according to the generalizations advanced above. The first structure, with a six-membered chelate ring, is less favored than the last two structures, which have only five atoms in a chelate ring. Reference to stability constants of similar compounds in Table 22-2 helps reveal which structure is favored. Suitable model compounds for the three possible structures are mercaptopropionic acid, glycine, and 2-mercaptoethylamine. For zinc ion the logarithms of the first formation constants are 6.8, 5.5, and 9.9, respectively. As only the last of these compares favorably with the value of 9.9 for zinc cysteinate, we may be sure that chelation occurs overwhelmingly through the N and S donor atoms. Figure 22-1 shows that S and N coordination is favored for zinc ion at all except the lowest pH values.

The principles just applied to the determination of the coordinating groups in zinc cysteinate may also be applied to proteins. Carboxypeptidase A, a proteolytic metalloenzyme, contains at its active site a zinc ion, which may be replaced by several divalent transition-metal ions. Stability constants for the binding of all these metal ions to the protein have been determined. Figure 22-2 shows a plot of the logarithms of the stability constants for metallocarboxypeptidases versus those for representative model compounds. The latter constants are chosen to represent likely modes of coordination in the enzyme:

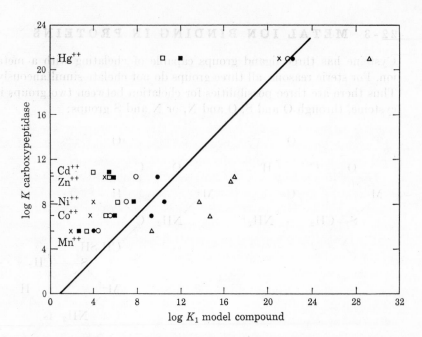

FIG. 22-2 Logarithms of the stability constants of several divalent metal ions with carboxypeptidase versus first formation constants for model compounds: glycine, □; ethylenediamine, ■; glutathione, ✕; mercaptoacetic acid, ○; cysteine, ●; 2-mercaptoethyliminodiacetic acid, △. A line of unit slope is drawn through points for mercuric complexes of mercaptoacetic acid and cysteine. When necessary, values have been corrected for metal ion binding to chloride ion and buffer in the media. [Stability-constant values for metallocarboxypeptidases were taken from B. L. Vallee, R. J. P. Williams, and J. E. Coleman, *Nature*, **190**, 633 (1961).]

glycine, N and O; ethylenediamine, N and N; glutathione, S; mercaptoacetic acid, S and O; cysteine, N and S; 2-mercaptoethyliminodiacetic acid, predominantly N and S with some O.

The coordinating groups of the enzyme should be indicated by the model compound which yields the same increments in stability constants for several metal ions as are displayed by the enzyme. Thus a slope of unity is expected in Fig. 22-2 for a model compound mimicking the binding groups in carboxypeptidase. A line of unit slope has been drawn through the points for mercuric complexes of mercaptoacetic acid and cysteine. The near identity of these values indicates that the strength of the mercuric complex is determined largely by the strong mercury-sulfur bond. The line of Fig. 22-2 passes to the right of the points for all the other metal complexes of mercaptoacetic acid but bisects the points for cysteine, implicating N and S donors in carboxypeptidase. In line with a principle mentioned in Sec. 22-1, we could have inferred sulfur binding from the greater stability constant for zinc than for nickel in the enzyme.

Further inspection of the figure reveals that no other model compound yields a line of unit slope correlating so many points. The agreements with glycine and ethylenediamine are the weakest; all those with a sulfur donor are stronger. The best straight line through the points for the multidentate ligand 2-mercaptoethyliminodiacetic acid containing N, S, and O donor groups has a slope of 0.85.

The inference from Fig. 22-2, along with other evidence, is that the coordinating groups in carboxypeptidase are a sulfhydryl group of a cysteine residue and an amino group. Of the metal ions readily available in biological systems, carboxypeptidase binds zinc most strongly and is evidently a zinc enzyme for this reason. Zinc ion is prevalent in the pancreas, where carboxypeptidase is synthesized. Owing to the relatively favorable zinc-sulfhydryl interaction, we might expect zinc to be bound by sulfur in other zinc proteins, as seems to be the case. Substitution of other divalent metal ions for zinc in carboxypeptidase often yields an active metalloenzyme, the activity of which occasionally exceeds that of the native zinc enzyme.

It is not essential that the line of Fig. 22-2 pass through the origin. Only constant increments between metal ions, indicated by a unit slope, are required. Since chelate ring size and other factors affect the absolute values of stability constants, a line of unit slope is not expected to pass through the origin. Nevertheless the line of Fig. 22-2 nearly passes through the origin and indicates that hydrogen bonding, hydrophobic bonding, restricted rotation, and other factors reduce what must be a larger chelate ring in the enzyme to nearly the same effective size as the five-membered ring of cysteine. Unlike cysteine, however, zinc ion is removed from carboxypeptidase A slowly over a period of hours even at acid pH.

The correlations just described need not be limited to metalloenzymes or to binding constants with macromolecules. For instance, a study of the activation or inhibition constants of several metal ions in an enzyme-catalyzed reaction, compared with the stability constants of the same metal ions with a variety of ligands, might provide clues as to the nature of the groups at the enzyme active site. Comparative metal ion studies of all kinds are extremely useful in elucidating specific sites in large molecules.

Most proteins do not occur naturally with a metal ion bound in such a specific site as in carboxypeptidase. Metal ions often combine with proteins in a rapidly reversible manner. Bovine serum albumin BSA binds up to 20 transition-metal ions. From Fig. 22-1 we expect that, at physiological pH, binding occurs at imidazole or favorably situated carboxylate groups, as seems to be the case. Figure 22-1 also reveals, however, that the single sulfhydryl group of BSA should be a unique metal binding site. About the third cupric ion added per molecule of BSA appears to react at the sulfhydryl site. High specificity in metal ion binding is also indicated by the heavy-atom derivatives of hemoglobin and myoglobin prepared by x-ray crystallographers.

Near physiological pH values, the first cupric or nickel ion added per BSA molecule combines at the N-terminal aspartic acid residue and chelates with the first two to three peptide nitrogens after ionization of the amide hydrogens. This special interaction yields reddish-violet and yellow colors for cupric and nickel ions, respectively, similar to the colors these metal ions yield in very basic solutions with excess biuret. Though it can occur only once per peptide chain, this reaction at the N terminus should be a general phenomenon of cupric and nickel ions in proteins.

22-4 LIGAND FIELD THEORY

The divalent metal ions of the latter half of the first transition series have identical charges and nearly the same radii, so that the entropies of hydration are similar. Thus differences in the equilibrium formation constants of complexes of these metal ions, which give rise to various values for the free-energy change on complex formation, are mainly due to the heat term ΔH. At least three not completely independent factors contribute to the heat term: ionic size, electronegativity, and angular polarization of d orbitals. The last effect, which contributes about 10% to the total bonding energy, has received considerable development recently under the heading of ligand field theory. Since this theory has been successful in correlating magnetic, spectral, equilibrium, and kinetic properties of transition-metal-ion complexes, a brief qualitative outline is presented here.

Although the s, p, and d orbitals in gaseous atoms are all spherically symmetric, the last two may be resolved into several components. Conventionally the p orbitals are expressed in terms of three components, p_x, p_y, and p_z, along the axes of a cartesian coordinate system, each component orbital of which may contain two electrons with paired spins. The regions in space which contain nearly all the electronic charge for the five resolved d orbitals are indicated in Fig. 22-3. The first two, usually designated $d_{x^2-y^2}$ and d_{z^2}, are directed along the axes so that all three axes are equally covered. The last three have lobes at 45° with the axes, each orbital lying in a plane of two of the three coordinates. These five d orbitals, all at the same energy level in a gaseous atom, are termed degenerate.

When six charged or uncharged ligand groups with a free pair of

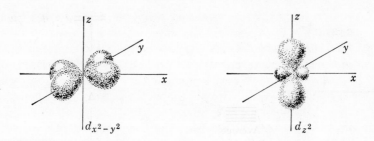

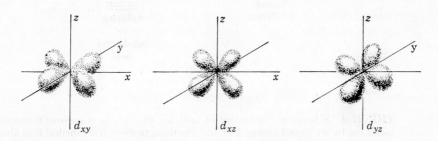

FIG. 22-3 Representation of d orbital components of a gaseous atom. (From E. M. Kosower, "Molecular Biochemistry," McGraw-Hill Book Company, Inc., New York, 1962.)

electrons are brought up to a transition-metal ion along the positive and negative sides of the three coordinate axes to form an octahedral complex, electron repulsion occurs between free ligand electrons and electrons in the d orbitals. Since the d_{xy}, d_{xz}, and d_{yz} orbitals lie between the high electron density regions of the ligand donor groups, they will be subject to less electron repulsion and undergo a smaller increase in energy than the d_{z^2} and $d_{x^2-y^2}$ orbitals. The result is a partial removal of the degenerate d levels of the gaseous atom into two groups as shown in Fig. 22-4. A planar complex may be obtained by removing the two ligands on the z axis of an octahedral complex, much reducing the electrostatic repulsion along this direction and further decreasing the degeneracy. Planar and other configurations are not considered further here. Ligand field theory describes the way in which metal ion electrons, through angular polarization, reduce electron repulsion of ligand electrons.

The energy separation between the split d levels of an octahedral complex, denoted as Δ, is a function of the electrostatic field and σ and π bonding effects. Weak, visible spectra observed in complexes of

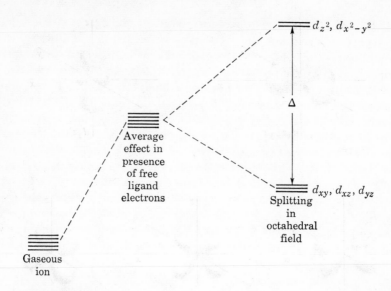

FIG. 22-4 Schematic illustration of splitting of d levels of gaseous transition-metal ion by six ligand groups with free electrons to give an octahedral field about the ion. This picture is strictly valid only for one or nine d electrons in a field of perfect octahedral symmetry, but it is useful for qualitative discussions of less restricted metal ion complexes.

transition-metal ions are due to transitions between the split d levels which are not fully allowed according to quantum mechanical selection rules. Electrons fill the lower d orbitals first, and, upon absorption of a quantum of energy corresponding to the energy separation of non-degenerate d orbitals, an electron jumps from the lower to the upper d level. If the upper d levels are filled, the transition cannot occur, and no visible spectrum appears. Thus zinc ion with 10 d electrons forms colorless complexes. Though only a single absorption band is expected in view of the above considerations, more are often observed, owing to several factors, among them a lesser symmetry than exists in pure octahedral complexes. Ligand groups can be ordered in a spectrochemical series according to the wavelength of absorption and the atom of a ligand bound to the metal ion. To a first approximation, the spectrochemical series of increasing energy (or decreasing wavelength), independent of transition-metal ion and charge on the ligand, is

$$I < Br < Cl < S < F < O < N < C$$

with unsaturated ligands lying highest; e.g., ethylenediamine < o-phenanthroline.

Each of the horizontal lines in the energy-level diagram of Fig. 22-4 represents a d orbital capable of holding two electrons, or 10 electrons for all five orbitals. The first three d electrons to be added in an octahedral complex pass, one each, into the d_{xy}, d_{xz}, and d_{yz} orbitals. The fourth electron may fill either a lower or upper orbital, depending upon whether the energy separation Δ between the split d levels is larger or smaller than the energy required to pair two electrons of opposite spins in a single orbital. If the fourth electron passes into an upper orbital, there are four unpaired spins; if it pairs with one of the electrons already in a lower orbital, only two unpaired spins remain. These two possibilities are described as *high-spin* and *low-spin* cases, respectively. Other terms previously used in place of high spin are *ionic* and *outer orbital*, while *covalent* and *inner orbital* have been used to describe low-spin complexes. In what follows we make the approximation that the spectrochemical parameter Δ, derived partly from an excited spectroscopic state, is applicable to the equilibrium distribution of ground-state molecules determined by magnetic susceptibility or electron spin-resonance experiments. Ligands high in the spectrochemical series produce a strong field (large Δ) about the metal ion and tend to yield low-spin complexes; ligands yielding only a weak field tend to give high-spin complexes when a choice is available.

As shown in Fig. 22-5, an octahedral system with five d electrons will give five unpaired electrons in a weak ligand field and one unpaired

FIG. 22-5 Disposition of electrons in octahedral systems of five and six d electrons in weak and strong ligand field limits.

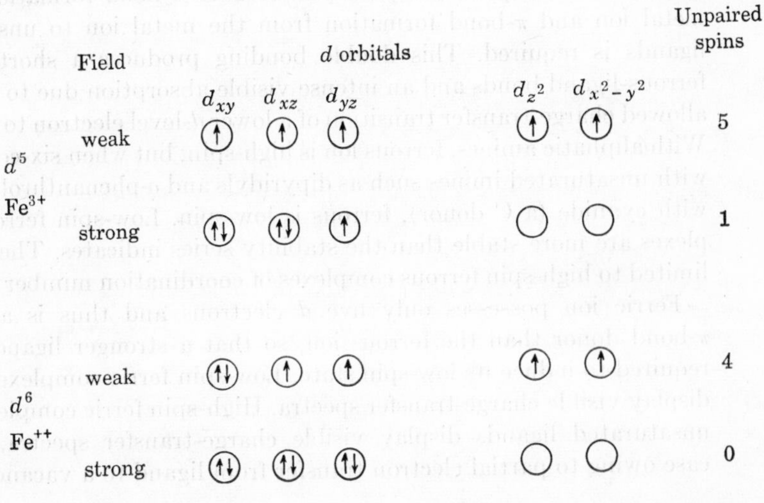

Field		d orbitals					Unpaired spins
	d_{xy}	d_{xz}	d_{yz}		d_{z^2}	$d_{x^2-y^2}$	
d^5 weak	↑	↑	↑		↑	↑	5
Fe^{3+} strong	↑↓	↑↓	↑		○	○	1
d^6 weak	↑↓	↑	↑		↑	↑	4
Fe^{++} strong	↑↓	↑↓	↑↓		○	○	0

electron in a strong field. Maximum spin multiplicity is achieved unless the field is so strong that the energy separation is greater than the exchange energy required to pair, in a single orbital, two electrons of opposed spins. Cases intermediate to the weak- and strong-field limits are usually ascribed to a mixture of high- and low-spin forms and not to an intermediate spin state within a single molecule. The 5 d electron case is exemplified by Mn^{++} and Fe^{3+}. Their high-spin complexes with saturated ligands give unusually weak visible absorption, because a change in spin multiplicity is required for a d-d transition to occur; hence the pale pink Mn^{++} and pale yellow Fe^{3+} in aqueous solutions. Similarly, the 6 d electron systems Fe^{++} and Co^{3+} yield four and zero unpaired spins in the weak and strong field limits, respectively.

At some critical value of Δ and exchange energy, the transition between high- and low-spin complexes occurs. Ferrous ion does not spin-pair until it reaches the unsaturated nitrogen group of ligands which are high in the spectrochemical series. Though fluoride ion provides a strong electrostatic field, it is not high in the spectrochemical series and does not reduce the exchange energy, so that FeF_6^{4-} is a high-spin complex.

The two upper levels in Fig. 22-4 with orbital components directed along the axes form σ bonds with the ligand. The metal ion acts as an electron acceptor of lone-pair electrons on the ligands, since the upper orbitals are at most partly filled in transition-metal ions. The three lower levels directed between the coordinate axes have a symmetry appropriate to π-bond formation with the ligand. In this case the metal is often, but not always, a donor of electrons to unsaturated ligands with incompletely filled π orbitals. In order to produce a low-spin ferrous complex, the push-pull of both σ-bond formation to the metal ion and π-bond formation from the metal ion to unsaturated ligands is required. This double bonding produces a shortening of ferrous-ligand bonds and an intense visible absorption due to the fully allowed charge-transfer transition of a lower d-level electron to a ligand. With aliphatic amines, ferrous ion is high-spin, but when six-coordinate with unsaturated imines such as dipyridyls and o-phenanthrolines, and with cyanide (a C donor), ferrous is low-spin. Low-spin ferrous complexes are more stable than the stability series indicates. The series is limited to high-spin ferrous complexes of coordination number 4 or less.

Ferric ion possesses only five d electrons and thus is a weaker π-bond donor than the ferrous ion, so that a stronger ligand field is required to induce its low-spin state. Low-spin ferric complexes do not display visible charge-transfer spectra. High-spin ferric complexes with unsaturated ligands display visible charge-transfer spectra, in this case owing to partial electron transfer from ligand to a vacancy in the lower d level of the metal ion. Because it has one less electron, ferric has a smaller radius than ferrous ion of the same spin type. Spin pairing also reduces cation size; this, coupled with the oxidation state effect, results in high-spin ferrous ion being larger than low-spin ferrous and high-spin ferric ions, which have about the same radius.

22-5 IRON IN HEMOGLOBIN

Myoglobin, hemoglobin, catalase, peroxidase, and cytochrome c all contain similar porphyrin rings, each coordinating four unsaturated nitrogen donors about an iron atom, yet these proteins exhibit different properties and perform varying functions. Variation in properties and function is provided by the conformation of the protein and the nature of the groups coordinated to iron above and below the nearly planar porphyrin rings. The redox enzymes catalase and peroxidase are high-spin ferric complexes which, it is inferred from spectral evidence, coordinate two carboxylate groups and one carboxylate and one amino group, respectively, above and below the porphyrin. Only when groups high in the spectrochemical series are coordinated in the fifth and sixth positions above and below the ring will a low-spin complex appear. Low-spin ferrocytochrome c coordinates two unsaturated nitrogen donor imidazole groups of histidine residues in the fifth and sixth positions and under physiological conditions cannot pick up oxygen, carbon monoxide, fluoride, or cyanide. The oxidized protein ferricytochrome c is also low-spin.

Myoglobin and hemoglobin are high-spin ferrous complexes with an imidazole group of histidine in the fifth position and a water molecule in the sixth. On replacement of the water molecule by carbon monoxide or oxygen at the iron atom, the ferrous ion becomes low-spin, and the paramagnetic oxygen molecule with two unpaired spins becomes spin-paired, so that the overall magnetic moment for the oxygenated proteins is zero. The color of the spin-paired ferrous complex is a deep red, due to absorptions associated mainly with the porphyrin ring. At least partly because a change of spin multiplicity is necessary, oxidation of either protein by oxygen is slow even though it is favored thermodynamically. When other oxidizing agents are used, high-spin ferric proteins called *metmyoglobin* or *methemoglobin* are obtained. Substitution of azide N_3^- or cyanide CN^- for water in the sixth position about iron in methemoglobin yields a low-spin ferric complex.

Despite the shortening of bonds to the single metal ion accompanying the conversion of myoglobin to oxymyoglobin or metmyoglobin, all three forms of the protein crystallize in the same structure. However, oxyhemoglobin and methemoglobin crystallize in an identical structure, different from that of hemoglobin. In the case of hemoglobin, the bond shortening on changing from high-spin ferrous to either low-spin ferrous or high-spin ferric ions is accompanied by an alteration in crystal structure. This alteration reflects profound changes in the interrelationships among the four iron-bearing subunits of hemoglobin.

The solubility of oxygen in aqueous milieu is insufficient for physiological functions; oxyhemoglobin provides the means for oxygen transport in mammals. With two pairs each of two polypeptide chains, $\alpha_2\beta_2$, and four iron-containing heme groups, a hemoglobin molecule picks up each successive oxygen molecule more easily than the previous one until a maximum of four oxygen molecules is attached, one at each iron atom. If we define successive equilibrium constants for oxygen pickup similar to the successive formation constants for a metal ion with several ligands in Sec. 22-1, where M now represents hemoglobin, and A oxygen, then $K_1 < K_2 < K_3 < K_4$ and $K_4 \simeq 10^2 K_1$ in human hemoglobin, with the last ratio even higher in sheep hemoglobin. These cooperative heme-heme interactions favoring the acquisition of more oxygen after the first is attached are particularly notable at the pickup of the fourth and last oxygen molecule. As noted in Sec. 15-2, heme groups are 25 and 35 A from each other, so that the so-called heme-heme interactions must involve protein chains in some way. Studies over a range of temperature reveal that the negative heat term becomes slightly less negative, but that the successively greater decreases in free energy upon oxygenation are due mainly to increasingly favorable entropy terms. Though the positive sign of the entropy term is the same as that observed in protein denaturation, the values are much less, and oxyhemoglobin is more resistant to denaturation than the reduced protein. Urea-denatured oxyhemoglobin has a lower dissociation pressure than normal oxyhemoglobin, particularly at the lower pressures of oxygen. Therefore, we may look upon the cooperative heme-heme interactions as inhibiting oxygenation of normal hemoglobin at low oxygen pressures. The relatively high dissociation pressure of normal oxyhemoglobin at low oxygen pressures has the physiologically beneficial result of releasing more oxygen to tissues of low oxygen content than would otherwise be the case. The dissociation pressure of oxyhemoglobin is considerably greater than that of oxymyoglobin, so that if hemoglobin which is 50% saturated with oxygen contacts an equivalent quantity of myoglobin, most of the oxygen transfers to the myoglobin.

Another physiologically significant property of hemoglobin is its greater acidity upon oxygenation. The reverse process, the decrease of oxygen affinity of hemoglobin upon acidification in the physiological pH range is called the Bohr effect (discovered by Christian Bohr in 1904). In those tissues which have a lower pH than blood, oxygen is released to the tissues from blood. The Bohr effect has been ascribed to a lowering of the pK_a of histidine residues on oxygenation of hemoglobin. Little or no Bohr effect is observed in myoglobin or hemoglobin H, which consists of four β chains. Evidently, an α-β chain interaction is required for appearance of a Bohr effect. On the other hand x-ray studies indicate that the main change on oxygenation of hemoglobin occurs in the β chains.

There are two plausible explanations for the appearance of heme-heme interactions and the Bohr effect upon oxygenation of normal hemoglobin. Replacement of water by a larger oxygen molecule at an iron atom may force conformational alterations upon the protein. Although shortening of bonds to ferrous ion upon oxygenation of hemoglobin at the iron atoms is by itself insufficient to account fully for heme-heme interactions and the Bohr effect, it may trigger the conformational changes required for the expression of these properties. Only the x-ray diffraction studies outlined in Sec. 15-2 seem to hold any promise for definitively assessing the possible role of iron in heme-heme interactions and the Bohr effect.

SELECTED BIBLIOGRAPHY

1 J. Lewis and R. G. Wilkins (eds.), "Modern Coordination Chemistry," Interscience Publishers, Inc., New York, 1960.

2 Biological Aspects of Metal Binding, *Federation Proc.*, **20,** Supplement 10 (1961).

3 R. J. P. Williams, Coordination, Chelation, and Catalysis, chap. 9 in P. D. Boyer (ed.), "The Enzymes," vol. 1, Academic Press Inc., New York, 1959.

4 F. A. Cotton and G. Wilkinson, "Advanced Inorganic Chemistry," Interscience Publishers, Inc., New York, 1962. Chapter 26 provides a useful, clear exposition of ligand field theory.

5 L. E. Orgel, "An Introduction to Transition Metal Chemistry," Methuen & Co., Ltd., London, 1960.

6 C. J. Ballhausen, "Introduction to Ligand Field Theory," McGraw-Hill Book Company, Inc., New York, 1962.

QUESTIONS

22-1 Predict probable formation constants for Mn^{++}, Fe^{++}, and Co^{++} with acetic acid.

22-2 From the values in Table 22-2, to what groups in cysteine would you infer that Mn^{++} is bound?

22-3 Answer Question 22-2 for histidine instead of cysteine.

22-4 For any metal ion in Table 22-2 for which stability constants are given for both imidazole and ammonia, calculate the ratio of metal ion–imidazole complex to metal ion–ammonia complex at unit pH intervals from pH 4 to 11.

22-5 Derive the expression for $pM_{1/2}$ at $pH = pK_a$.

22-6 Plot $pM_{1/2}$ versus pH from pH 4 to 10 for zinc ion for the ligands of Table 22-2.

22-7 British anti-lewisite or 2,3-dimercaptopropanol is an effective antidote for poisoning by heavy metals. The hydrophilic hydroxy group hinders passage into cells of the chelate that is formed. What do you estimate is the formation constant of the ligand with mercuric ion?

22-8 Enumerate the factors affecting metal ion selectivity in biological reactions.

22-9 Explain why cupric ions are bound much more strongly to glycylglycine than to glycylproline.

22-10 Mercuric ion forms a dimer with two molecules of mercaptalbumin, the fraction of albumin containing a single sulfhydryl group. The initial reaction of mercuric ion with the protein is fast, while the addition of the second protein molecule to the mercuric complex is slow. What explanation can you give for the slow reaction?

22-11 In myoglobin and hemoglobin, a histidine residue is near to but not normally attached at the sixth coordination position about iron. In some abnormal human hemoglobins, this histidine residue may be replaced. When replaced by tyrosine, HbM, the iron is oxidized to the ferric state, and the oxygen-carrying capacity of the iron is destroyed. Replacement of the histidine by arginine does not destroy the oxygen-carrying capacity. Assuming that the tyrosyl residue can coordinate with iron, account for the ability of phenolic groups to favor Fe^{3+} over Fe^{++} more than either histidine or arginine.

22-12 The standard reduction potential (Sec. 2-6) of the aqueous Fe^{3+}/Fe^{++} couple is $+0.77$ volt, and that of the iron couple in hemoglobin is $+0.14$ volt; the reduction potential of the oxygen electrode (Question 2-19) in neutral solutions is about $+0.80$ volt. Is the ferric or ferrous state of iron in hemoglobin the more stabilized with respect to the aqueous ions? Should oxidation of ferrous iron in hemoglobin take place? If so, suggest reasons why oxygenation rather than oxidation occurs.

Appendix

Functions α and γ of Sec. 11-3 for Viscosity and Frictional Coefficient†

Spheres to Rods				Oblate Ellipsoids	
α	$\gamma \times 10^{-6}$	p	$1/p$	α	$\gamma \times 10^{-6}$
1.95	4.11	1		1.95	4.11
2.18	4.60	1.5		1.98	4.19
2.40	5.10	2		2.03	4.30
2.77	5.98	3		2.12	4.50
3.04	6.69	4		2.18	4.64
3.25	7.28	5		2.22	4.73
3.42	7.78	6		2.25	4.81
3.66	8.60	8		2.30	4.91
3.84	9.25	10		2.32	4.97
3.97	9.79	12		2.34	5.02
4.12	10.5	15		2.36	5.06
4.30	11.3	20		2.39	5.12
4.42	12.0	25		2.40	5.14
4.52	12.6	30		2.41	5.16
4.66	13.4	40		2.42	5.19
4.76	14.1	50		2.42	5.21
4.84	14.7	60		2.43	5.22
4.96	15.5	80		2.44	5.23
5.05	16.2	100		2.44	5.24
5.30	18.4	200		2.45	5.25
5.43	19.6	300		2.45	5.26

† R is in angstrom units, and $[\eta]$ in deciliters per gram.

Functions α and γ of Sec. 11-3 for Viscosity and Frictional Coefficient†

	Sphere to Rods				Oblate Ellipsoid	
α	γ × 10⁵		l/b	α	γ × 10⁵	
1.98	1.01		1	1.98	1.11	
2.18	1.00		1.5	1.98	1.10	
2.40	2.10		2	2.92	1.30	
2.77	3.08		3	3.12	1.50	
3.04	6.06		4	3.68	1.61	
3.32	7.25		5	3.92	1.73	
3.42	7.75		6	3.36	1.89	
3.68	8.50		8	2.30	1.91	
3.84	9.95		10	2.10	1.97	
3.96	9.70		12	2.31	3.03	
4.12	10.5		15	2.50	3.08	
4.30	11.3		20	2.30	3.74	
4.32	12.0		25	2.10	4.11	
4.52	12.5		30	2.41	4.16	
4.66	13.4		40	2.42	4.16	
4.76	14.1		50	2.42	5.21	
4.84	11.7		70	2.18	5.22	
4.99	15.3		80	2.44	5.93	
5.08	16.2		100	2.11	8.31	
5.30	18.3		200	2.18	5.36	
5.43	19.0		300	2.15	5.30	

† R is in angstrom units, and [b] in deciliters per gram.

Index